1.13

Legend:

11 Basildon Estate gravel pits - now the Childe Beale Wild Life Trust.

12 Basildon Es... there.

13 Crown Hill...

14 Harley Wo... hundreds of... furniture fa...

15 No. 11 Low...

16 Manor Farm... Mortimer i... ...of the Basildon Estate was sold off.

17 Site of the steam powered pumps that kept the troughs on the Great Western Railway main line filled, enabling steam locomotives to pick up water as they passed over the troughs, some in excess of 80 m.p.h. The troughs were about half-a-mile long, stretching back to Skew Bridge.

18 Skew Bridge, which carries the Reading-Wallingford road over the GWR main line west of Pangbourne.

Map labels:

Stapnalls Fm

Gatehampton Fm

Coombe End Fm

17 Ferry

Church Fm

Basildon

River Thames

...ildon House

Park Fm

Home Fm

18

11

Coombe Lodge

Bozedown Ho

Home Fm

Whitchurch

Lock toll

Pangbourne

Lower Bowden

A329

Upper Bowden Fm

Nautical College

Flowers Fm

Rectory

Andrew 1998

Bere Court

Tidmarsh

Mill

A LIFE WITH STEAM

A LIFE WITH STEAM

JOE CHALLIS

Published by Finial Publishing on behalf of
Buxworth Steam Group, Barren Clough Farm, Buxworth, High Peak,
Derbyshire SK23 7NS United Kingdom

First published 1998

ISBN 1-900467-04-6

Designed and produced by Finial Publishing
36 Park Road, Swanage, Dorset BH19 2AD

Typeset in 11 on 13 pt Garamond

Printed in England by
The Dorset Press, Dorchester, Dorset DT1 1HD

Colour separations by
Dorset Imaging & Scanning Company Ltd, Poole, Dorset BH17 7BX

JACKET

Text: Andrew P. M. Wright

Photographs

Front: *Joe Challis pictured with the unique Wilder piston valve engine No.1, BL 4150 at the 1997 Great Dorset Steam Fair.*
Photograph: Buxworth Steam Group.

Rear: *Ploughing on the Basildon Estate c. 1930.*
Photograph: Rural History Centre, University of Reading.

Inside: *The author with Dr. Tony Marchington's Fowler BB1 ploughing engine and tackle at Lyme Park, Cheshire in July 1985.*
Photograph: Buxworth Steam Group.

ENDPAPERS

Drawn by Andrew Maltman
Adapted from Ordnance Survey Sheet 113, Reading , 1933.
By kind permission of Ordnance Survey, Southampton SO16 4XH.

Contents

Acknowledgements

I would like to extend my sincere thanks to the following for their encouragement and support during the preparation and production of this volume.

First of all, I have to acknowledge the friendship and support offered by that great steam enthusiast Dr. Tony Marchington. During many visits to Barrren Clough Farm - the home of Frank and Milly (Tony's parents) - I was made very welcome. Between them, they started me back in the steam scene and I am sure that if it had not been for them, I would not have joined the Steam Plough Club or met many of the steam plough enthusiasts I know today. I must also thank Tony for sponsoring the publication of this book.

To my colleagues in the Steam Plough Club, I extend my gratitude for their friendship and in particular for their encouragement in building on the series of articles that I wrote and which were subsequently published in the Club magazine. These articles form the foundation of this manuscript. Thanks also to Robert Oliver (Chairman) for finding the time to write an introduction to this book and for permission to use the Club's logo throughout this book.

The enthusiasm shown by many of my friends in the National Traction Engine Trust (NTET) regarding the publication of this book has been very encouraging and I am extremely grateful for their support.

My heartfelt thanks to James Hodgson and Neil Mackinlay, the current owners of the unique Wilder No. 1 piston valve engine BL 1450, which I was first re-united with at the 1996 Great Dorset. I met up again with 'my' engine (now almost completely restored) at the 1997 event. I cannot express my gratitude enough to James and Neil for allowing me to get my hands on BL 1450 again and they are to be congratulated on a superb restoration.

I also acknowledge the invaluable assistance given by David Spooner of Wokingham for, first of all, converting my manuscript into a form acceptable to a publisher and, secondly, checking the final proofs.

Thanks to David Clifford and John Villers of Finial Publishing for transforming my manuscript into a highly readable book; for researching additional material for inclusion; investigating sources of photographs and for setting up photographic sessions - all of which I thoroughly enjoyed.

I am extremely grateful for the assistance of Richard Jordan-Baker, Oliver Garnett and Ed Gibbons of The National Trust, Barbara Holden, Rural History Centre, University of Reading and Ordnance Survey, Southampton for their help in researching photographs, maps and other relevant material.

All the photographs contained in this book - unless stated otherwise - are from my personal collection. Finally, to anyone I might have omitted, please accept my sincere apologies.

Joe Challis

Introduction

Like the traction engine and the steam roller, which both faded from the scene due to Government interference and excessive taxation, the plough engine has experienced a renaissance in recent years.

Today, most peoples' perception of traction engines comes from the traction engine rally. This sprang up in the 1950s, when enthusiasts who had preserved engines from the scrap merchant's cutting torch, got together to show their engines off to the general public. From a humble beginning, it has developed into a very large and well organised part of today's summer leisure industry. Engines that would have been scrapped in days gone by, are restored with new boilers, fireboxes and other parts. Specialists firms using traditional skills are able to bring back to life engines that were thought to have been past saving, both in the traction engine and the steam railway preservation movement. Traction engine rallies enable the public to see engines performing the tasks that they did in commercial use. Many rallies now have steam ploughing as a part of the show. This enables visitors to see how the double engine system, first used in the 1850s, can still do a good job today. Some farmers who own plough engines still plough part of their farm each year with steam.

While the preservation movement was growing, another use of the plough engine was quietly continuing. Landowners with large lakes on their property, which need dredging to clear the silt out, would employ companies with steam plough engines to do this work. Today, there are commercial companies still using engines built in the early 1900s to do this work. Several marinas around our coasts have been part constructed in this manner.

The National Traction Engine Trust, the overall preservation body for traction engines in this country, was founded as The National Traction Engine Club in 1953 and is today having to contend with legislation emanating from Brussels, European laws knowing or caring little about the slightly eccentric goings-on of the steam enthusiast in Britain.

Harold Bonnett founded The Steam Plough Club in 1966 to encourage interest in the plough engine. At that time, there was serious thought that steam ploughing could become extinct with the working engines and ploughmen becoming fewer and fewer. Today, however, more and more plough engines are under restoration and over 170 plough engines appear in the Club engine list. Working demonstrations are given and an archive section exists to answer questions on engine and company histories. The Club also publishes a quarterly magazine, in which some of Joe Challis's writings have appeared and it now has a membership of nearly 500, including a growing International group.

Robert F. Oliver (Chairman) The Steam Plough Club, 1998

'This photograph was taken in 1986 in the yard of the Navigation Inn, Buxworth, Derbyshire and shows me with that great steam enthusiast Tony Marchington and and two young friends with his Fowler BB1 Ploughers **Fame** *and* **Fortune** *...!'*
                                                                                    JOE CHALLIS

Preface

I first met Joe Challis on a beautiful summer day in 1982 on the occasion of that year's Woodcote Rally. At the time, I was living nearby in the village of Beech Hill, just south of Reading, and had taken time out to visit that marvellous little rally of national repute. Walking along the lines of exhibits, my attention was drawn by an elderly gentleman sitting in front of his caravan by a table on which was displayed a marvellous 2in. scale miniature of a BB1 Fowler ploughing engine.

"That's a miniature of a Fowler BB1", I said, trying to sound knowledgeable.

"Yes", replied the gentleman, "I'm working on the other one of the set to exhibit them both together one day".

"That's wonderful", I said, "I am a great admirer of Fowlers, and ploughing engines in particular, to the extent that I bought a set with the plough, living van and water cart, a couple of years ago", trying to sound even more impressive.

"Oh, really?" said Joe, "that's tremendous. I was foreman on a set at the age of 19, and drove for Wilders of Wallingford and Wards of Egham before I was married".

I stood there, flabbergasted. What could I even pretend to know when compared with this man's undoubted knowledge and experience of ploughing engines?

"Are you a member of the Steam Plough Club?" I asked.

"No", Joe said, "What's that?".

It was then that I realised that I had probably made the greatest industrial archaeological find in the history of steam ploughing; and so it turned out, for Joe Challis is now recognised as the greatest living expert on steam plough engines.

The following day, Sunday, I visited Woodcote again - this time with photographs of my engines - and over cups of tea Joe and his lovely wife, Gladys, here began the process which eventually led to the writing of this book.

From that first meeting at Woodcote, Joe and I became very good friends as, over the years, he has shared with me, and others, his vast wealth of knowledge and understanding of steam engines in general and steam ploughing in particular.

At first Joe was very much a private treasure, teaching me and my immediate family (my father, Frank and my brother, Allan) the rudiments of steam ploughing. Joe taught us how to get ropes to coil properly, how to splice steel rope and where to find long-lost quantities of marvellous, original, black, steam oil in rusted, but still intact, 45 gallon drums.

Soon, however, Joe's name started to appear in reports in *Steam Plough*

Times and in the columns of *World's Fair* and it was clear that the stalwarts of steam ploughing and preserved steam traction engines in general were beginning to tap into his knowledge. Joe was soon a celebrity.

In 1985, I ran the Lyme Park Steam Rally. This became famous subsequently not only for the vast numbers of people it attracted (some of whom were destined to sit in traffic and never see the event), but also for the BBC television documentary film 'A Gambol on Steam'. The film has been shown on TV on many occasions since, and the predominant observation from people who have seen it remains the same: Joe standing against the back wheel of one his beloved Fowler BB1s, exclaiming "I have really enjoyed myself - I never thought I would do this again".

More recently, Joe has been quite active at steam plough functions and has witnessed a renaissance in the popularity of steam ploughing, which I know he never anticipated.

This, his life story in steam is a fabulous book. I read it in manuscript from cover to cover and was touched not just by the complete immersion in steam traction engines and steam ploughing which it provides, but also by the tremendous depth of warmth and appreciation which can only come from a man in his 80s, looking back on a life well spent.

Joe's description of his early life on the Basildon Estate, near Reading, comes over as fresh and descriptive as if it were yesterday. Nature provides a backdrop to every event, as only a true country man would recall and his turn of phrase is as descriptive as any that I have read. "If ever you have travelled the Crowmarsh to Goring road, you will have noticed those big, rolling corn fields stretching from the River Thames far into the Chiltern Hills." With that phrase, Joe creates a landscape.

There are also moments of vivid humour. "If you have ever driven a three wheeler car, you will know that it is not the thing to take up a three-ply cart track."

Joe finishes his story in professional steam as a steam roller driver during the Second World War, by which time many steam ploughing engines were reduced to hedge pulling and demolition work in preparation for the M4 and later extensions of the airport at Heathrow.

From then, he jumps on to preservation days and his building of the miniature which I first came across on that very fortunate day in the summer of 1982, when the two of us first met.

There are also useful tips for modern preservationists who are lucky enough nowadays to own or operate a preserved pair of plough engines.

I consider myself very privileged to be counted amongst Joe Challis's friends. He has produced the most sensuous and, at the same time, most knowledgeable book on traction engines ever written. It will stand as a monument to Joe Challis and his life in steam for as long as people carry interest in steam ploughing and that glorious period of English history and engineering.

Tony Marchington

ENGINE AND WINDLASS.

PLOUGH.

ANCHOR,

[*See following pages.*]

Photograph: Rural History Centre, University of Reading.

'Reproduced from Ransomes & Sims' Catalogue of 1859, is this illustration of a 'Fowler's Steam Plough'. This revised tackle consisted of a portable steam engine, equipped with a double drum windlass, a long iron rope and a four-wheeled anchor cart. Note the wooden trough on the top of the cart which could be filled with soil to provide additional ballast to press the disc wheels into the ground. Also evident are the gears by which the anchor cart could be winched into a new position as the ploughing progressed. Of particular interest, is the hand signalling which controlled the movement of the balance plough backwards and forwards across the field ...!'

JOE CHALLIS

The Development of Steam Ploughing

H arold Bonnett in his book 'Saga of the Steam Plough', suggests the quest for 'power farming', had commenced at almost the same time as the birth of the steam engine. The first rumblings appear to have occurred in 1619 when James I granted a patent to two early inventors to 'Ploughe Ground, without Horse or Oxen'. Bonnett's research indicates that 'the Marquis of Worcester ... had by 1663 devised and constructed a crude but workable steam pumping engine' and 'it is not so unlikely, therefore, that the patentees had at least heard court gossip of the investigations already afoot to utilize steam power'. Similarly, in 1767, another inventor came forward with an idea described as 'A Fire Engine for Ploughing' and was confident enough to 'have sold most of his horses, and advised his farmer friends to do the same, believing his proposed steam engine would rapidly do away with horses for ploughing'.

Despite this early optimism, the first practical steam engines would not be built until the early 1800s, with Thoman Newcomen and Captain Thomas Savery leading the field. With regard to this period, Bonnet states that 'if we leave the infant railways with their 'Puffing Billy' locomotives, the steam engines so far constructed were, apart from such isolated examples as Trevithick's road engine of 1801, or the lightweight designs for steam road carriages, chiefly of the stationary type. These heavy, cumbersome and low-powered engines were not good enough for the inventors who wanted a separate, light and mobile engine which could be hitched to the front of the plough in place of the team of horses or oxen'.

Bonnett suggests that the 'first steam engines seen by many country labouring men were the portable or horse-drawn types introduced from as early as 1832 by the more mechanically minded and progressive landowners. These engines were not employed for ploughing, but for threshing or grinding corn, pumping water, cutting chaff and other stationary jobs'. Nonetheless, despite the inventiveness of British agricultural engineers at this period and a plethora of steam power on British farms, apart from a few oddities, as yet nobody had worked out a way to successfully harness the steam engine to plough a field cheaper than could be done by using teams of horses!

Bonnett states that there 'was no engine really suitable for them. It is not surprising, therefore, to find that others had already given some thought to a system by which the heavy power plant itself stood still while it hauled the implement. A rope, chain or other flexible band was to be used to pull the mobile implement between the standing engine, and a pulley anchored on the opposite site of the field'. At the vanguard of this development was 'A farmer named Hannam, living at Burcote near Abingdon in Berkshire, ...

one of the first to be associated with the introduction of what came to be known later as the 'Roundabout' system of ploughing or cultivating. This method took its name from the pecularity of having a long free-running haulage rope carried over guiding pulleys, right round the outside of the field. The rope started from and returned to the winding winch, which stood near the single engine. Like some 5,000 other British farmers of 1850 Hannam had an ordinary farm type portable steam engine, i.e. one drawn from place to place by horses. As these engines were expensive items to purchase, and not always fully employed threshing, grinding corn or cutting chaff, Hannam had ideas about using their spare time to till the fields'. Other farmers followed in Hannam's footsteps, improving the 'rope, or indirect' of haulage as they went, while others concentrated on the application of the 'direct haulage' method of steam cultivation.

The most famous name in steam ploughing is undoubtedly John Fowler (1826-1864). His first claim to fame was his work in trying to alleviate the famine conditions in Ireland after he spent a holiday there and saw tha awful situation caused by the poor undrained land and the results of this among the poor. He developed a drain making implement to draw a drain in the earth across a field to assist the water to flow away. Bonnett records that in 'January 1855, Fowler addressed the Royal Society of Arts in John Adam Street, London. His talk provoked a good deal of questioning about the real prospects of ever being able to plough by steam. Present at the RSA lecture was another steam plough pioneer - William Worby - who was convinced that a 6 h.p. engine could be made to plough an acre per hour on light land. When he heard that, Fowler quickly replied, 'If you believe this, I will give you an order home with you to make a set of tackle at once'.'

Bonnett suggests 'There must have been some long hours and late nights in the workshop [Ransomes & Sims works at Ipswich], because by 10th April that year the tackle was set up and at work at Nacton in Essex. It consisted of a Ransome's portable engine, a double drum windlass, long iron wire rope, rope anchors and a pole-steered balance plough [another recent invention]. To everyone's delight, the thing worked. The promised acre an hour was accomplished quite easily ... The only misgiving they seem to have had was the amount of labourers' work necessary to dig holes for the shifting positions of the rope anchors, as the ploughing advanced down the field. Shortly afterwards the Nacton-type of ground anchor was replaced by a four-wheeled anchor cart. This cart was loaded with earth to give it weight, and the wheels were of the sharp edged disc pattern, which cut down into the soil, and so resisted the inwards pull of the rope. It was far easier to pull this cart along than to use a gang of labourers continually digging holes for anchors'.

Bonnett records that, building on the experience of others, 'In 1856 Fowler patented a system for ploughing with two engines, using one engine on either side of the field ... With two plough engines working as a pair, there was no need to use horses to move the rope winches, or to pull out the long rope before making a start. Although these engines were 'self-moving' ie both 'The engine and anchor cart of this tackle were each able to move themselves forward along the field headlands by winding in a rope anchored ahead, the engines still had to be moved by teams of horses'. Therefore, as Bonnett states 'The next logical step was to devise a satisfactory, self-moving plough engine'.

The farmers were getting tired of taking out a team of horses whenever a move about the field, or from field to field, was necessary. Fowlers had been busy on this possibility for some time, but it would not be until 1858 that they turned out their first practical self-moving traction type plough engine. As was usual in those days, it required a horse in shafts at the front to steer it [steering-gear not yet having been perfected]'. Fowler continued with his steam plough experiments, often with outside inventors, improving the tackle as he went and he was so successful that 'By 1860 there was no alternative but to start his own works and that year he opened his 'Steam Plough Works' at Hunslet, Leeds. His first really satisfactory two engine set left these works in 1861' and another 'important event was the patenting, in 1863, of an automatic gear for coiling the ropes on the engine drums'.

Conquering all before it, steam power now not only powered Britain's railways, mines and factories, but began to reign supreme on the nation's agrarian scene as well. Bonnett states that by 'the end of 1863, it could be said that at last steam ploughing was established on a paying basis' and that 'in spite of teething troubles, the fact remains that on the whole the idea of ploughing and cultivating by steam began to be accepted as a normal, everyday affair on the farms of this country'.

From 'Saga of the Steam Plough' (David & Charles) by kind permission of the publishers.

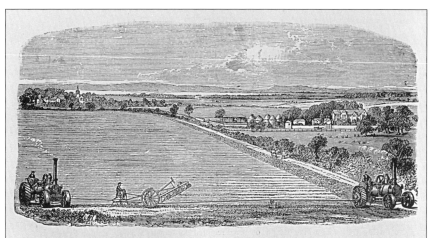

Plan of Working. Fowler's Double Engine Steam Plough System No. 3.

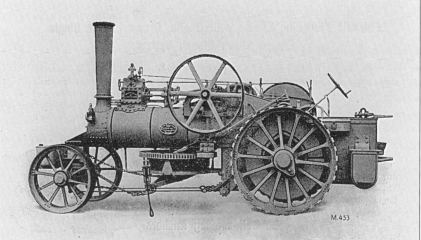

Fowler's Ploughing Engine for the Double Engine Steam Plough System No. 3.

Photograph: Rural History Centre, University of Reading.
Reproduced from Ransomes & Sims' Catalogue of 1859.

Glossary

Acreage money: Paid to drivers at the rate of £1-7s-6d a week, plus $^1/_2$d per acre for harrowing; 1d per acre for cultivating plus 2d per acre for ploughing. Paid out at the end of the season.

Angle irons: Made from 3in. angle-iron rolled to fit on the rim of the front engine wheels, in four sections and fixed with nuts and bolts. They would cut into the field to a depth of 3in. and so help to stop the engine from sliding sideways with the pull of the rope.

Anti-balance plough: A plough fitted with a axle in the centre that travelled forward when the plough pitched into the ground, thus putting extra weight onto the end of the plough that was in the ground.

Auxiliary lever: These were only fitted to compound engines. A compound engine has two pistons and cylinders, the steam from the boiler going to the smallest cylinder first, then the exhaust from this to the big cylinder, so using the steam twice. The Auxiliary Lever opened a valve from the boiler into the big cylinder and so more than doubles the power of the engine.

Avelings: Aveling & Porter of Rochester were engine manufacturers and although they made more steam rollers than the rest of the engine builders in the United Kingdom put together, they made very few ploughing engines, Fowlers of Leeds having the edge on all other firms at this time.

Axle-keys: On steam engines, there is a train of gears from the crankshaft to the rear axle and the main spur gear is keyed to the axle to make the drive. The key is a piece of 1in. square steel sunk into the axle in a slot cut with a milling machine. There is also a keyway cut into the spur wheel and so makes the drive.

Baler: A machine that was usually driven from the threshing machine and baled the straw into oblong bales. These were tied with wire and weighed around 1 cwt.

BB1s: 16 hp Compound ploughing engines, which were the most popular of all the ploughers built by Fowlers of Leeds for use in the U.K.

Big wheel: Top gear.

Big wheels: The rear wheels of most steam engines are always referred to as the 'big wheels'. For instance, the rear wheels of a Fowler BB1 ploughing engine have a diameter of 6ft 6in. and on many occasions, the 'big wheels' provided the only shelter for a ploughing team unfortunate enough to be caught in a heavy downpour

Bomford & Evershed: Pioneers in the use of steam rollers equipped with scarifiers for breaking up the road surfaceprior to relaying.

Chain bucketing: When travelling from job to job, water had to be picked up for the engines where ever possible. This was frequently too far from the road for lift pipes to reach and water, therefore, had to be carried in buckets. The gang of four would space themselves between the source of water and the engine and hand a full bucket of water up and empty one down, each bucket holding 3 gallons.

Clayton & Shuttleworth: A British firm that built many steam rollers and traction engines.

Coiling gear/pulleys: Under the rope drum of a ploughing engine, is a coiling gear to coil the rope up and down properly, so that the rope does not cross over itself, as this is harmful to the rope. The pulleys are at the end of the coiling lever, with the rope passing between them.

Compound ploughers: Most of the ploughing engines built after about 1920, were compounds as they were more economic than the single cylinder types. The steam was used twice, the used steam from the small cylinder being passed into the bigger cylinder, thus almost doubling the power.

Crankshaft: the first motion shaft of the drive to the wheels and rope drum, propelled by the piston and connecting rods.

Cross strake marks: Plates across the rims of the wheels to make grip on soft ground. These are set at an angle with the inside of the wheel (nearest the boiler) to touch the ground first. They leave a 'V'-shaped mark on the ground or road, thus making it easy to recognise which direction the engine is headed.

Cultivator points: Cast iron points fitted to the end of the tines, which were changed as they wore down.

Cultivators: Implements used with ploughing engines, most having 11 or 13 tines which could be set to go into the ground up to 2ft 6in. deep.

Cup box: On threshing machines, the corn finds its way to the lowest part of the machine before going back to the top to go through a grading screen and then into sacks. The corn is picked up from the Cup Box and taken to the top by a 6in. belt fitted with steel cups.

Damper: A a round plate slightly larger than the top of the engine chimney, placed on the chimney at night to stop the fire from drawing up.

Die block: Fitted to the rope coiling gear and runs in a cam which is driven by gears at the bottom of the rope drum, so lifting the coiling lever up and down.

Differential gear: Fitted to the rear axle of steam engines, allowing one driving wheel to travel faster than the other when going round corners. The wheel on the outside of the bend has further to go than the inside one and so has to turn faster.

Double-tined: When cultivating, most farmers preferred double-tining, thus ensuring that the soil was moved twice. Cultivators had two wheels on the main axle and one at the front for steering. This was run along the line of the outside tine on the previous pull. This method ensured that half the tines were breaking virgin soil and the other half were moving soil that had already been broken once.

Drain taps: Located on the ends of the cylinders of steam engines. Always opened when the engine is going to stand for a while and are also always opened for the first start in the morning, so allowing condensed steam to escape.

Drainer: (see Mole drainer).

Drug bat: A big iron shoe that is anchored to the frame of a wagon or machine and which is placed under the road wheel and slides along the surface of the ground or road, thus forming a brake.

Drum gear/ring/bearings: The gear ring is the gear wheel bolted to the top of the rope drum and driven by a gear wheel from the vertical shaft under the crankshaft. The bearings are large bronze bushes that the rope drum and upright shaft run on.

Eleven-thirteen (11-13): Most cultivators were fitted with 13 tines and often on very hard or heavy ground, the two outside tines were removed and so used as 11 tine. A smaller cultivator was known as a 9-11.

Expansion engine: A steam engine with a special valve gear. Most of these engines were manufactured by Wallis & Steevens of Basingstoke.

Five/Six furrow plough: The number of furrows turned over at each pull (most Fowler ploughs were five or six furrow).

Flywheel: Situated usually on the left side of a steam engine and ensures that the engine runs evenly.

Footboard: This is a platform along the side of the engine to walk along when oiling the link motion etc.

Fordson TVO tractor: Early farm tractors built by Fordson and were started with petrol and run on petrol until the engine was warm, then changed over to T.V.O. (Traction Vaporising Oil) which is similar to paraffin.

Foster tractor: A small steam traction engine made by Fosters of Lincoln.

Four shaft engines: This is the number of drive shafts for the gear train. Two shafts between the crankshaft and axle. Some engines are three shaft and with this type the crankshaft runs in the same direction as the road wheels, whereas with four shaft, the crankshaft runs the opposite way.

Fowlers: Fowlers of Leeds were the builders of 99% of the World's steam ploughing tackle.

Fry steam wagons: There were a fleet of Overtype Foden steam wagons, owned by Frys.

Furrow wheel: The wheel on a steam plough that always runs in the furrow when ploughing and which is about 10in. larger in diameter and narrower than the land wheel on the other side of the machine.

Gauge glass: A glass tube fitted to the back of the boiler and in front of the driver, which shows the water level in the boiler.

Governor belt: A narrow - usually leather - belt which drives the governors from the crankshaft. The governors are for controlling the speed of the engine and opens or shuts a steam valve to the cylinders as the load fluctuates.

Hampshire pokers: A long poker with a 'T' piece welded across the end for removing clinker from fire bars.

Harrows: A light cultivator. This has wings that fold up for travelling on the road and when opened for use in the field, is about 12ft wide. It is used to break down the soil after it has been broken up with the Eleven-Thirteen cultivator.

Hornplate: The main side plates of the boiler that carry the bearings for the drive shafts and crankshaft. Also the tender is bolted to them.

'Horses head': A part of a straw baler which moves up and down and pushes the straw into the machine for the main ram to push it along to form the bales. The device is known as the 'horses head' because of its shape and because it has teeth at the end which gives it the appearance of a horse with its mouth open.

Injector: Feeds water into the boiler and is a complicated piece of machinery with jets and cones inside. The injector is fed from steam from the boiler and takes water from the tank and feeds the boiler at a higher pressure than the steam that is fed into it.

Injector feedpipe check valve: As the water is fed into the boiler, it lifts a check valve to let the water pass into the boiler and when the injector is shut off, the valve drops onto its seating and shuts off the pressure from the boiler.

'Jingle Bells': These were very early Fowler engines owned by Wilders of Wallingford and were so named because of the ringing noise from the four big bevel gears that operated the rope drum.

K7s: 12 hp Fowler compound ploughing engines, K7 being the type.

Lift pipe: A flexible hose connected to the lifter and fitted with a strainer to stop leaves etc from being sucked into the water tank. Usually 30ft long.

Living van (ploughing): The home of the steam plough gang all the week and often week-ends. There were beds for five, a cooking stove (coal fired) and underneath two big lockers which were always well stocked with drums of oil, coal, plough shares and cultivator points.

Living van (roller): A smaller type of van and was often the home for the roller driver and his wife.

McLaren single: A single cylinder engine built by McLaren of Leeds.

Marshalls: Steam engine builders of Gainsborough, Lincolnshire.

Mold/Mould boards: Shaped steel plates on a plough that turns the soil over after it has been lifted by the plough share.

Mole drainer (see Drainer): An implement with a large steel blade with a steel mole at the bottom which is pulled through the soil up to a depth of 3ft and so leaving a 3in. channel under the ground or road, almost like a drain pipe.

'Monkey's head': The wheels that the rope passes through on the end of the coiling lever.

'Monkey tail' regulator: Most regulators are vertical or horizontal and pulled or pushed backwards or forwards. A 'monkey tail' regulator is longer and lifted up and down.

Motion bright work: The connecting rods and valve operating rods.

Oscillating cylinder: A type of steam engine which has no connecting rods. The piston rod is coupled to the crank and the cylinders oscillate with it.

Overtype Fodens: Steam wagons made by Fodens of Sandbach with the engine on the top of the boiler.

Oxford chimney and smokebox door: John Allens of Oxford built some steam engines, but a good proportion of their output were parts to fit Fowler engines, these being mainly cast iron chimneys and pressed steel smokebox doors.

Paddle: A very small spade on a long handle used on a plough to remove weeds etc.

Perch bracket: The bracket under the smokebox of steam engines which the front axle is fitted to.

Piston valve compound: Most early steam engines were fitted with flat slide valves working over steam ports. Some later types were fitted with small pistons to open and close the steam ports on singles and compounds.

Ploughing engines: Always larger than traction engines, ploughing engines were fitted with a rope drum under the boiler. They worked in pairs, one each side of the field, pulling the implements with steel wire ropes.

Plummer blocks: A casting fitted with bearings for a shaft to run in.

Press: An implement used with the plough which has a heavy steel frame and axle and fitted with five or six heavy cast iron wheels with 'V'-shaped rims that press grooves between the furrows for the corn to fall into when broadcast over the ploughed field.

Priming: This occurs when water gets into the cylinder with the steam and is caused by several different causes, such as pressure being too low, too much water in the boiler or dirty water. The main offender is water from a pond where ducks have been, the oil from the duck feathers frothing up and then entering the cylinder.

Pug mills: A machine that compresses clay before it goes into a brick making machine.

Pump rod: The connecting rod from the eccentric on the crankshaft to the pump plunger.

Push saw bench: A saw bench where the timber is pushed onto the saw blade by hand.

Rack bench: A saw bench with a travelling table to carry the timber to the saw blade. Some were operated by hand, others were mechanically operated.

Rams: For pushing something, often by hydraulic pressure.

Regulator: For operating the steam valve from the boiler to the cylinder.

Road bands: These were fitted over the spade lugs (or spuds) on early tractors for travelling on the road.

Road gearing guards: The guards covering the train of drive gears from the crankshaft to rear axle.

Road wheel pin: A large pin through the hub of the rear wheels on steam engines to make the drive. On ploughing engines these were of 3in. diameter.

Roberts folding elevator: Used to take the straw from the threshing machine to the straw rick and could be raised as the rick built up. They could be folded up for travelling on the road.

Rope drum: A drum fitted under the boiler of ploughing engines and driven from the crankshaft to wind in the steel wire rope that pulled the implements. Traction engines had a small drum on the rear axle.

Savage roundabout organ engine: Savages of Kings Lynn, Norfolk were the builders of most of the steam roundabouts seen at fairgrounds. The organ engine was a small vertical single cylinder engine to drive the bellows that operated the organ.

Sawing tackle: A steam traction engine and saw benches.

Scarifier: A piece of equipment fitted to most steam rollers for breaking up roads for reshaping.

Scotch block: A wooden block carried on most steam engines to place behind the wheel to prevent the engine from running back when changing gears. On ploughing engines, it was most important as they were out of gear when pulling the rope in.

Second motion shaft: The next drive shaft to the crankshaft.

Shackles: A 'D'-shaped link for connecting the steam plough rope to the implements.

Shares: A cast iron point fitted to the nose of each plough.

Shunting pole: A heavy wooden or iron pole about 8ft long used for pushing the threshing machine between the ricks.

Single furrow wooden plough: An early horse-drawn plough with a wooden frame and a single iron plough and share.

Skids: Heavy lengths of timber used when loading timber wagons, the logs being rolled up the skids onto the wagon.

Slabs: Large baulks of timber.

Sleeve: A tube shaped piece of metal.

Slide valves: The valves of a steam engine that are operated by the link motion to open and close the steam ports to the piston.

Snatch block: A large pulley block used with steam engines, which gears to half speed whatever it is attached to.

Spud pins: Pins that fix the spuds to the wheel rims.

Spuds: 'T'-shaped sections that are fixed to the wheel rims for travelling on soft or sloping ground.

Steam gauge: A gauge fitted to the top of the boiler and facing the driver to indicate the pressure inside the boiler. Single cylinder steam engines usually operated at 120 psi and compounds at 180-200 psi

Steam Plough Club: Founded on 3rd December 1966 by Harold Bonnett (for more information see page 306).

Steam plough gang: The number of persons needed to operate a set of steam ploughing tackle and consisted of a foreman, two drivers, one plough or cultivator man and a cook boy.

Steam ploughing tackle: Consisted of two engines, a living van, a water cart, a plough, a cultivator, a set of harrows and a mole drainer.

Steam ports: the ports that are opened and closed by the slide valves.

Tank steerage engines: Early ploughing engines were fitted with this type of steering. Instead of having a drum in front of the firebox operated by worm and worm wheel (as fitted to later engines), tank steerage engines were fitted with a pair of cogwheels under the tank at the rear of the engine, the driver having to turn the steering wheel to the right to go left and to the left to go right.

Tender: The rear end of the steam engine ie the water tank, footplate and coal bunker.

Third motion shaft: The second shaft of the gear train that is driven by the second motion shaft. This applies to four-shaft engines only.

Three speed Fowlers: Engines used for hauling and were also used by showmen. Most traction engines were two-speed. The third gear on

Fowlers was situated inside the flywheel.

Threshing machine: A machine generally driven by steam engines to extract corn from straw and grade it.

'Tickling stick': A small lever that operates the valve which allows high pressure steam into the low pressure cylinder on compound engines.

Tines: Spikes on a cultivator that dig into the soil.

Traction engines: Steam engines used for farm work, hauling and the like.

Turntable ring: Farm wagons had an undercarriage at the front end that turned for steering and under the bed of the wagon was situated a steel ring for the undercarriage to slide round on.

Two wing-tines: Fowler cultivators with a tine outside each rear wheel, known as 'wing tines'.

Vee-Bar: A 'V'-shaped bar at the top of the cultivator or harrows that the two engine ropes are shackled to.

Water cart: Used to supply water to the engines and pulled by two heavy horses The water cart usually held 2000 gallons.

Water lifter: Fitted to the tender of a steam engine and was operated by steam to suck water from ponds or streams. On the larger road engines, the water lifter was fitted to a belly tank located under the boiler.

Whistle: Fitted to the top of the cylinder. On ploughing engines whistles, were used mainly when working over hills, the two engines when visually out of sight of each other, communicating audibly by a system of simple signals - one blast for 'stop' and two blasts for 'go'.

White's injector: These were fitted to most Fowler BB1 engines and was the only means of getting water into the boiler. If kept clean inside, these injectors were very reliable, but did not operate so efficiently if the water in the tank was warm.

Recommended Reading

1. 'Men of Iron', published by the Wallingford Historical &
   Archaeological Society 1983. Edited by Judy & Stuart Dewey.
   Printed by Parchment (Oxford) Ltd.

2. 'Ploughing by Steam' by John Haining & Colin Tyler.
   Originally published by M.A.P. Ltd, 1970.
   Paperback Edition (ISBN 0-906798-49-3) first published by
   Ashgrove Press Limited, 1985

3. 'Saga of the Steam Plough' by Harold Bonnett. George Allen &
   Unwin, 1965. Second Impression (ISBN 0-7153-5742-5),
   David & Charles, 1972.

4. 'Steaming On - Engines & Wagons from the Golden Age of
   Steam Power' by Eric Sawford (ISBN 0-7509-1484-X),
   Sutton Publishing Limited, 1998.

Personalities

The following list contains the names of some of the people encountered by Joe Challis during his lifetime with steam and recalled in this book:

Aubrey, Ben (Ropeman, Wards)

Baker, Bill (Lorry driver, Basildon Estate)

Bantick, Bill (Works Foreman, Wards)

Becket, Guss (Wilders)

Bennett, Fred (Cultivator an, BB1 steam ploughing gang, Wards)

Breakspear, Bert (Wards)

Case, Jack (Roller driver, Fords)

Challis, Bert (Brother)

Challis, Cecil (Brother)

Challis, Jack (Brother)

Chesterton, Mr (Basildon Estate Manager)

Collins, Jim (Driver BB1 ploughing gang, Wards)

Cooper, George (Fitter, Wards)

Cresswell, Dan (Basildon Estate steam driver, then Wilders)

Day, Jim (Driver, Wards)

Deacon, 'Peggy' (Night watchman, Goring)

Downham, Billy (Communication man)

Edwards, Jack 'Bandy' (Ploughman, Wilders)

Elliott, Walt (BB1 ploughing gang, Wards)

Flowers, Bill (Sawmill owner, Pangbourne)

Ford, Harry (Blacksmith, Basildon Estate)

Ilesdon, Wally (Driver, Ploughing gang, Wilders)

Jefferies, Charlie (Driver, Ploughing gang, Wilders)

Johnson, George (Driver, Basildon Estate, then Wilders)

Jones, Fred (Cultivator man, Ploughing gang, Wilders)

King, Bob 'Kingey' (Apprentice moulder, Wilders)

Kirk, Bill (Blacksmith, Basildon Estate)

Little, George (Manager, Wilders)

Marchington, Frank (Buxworth Steam Group)

Marchington, Tony

Marchington, Milly

Marchington, Allan

Morrison, Major James Archibald (Owner of Basildon Estate)

Newman, George (Wilders)

North, Harry (Gang foreman, Fords)

Noyce, George (Yard foreman, Fords)

Parkes, George (Ploughing gang foreman, Wilders)

Parkin, Mr (Fords)

Perry, Jim (Lathe operator, Wilders)

Platt, Albert (Chain gang, Wards)

Pullen, Mr (Divisional Surveyor, Fords)

Quatermain, 'Jip' (Ploughman, Wilders)

Richings, Jack ((Steam crane driver, Basildon Estate)

Roslin, Bob (Fitter, Wards)

Saunders, Fred (Boilersmith, Wilders)

Saunders, Jack (Fitting shop foreman, Wilders)

Smith, Jim (Steam plough foreman, Basildon Estate, then Wilders)

Steele, Frank (Driver/steersman, Wards)

Stewart, Charlie (Boilersmith, Wards)

Walters, Lad (Wilders)

Ward, Jack (Threshing man, Wards)

Ward, Sydney (Wards)

Wells, Bill (BB1 ploughing gang, Wards)

Wickens, Barry (Driver, Wards)

Wickens, Albert (Ploughing agent and landlord of 'Perch and Pike' public house, South Stoke)

Wilder, John (Wilders)

York, John (Travelling foreman, Fords)

'Out of necessity, many of the children who attended the Basildon schools with me, would spend most of their Summer holidays doing exactly what these children are doing, gleaning in the Estate fields, picking up ears of corn left by the reapers. However, I personally never went gleaning. All my spare time was spent with the steam plough tackle ...!' **JOE CHALLIS**

Chapter 1

'The Steam Bug'

I was born on 6th October 1912 at Primrose Cottage, Hook End Lane, Lower Basildon, Nr. Reading, Berkshire, the second son of a family of eight, four boys and four girls. Upper and Lower Basildon were then very small villages two miles apart and were part of the Basildon Estate owned by millionaire James Archibald Morrison. This was a very large Estate reaching from Pangbourne to the Berkshire Downs with quite a big slice on the Oxfordshire side of the River Thames, in all about nine square miles. The mansion and park lies between the two villages and is now a National Trust property.

On the Estate there were many teams of heavy horses to pull the grass mowers, corn binders, corn drills, harrows etc, but the heavy work of ploughing and cultivating was done by iron horses, a pair of Fowler 12 hp compound ploughing engines which I would think must have been K7s. Also to do the threshing, hauling timber and cattle food and bringing a constant flow of building materials from Pangbourne Station there was an 8 hp single cylinder Fowler traction engine. Between the Thames and the Reading to Oxford road, which is now the Child Beale Wildlife Trust, were the Estate gravel pits where gravel was dredged out with a steam crane which had a grab holding about two cubic yards and so did not take long to fill the trucks for the old Fowler to struggle up the steep slope to the main road.

The Estate, therefore, relied very much on steam power to keep it going. My father was the steam boss there and would be working with the ploughing engines while the rush was on, filling in between time with the traction engine. He was very experienced with steam engines starting with them as a boy for Thomas Baker & Sons of Compton in Berkshire. They had steam threshing tackle and I would think ploughing tackle as well. They also had a foundry and made farm machinery, supplying most of the farms in the area with plough shares, although their main product was horse drawn water carts. They were taken over many years ago and the site is now used for making mobile cranes.

Basildon Estate saw mill which was just inside the park, about one mile from my home, was also powered by the Fowler traction engine. She would be run back under the shed and a chimney extension (to carry the smoke away from the saw benches), was lowered down onto her chimney and there she would be for, perhaps, two or three weeks at a time until enough gate posts, fencing, building timber etc had been cut. This was where I was first

1

bitten by the steam engine bug. From the age of about four years when the engine was at the saw mill on Saturday mornings, I would be perched on the carrier of father's bike and away we would go to get steam up for seven o'clock. He would show me how to keep the fire made up, watch the steam and water gauges and when to turn the pump on or off. I loved to go home at midday with my hands and face black with oil and coal dust.

By the end of World War One, I was six years old and had learned quite a lot about steam engines. My older brother, who was seven years older than myself would soon be thinking of leaving school and starting work with the steam engines on the Estate. He was by now quite useful with the ploughing engines as he had spent hundreds of hours with father in the evenings, Saturday mornings and school holidays and could drive them quite well. He was like father, tall and hefty, being six foot, weighed sixteen stone and was as strong as a horse. My two younger brothers turned out to be the same. This is where I thought I was going to lose out, as I was very small for my age. I was the titch of the family but even so I was as tough as nails.

By now I was steam engine mad and thought of nothing else and would walk miles to be near a steam engine of any type or shape. I could very often see some nice engines on my way to and from school, as I had to walk about a mile to the Lower Basildon School which was at the side of the main Reading to Oxford road in the middle of the village. At that time, there was a haulage firm in Reading by the name of Charles Openshaw, which had about half a dozen big three-speed Fowlers and used that road most days with loads of bricks and tiles from the Tilehurst brick yards. They also did a lot of work for Pickfords of Reading. These were beautiful engines and were always spotlessly clean with gleaming brass work and each one had its polished name plate on the side motion covers.

I still remember the names of most of them, they were *Big Ben*, *Mons Star*, *Princess Royal*, *Princess Mary* and *Majestic* but I am pretty sure that there was another one. They were all on iron wheels in those days and our stretch of the road that they used was an accident black spot. From the Reading direction they had to go down Crown Hill, which was then quite steep and went through a chalk cutting at the top, then a fairly sharp left-hand bend at the bottom which leaned the wrong way and this is where the accidents happened. As the engines turned the left-hand bend, the load tended to push the back of the engine across the road. At this very place, on my way home from school one day, I came across one of Jacob Studt's big Burrell road engines, which had been hauling three large wagons (Jacob Studt was the famous travelling showman). The wagons had completely left the road, toppling over into a gully, the engine coming to a halt with its rear wheel up against an elm tree. One wagon had contained glassware, but its contents were spread everywhere. She laid there for a couple of days until pulled back onto her wheels by a showman's engine.

I used to watch the Openshaw gangs start off down the hill very steadily, edging their way to the bend with the truck brakes full on, then stop at the bottom to unwind the brakes, fire up and then slog their way up Grotto Hill and away towards Streatley. I was late for school more than once by hanging around waiting for these beautiful old engines to come along, then to watch them down the hill. I would stand on the fence at the top of the bank, where I was perfectly safe and look down on to them as they slowly made their way down the hill which was dreaded by everyone in those days. I suppose they would leave Reading about 7 o'clock and usually reached Lower Basildon between half past eight and nine o'clock. The eighth mile stone from Reading is at the top of the hill and reads Oxford 20, Reading 8, Wallingford 7 and Abingdon 17.

Often during the summer evenings, or perhaps a Saturday afternoon, I would make a change by watching the trains go through the village. All that I had to do was walk to the end of the lane, cross the Reading road, go about 200 yards down the meadow to where the railway crosses the Thames, then climb up the bank, stand on the railway fence and wait for those great Swindon built engines to come hammering through. Some of them, like for instance 'The Cheltenham Flyer', would be doing 80 mph, a great sight and to add to that, this was where they picked up water.

On the opposite side of the lines to where I used to stand, was a pump house with two steam driven pumps. These were used to keep a huge tank, built up on brickwork, filled up with water. This in turn kept the troughs filled with water. These troughs were about 18in. wide by about 9in. deep and reached for about half a mile. As soon as they reached this point the fireman would wind a big handle round and drop the scoop into the trough and in a very short distance you could see water overflowing from the tender, sometimes as far back as the third coach. At that time, I could tell you the number of each engine according to its name, first the 'Hall' class then the 'Castles' and finally the 'Kings' all very fine engines and I loved to watch them go by, but somehow I never fancied going to work with them.

At the top of the field which sloped up from where we lived, was the Estate lime kiln. This was on our side of a track cut across the hillside. On the opposite side of the track lies the chalk quarry, about a 50 foot face of some of the best chalk you will ever find. On the face is a cave, from which were taken a large number of the Roman flint axes and spears, now to be seen in the Reading Museum. Another road had been cut across the hill, so that the lime could be loaded from the bottom of the kiln, this road sloped steeply coming out onto the notorious Crown Hill. When the old Fowler

3

traction engine was pulling out on to the main road whilst hauling two trucks well loaded with lime, she could be heard a long way off, a sound I loved to hear. The trucks of lime would be drawn into the fields and each one in turn would be slowly pulled along with two or three farm labourers throwing its contents over the field with the aid of shovels.

One afternoon I was on my way home from school and could hear the crisp bark of the Fowler on its way up from the kiln. By the time she reached the main road I was standing on the bank waiting to see them edge their way down the hill. She was stopped with the front wheels on the main road and blowing off like mad. While the injector was cooling her down and filling the boiler ready for the steep slope down, two of the gang were winding on the brakes of the trucks. There was a beam on hangers with blocks direct onto the wheel rims with a handwheel and screw to pull them on. The other two members of the gang walked away from the engine to stop any car or lorry that might be coming either way, as all the road was needed to get round and back into the side of the road before they reached the off-camber left-handed bend.

As they made their way down the hill, I walked along the top of the bank by the side of them (this was always my path to and from school). Safely round the bend and onto the flat she was brought to a halt. While the brakes were being released father was firing up ready for the short journey up the lane past home to a field about a quarter of a mile away. He closed the fire hole door, wiped his hands and, hopping up onto the rear wheel of the engine, lifted me off the bank and onto the footplate with him. After a short dressing down not to get my clothes dirty, away we went.

This was to be my very first ride on the road with a steam engine and it sticks in my mind as if it were only yesterday. I was standing on the footplate behind my father, making sure that my school clothes were not getting dirty, watching his mate spinning the steering wheel round to turn into Hook End Lane. As the lane leaves the main road, there is a short slope up then down the other side and in sight of our home. As we started up the slope, father said to shut my eyes and keep them shut while we pulled up there. This was so that they did not get filled with hot ashes (I suppose the engine was now in top gear). We were over the hill and down the other side with my eyes still shut and in sight of home, when father gave a blast of the whistle and I nearly jumped out of my shoes.

By the time we reached home, mother was standing at the door waiting for me, as she knew it was time for me to be home, but the engine did not stop. Father held me above his head so that she could see that I was safe with him and away we went up the road and into the field. The rear truck was uncoupled and the labourers took up their places on top of the half burnt

4

chalk and away we went to the far side of the field so that the lime could be spread on the way back. They had sized up the direction of the wind and this way the dust was being blown away from us. A few shovels of coal on the fire, a drop of water in the boiler and we were ready to be away at crawling pace while the lime was being shovelled out as far either side as they could throw it.

To my great surprise, father said "You are safe here now you can have a go" (I had been badgering him for a long time to let me see if I could drive the old girl). He had shown me how to start it out of gear and I had known for a long time which way the reversing lever had to be for the centre that the crank was on. I also had the feel of the regulator, so I started off pretty well and kept it ticking over all the way across the field. I was highly delighted and was now ready to go home and tell mother what I had been doing. I was also getting hungry, so while they were hooking up to the other truck, I made my way home to get cleaned up and have my tea. From the time father reached home and I went to bed, I talked of nothing else and the same the next few days with my school pals.

I was now seven years old and eager to learn as much as I could about steam engines and was, therefore, constantly asking questions about different parts of the old Fowler engine. Father would draw the part, explain what it was called and what it had to do. My brother had now left school and was working on the Estate with the engines. He was by now very useful, as he had been well trained by father and could also give me a lot of help. We slept together and talked of nothing else but steam engines. Every evening after his day's work, he would tell me just about everything that had happened during the day and how he had been driving the ploughing engines. He told me that although the ploughers were very much bigger than the Fowler traction engine, they were much easier to drive (something I could hardly believe), but later found out how right he was.

As time went on, I was getting the odd chance to drive the old Fowler on some of the farm roads with the thrashing tackle behind it, or to bring a couple of trucks of bricks out from the brick kiln. By now, I was getting quite good, as I could start off with a good load behind without too much of a snatch. If she was on the wrong centre for starting forward, I could pull the reversing lever back and use the regulator just right to turn it back right for going forward, but would often have to use both hands to push the lever forward again, then work fast to give it enough steam to get going. I was always told you don't have to be a big he-man as it's the way that you do it. This I found to be true.

With World War One now well behind us, lots of new things were happening on the Estate. New farm buildings were going up, new houses being built, more land had been bought up and by now the engines were really earning their keep. As a matter of fact, the hauling from Pangbourne Station at times was more than the traction engine could cope with, as there would often be ten or twelve trucks of coal at a time arriving at the station to feed the engines, brick kilns, lime kiln and gravel digging crane. Things were getting stretched to the limit and something would have to be done.

This is when the first lorry came to the Estate. It was a Seldon 6-tonner, one that I had never seen before or since. It was not long before a second lorry came on the scene, this time a second-hand German army wagon and trailer both of which had seen service in France. It was a huge thing and used nearly as much petrol as the steam engines did water. This was a Hanz Lloydd on solid tyres and the trailer on steel tyres, about $1\frac{1}{2}$in. thick. With two lorries now in use, the steam engine could get on with the threshing, sawing etc and was now spending quite a bit of its time at the brick kiln, where much new brick making machinery had been installed. There were now many more workers on the Estate and a few of these were trained as steam engine drivers, so that the ploughing engines could be worked full time as they were now going outside the Estate to help out neighbouring farmers.

As Lower Basildon school was only an infant school, when pupils reached the age of nine years they had to go to Upper Basildon school. This meant that I had two miles to walk morning and night, but this did not bother me at all as there were many footpaths that the gamekeepers had made. These took me through the woods and across the fields, thus giving me a better chance to call in on the ploughing engines. They could often be seen working somewhere on the chalky hills around Upper Basildon and my brother was now a driver on one of them and keen to show me all the ins and outs of steam ploughing. By now the ploughing engines were working from seven in the morning round to nine o'clock in the evening, through the long days of spring and summer. A full time steam plough foreman was employed by the Estate so that father could put in full time with his beloved Fowler. We had a very large garden to keep dug and planted so he liked to get home in reasonable time to do just that. The chap that had come to take over the ploughing tackle turned out to be quite a nice guy. His name was Jim Smith but I don't remember where he came from to Basildon. There were many steam plough contractors around in those days and I suppose he must have come from one of them as father reckoned that he knew all the answers about steam ploughing.

I was now at school with the older boys, some of them near school leaving age, which was then fourteen years. They all seemed to be keen on football and cricket and did nothing else at play times and mid-day meal

6

times. I had no interest whatever in this and at mid-day would wander off into the woods to go bird-nesting or just wander around the hills and fields, perhaps listening for the crisp bark of the old Fowler traction engine which was nearly always around Upper Basildon with loads of coal for the brick kiln, or timber for the saw mill, or perhaps cattle food for one of the farms, or with the threshing tackle behind it on its way from one farm to another. The country around Upper Basildon is very hilly and I could often hear the old girl, although very often, perhaps, half a mile away and out of sight. The worst hill being Kiln Hill, which is on the road from Pangbourne to the brick kiln. It was then just a flint road over clay and like a sponge, so that with two trucks of coal behind, it was just about as much as the old Fowler could manage. Father used to tell me that if you put a matchbox under the front wheel it would hardly be crushed. With the ploughing engines it was a different story. If you could not see them, you would not hear them, as the fields were light soil and never cultivated or ploughed very deep to avoid bringing chalk to the top and, of course, a compound always has a soft exhaust note compared with a single cylinder engine.

By walking through the woods to school, I was not seeing so much of the Charles Openshaw engines, but I was getting to know more about the ploughing engines. There were not many evenings that I did not find my way to them and spend an hour or two on the cultivator with Jim Smith, or stand on the footplate of one of the engines to watch the rope clutch being dropped in as the crankshaft ticked over, then to see the speed build up after the cultivator was dropped, often so fast that the spokes of the flywheel could not be seen.

After a day's work, while we were all sat at home taking a rest before going to bed, I was for ever asking questions about the engines such as: Why did the compound ploughers run so much faster than the single cylinder traction engine, even though they had far more moving parts, especially since they were both made by the same firm? The answer was soon there, the K7s were shorter stroke and the crankshaft was well balanced. They were also geared lower than the single-cylinder ploughing engines and so were designed to run fast (I had not yet seen a single-cylinder ploughing engine). Another question was, why as the cultivator got nearer to the engine, was the regulator being gradually opened more, yet the crank was gradually getting slower and, more often than not, the steam pressure was getting higher, which to me made no sense at all. It was quite a time before the penny dropped, while it was being explained what this is all about. You start off with the drum nearly empty and as the rope builds up on to the drum, so does the speed of the cultivator, therefore the going gets much harder, the rope speed is nearly twice as fast with a full drum as with an empty one.

As the summer of that year went on, I was spending more and more time with the ploughers. My brother by now had built me up a bicycle which I soon learnt to ride and was taking it to school, so that I could be home by about four o'clock, change into some old clothes, have a cup of tea and be away to the ploughing tackle for the rest of the evening. I nearly always had some idea where to steer for. Every night I would ask my brother Bert where they were likely to be on the next day. Alternatively, I could always find them by the wheel tracks, as I learned from a very early age how to tell by the angle of the cross strake marks on the road which way the engine had travelled.

By now, I was often spending hours on the cultivator with Jim Smith, who seemed to like to have someone to chatter to as he made his way backwards and forwards across the field in the dust from the wheels. He had shown me how to sit on the seat safely when riding as a passenger. There is nothing to catch hold of, so it can be a rough ride at times, especially when crossing the furrows. When the wheels drop into the furrow, the tines go deep into the ground and the cultivator will actually stop for a fraction of a second then lurch forward. This is caused by the rope stretching, the more rope you have out, the more it will stretch. The seat on the Fowler cultivator is just a wooden tool box, with a lid that overhangs each side of the box by about 6in.. You sit travelling sideways and astride the box, catching hold of the overhanging end of the lid, never anywhere else, because often if you go over a bump while travelling at a fair speed, the lid of the box, with you sat on it, will jump up and if it comes down on your fingers, they would be well and truly flattened. It was not long before Jim was letting me steer the cultivator and had pointed out to me how to make the thirteen tines count as fifteen.

Most Fowler cultivators were what was known as eleven-thirteen, there being eleven tines equally spaced in the main frame with two wing-tines, one outside each main wheel. These would be taken out when working on very heavy or hard ground. Jim had told me never to look at the front wheel, but look straight ahead and it soon came to me that by doing this you can judge your position so that the wing-tine is running about the same distance away from where the outside tine came in the last pull. I could turn the steering back into line for going straight after turning round, but I had to let go of the steering wheel and stand up, using both hands to pull the lever to drop the tines in again. The cultivator and harrows are lifted and latched automatically every time the implement turns at the end of the pull by the vee-bar to which the ropes are attached and they are held there until the lever is pulled to let them down again.

I was by now getting on well with Jim and most evenings as soon as I arrived on the scene, he would start chattering to me about the engines, the implements or if he happened to be on the cultivator, he would beckon me to jump on and have a ride. When I told him I could drive the Fowler traction engine, he said that if I could drive that, then surely I could drive these, so as soon as the cultivator man was back from his tea break I was taken across the field to my brother's engine and pushed up onto the footplate to have a go. Well, I had stood up there many times before and knew that the levers were all too high and too far away for me to reach properly, but now I had been given the OK by the foreman, I was certainly going to have a go.

While the rope was running out, I started the engine running and got it nicely ticking over with the reversing lever forward, so that as soon as the drum had stopped turning, I could pull the lever back and lift the clutch lever at the same time (this was the right-hand engine which pulls the rope in with the lever back). My brother could see that no way could I reach the two levers at the same time, so he said to look after the reversing lever and regulator and he would see to the clutch, so I yanked the lever back with both hands and in went the clutch nice and quiet. A little bit more on the regulator and I could see the cultivator turning nicely. This was OK until the cultivator was dropped. I had not worked fast enough with the regulator, so she stopped. However, my brother was waiting for this and he reached forward to push the auxiliary lever and we were away again, soon building up speed. I thought this was great, but I could see that I would not be able to see when the rope eye was getting near to the coiling gear pulley or 'monkey's head' as they were commonly known, so I handed over to brother Bert to finish pulling in the last few yards. I had about half a dozen pulls that evening and was really chuffed and could not get home fast enough to tell father what I had been doing.

When I reached home the next afternoon, mother told me that I had not got far to go that day as they were round in Rainbow Bottom. This was only a few hundred yards from home, so on with the old clothes, have a quick cup of tea and a sandwich and away up the lane to the engines. They had cultivated the flat part of the field and started working up the hill which was fairly steep at the end that my brother's engine was working, so he said that I had better have a few pulls before we got onto the steeper part of the hill. Now in the big locker under the living van, there was always a few lengths of railway sleeper ready to split for lighting-up wood, if none could be found in the hedgerows or woods around the fields. Bert had found a short piece of chain and a couple of staples and had fixed two of these lengths of sleeper together. These were hanging on the plough coupling of the engine and they were soon pulled across the coal bunker and laid on the footplate for me to stand on. This was great, a bit awkward for firing up, but I could now reach the levers so much better, though I could still not see over the rear gear guard to see when the rope eye was near the pulleys without leaning right over. To do this, I had to let go of the regulator which I soon got off to a fine art.

By now, we were getting onto the steep part of the field and at each move forward the scotch block, which was always hanging on a long chain hooked to the side of the tender, had to be pulled up behind the wheel and the engine carefully let back onto it. If the hill was fairly steep, you did not rely on just the block. On the back of every ploughing engine in those days was a big sling chain, with one end fixed to the coupling pin and the hook end usually hanging in the back of the coal bunker or on the plough coupling. Before the driver started to pull the cultivator, the sling chain would be threaded through the wheel and the hook put over the chain so that, if the block got pushed into the ground and the wheel mounted it, the chain would tighten and hold it. With all this to do at every pull, Bert took over while I had a few rides on the cultivator with Jim.

The chap driving the left-hand engine was Dan Cresswell. He had spent quite a lot of time in the Navy and had gone through the war as a stoker in a battleship. His plougher was still on fairly level ground, so as we turned round he shouted down for me to come and have a go on his engine. I didn't need telling twice and was soon up on the footplate with him and getting used to the feel of the regulator. It was very much the same as Bert's engine. The only thing I had to remember was she had to run with the lever forward instead of back. This I soon got the hang of and although I had not got any blocks to stand on, I could see the pulleys and could watch the rope eye right up to them, there being no gearing to look over on the left hand side. I spent most of the evening on this engine. It was a bit of a struggle to reach the gear lever to move up after each pull, but I managed it, soon realising that it was a full time job. The field was not very wide and by the time I had moved forward, put it out of gear, turned the injector on, put a few shovels of coal on the fire, the drum had stopped turning and it was time to pull back again.

With the daylight beginning to fade, I made my way back home, had a good wash and was telling my parents all I had been doing. By this time Bert had arrived home and we were soon ready for bed, to chatter about what had been done. I was now steam plough mad. Bert and I thought and talked of nothing else and at weekends we had steam ploughing for every meal when we were together. I had made up my mind that there was nothing else I wanted to do when the time came to leave school, but this was still four years away. Four years is a long time when you have made up your mind and are just waiting for that day to come. Most evenings and Saturday mornings and most of the summer holidays of that year, I would be away on my bicycle to find the ploughing engines for a drive whenever possible. I was waiting for the autumn, when they would park the cultivator somewhere and get down to ploughing, most of this being done after harvest was finished.

As soon as the plough was put into action, I was there to have a ride on it, as up to now I had not even sat on it while moving. The plough, which was supplied to the Estate with the rest of the set, was a five-furrow anti-balance job and was kept in good condition and could do some very nice work. I gathered there was a lot of keen competition going between the carters with their horse ploughs and the steam gang.

With a few rides on the middle seat of the plough watching the corn stubble being turned nicely under, it was time to get behind the steering wheel. Now, I had sat at the steering wheel several times before while it was not in use and the axle was in the centre position. This way, I could reach the steering wheel with no problems, but it was a different story when the plough was in action. The plough was pulled down ready for the return trip. I scrambled onto the seat and as soon as the rope tightened and the plough bit into the ground, the axle moved to its working position. I was leaning forward and nearly off the seat and, of course, there is no footrest. So there I was, just about dangling on the edge of the seat, but I had kept a fairly straight furrow and was highly delighted.

Just before we reached the far side of the field, Jim, who had been riding on the middle seat, explained to me that a few yards from the end of the pull, I must turn the wheel quickly and steer the plough towards the front of the engine, then sharply back again. By doing this, you don't have to do too much to swing the furrow wheel over into the last furrow of the previous pull. With this being done, I am back behind the steering wheel again and making our way back across the field, but for a few dozen yards I was a bit foxed as to what was going on. I was first tight to the land side of the furrow, then across the other side. Looking back to Jim perched on the spare seat, I saw he was laughing all over his face. Then he shouted across to tell me what I was doing wrong.

What I had not been told was that only one end of the plough steers in the normal way, ie by turning clockwise to go right and anti-clockwise to go left. The other end does the reverse, ie you turn clockwise to go left, etc. I was then told that the single-cylinder ploughing engines, with the old type tank-steerage also steered that way. I had not yet seen engines of this type and was anxious to see what they were all about.

After reaching home that evening and talking to father about them, he explained to me how this back to front steering worked and how lethal the old tank-steerage engines were to handle on rough ground. He told me that the nearest ones of this type to us were at R J & H Wilder of Wallingford. They had four such sets and I would no doubt see some of them when I got around a bit further from home. One of their sets came to work occasionally as close as Goring, which was only two miles away.

Every bit of time I had spare right through the autumn, I would make my way to where the engines were working to get as much time as possible on the plough and was now quite a dab hand at it, having learned all the wrinkles there were to be known about the job. One of the main things being, that you don't sit directly behind the steering wheel, but lean out the side and look straight up the furrow. This way, not only can you keep a nice straight furrow, but most of all, if the rope on the engine should happen not to be running just right and the engine is leaning slightly towards the work, then when it reaches the top of the drum, it will sometimes put two coils on the top of each other. They will then drop with a bang and the axle of the plough will fly back into the centre position and you have got yourself a smack in the face with the steering wheel. Sometimes, when this happens, the two coils of the rope that have dropped will cross over each other and you are then in dire trouble, as they are then tied in a knot and take a bit of putting right.

I was now eager to drive the engine and pull the plough across the field. So, one evening when they were working close to home and were ploughing fairly shallow and pulling was quite easy, Bert got me on the footplate to have a go. He explained to me that for ploughing you don't pull quite so fast as cultivating. Also, when the plough is steered sharply to the front of the engine at the end of the pull and the plough wheel comes out of the furrow, it lifts the plough out of the ground and it is then so easy to pull the plough into the cylinder of the engine with serious results. This I soon got used to and could judge this so much easier, as I could see the end of the plough so much better than I could the cultivator.

I was still getting quite a bit of time in with the old Fowler traction engine, chiefly Saturdays and at times even on a Sunday, as things were now getting a bit hectic. There were so many new things turning up at the station. The lorries were a big help, but it was still full time work for the steamer. There was much more new livestock, which had to be fed only the best and there were few days at a time when there was nothing in the station to be moved to one farm or another on the Estate. There was also much new machinery for the brick kiln, as many more bricks would be needed for all the new farm buildings and houses that were being built. I said to father, "You are going to be busier than ever if you are going to keep running back to the brickyard to drive this lot for a few days at a time", as he had been doing in the past. The answer was that "There is a new portable steam engine on the way to drive this in the summer and the sawmill in winter". I had never heard of a portable steam engine and was eager to know what they were like. I was soon told that it was an engine on four wheels with no gears to drive it along, so that it has to be pulled from place to place by another engine or sometimes by horses. I was longing for the day when this would turn up.

I didn't have to wait too long. Father came home one night and said that he was going to Pangbourne in the morning to unload the new portable and pull it into the brickyard, which was only about a quarter of a mile from the school. I only had to run a hundred yards or so along a footpath through Emery's Copse and I was at the bottom of Kiln Hill. Father had told me he had no idea what time they would be there, as it would depend on what sort of luck they had unloading it from the railway wagon. "You will no doubt hear us long before we get there" he said. By what I could gather, it was a real big portable and from Pangbourne to Upper Basildon is up hill all the way and in places quite steep.

I went to school the next morning and told a few of my pals what was on the way. We soon made up our minds how we were going to spend our midday meal time from 12 noon to 1-30pm. We sat at our desks listening and hoping that they would not reach the village before mid-day, so that we could see them tackle the big hill. Twelve o'clock came and not a sound of a struggling steam engine, so we walked through the copse and played in the sand pit which was near the road to the brick kiln. Then, true enough, we could hear the old Fowler in the distance and could tell it was gradually getting closer to us, before it all went quiet for several minutes. We thought they had run into trouble, or had stopped for a meal break, but we were wrong. They had been free-wheeling down the slope between the two pubs - the 'Beehive' and the 'Red Lion' - and as we could after all hear, they were now on their way up the slope to the bottom of the steep hill. We could also see the smoke rushing up through the trees. For us, however, time was running out and it was time for getting back to school. We were not going to see the them tackle the hill after all. I desperately wanted to see this new engine, so I hung on for a few more minutes, until there, hanging on the back of the Fowler, was the biggest Robey portable I have ever seen in my life. An 8 hp Fowler is not one of the smallest of engines, but it looked like a toy in front of the Robey, which was very high and obviously looked top heavy with its huge cylinder block and two massive flywheels perched high above the boiler.

They stopped at the bottom of the hill and I had a word with father who

13

wasn't very happy and said, "This is where the trouble begins. We've already had to lock the differential gears to get up Pangbourne Hill and have been in low gear all the way". We realised that we could not stay and see them climb the hill, as it was time to be back in school. We dashed off, leaving them fitting a set of spud pins in both wheels, which was, of course, illegal, but the Estate did a lot towards the upkeep of this road. They were then about the only users of it and were constantly repairing and patching it with gravel or broken bricks etc, as it was just a bed of clay with a layer of flints on the top. When anything heavy went over, it was as if it was made of rubber.

When father reached home that night, my first words to him were "How did you get up the hill?". The answer was "We had real trouble. We got just about half way up and she started to dig herself in so we had to block the portable up, uncouple the engine and then rope the portable up in stages. The biggest problem was getting out of the holes she had dug. We couldn't drop back so we put a few spuds on her and went forward. Then we had to let the new portable back on the rope so that we could manoeuvre it over to straddle the holes that the Fowler had dug. Then slowly but surely, with two big scotch blocks following close behind the wheels, we reached the top and into the brickyard".

A few days later, the Robey was in position and raring to go. On the Saturday morning, I was there to see the first try out of this giant and all the new machinery. I left home with father that morning about 6am to travel the two miles to the brick works. We soon had a fire on the go and it was not long before the steam gauge started to move, as she had been steamed up on the Friday to get the drive belt sorted out. By about 8 o'clock, some of the officials from the Estate had arrived ready to see the new engine, pug mills etc, being put to the test. With everybody in their places, the wheels started turning and everything was to be loaded to its maximum to see just what could be turned out. With everything fully loaded, this massive engine just made mincemeat of it all. Its tall chimney pushing smoke high into the sky, you could hardly hear it running. Father had already told them it would be powerful enough to drive three such loads, but it was purchased on the recommendation of the manufacturers of the brick making machinery (who were no doubt working with the Robey concern) and as father always said, they had built this huge engine which nobody wanted and now was the time to move it.

I now had one more steam engine to visit whenever I wished and I often look back over the years and think how lucky I was compared with most. I loved steam engines and dreamed of nothing else and there I was living in the middle of the Estate which now had four steam engines and a steam crane, all within a couple of miles of home. There was also the main Great Western line on my doorstep and the A329, Reading to Wallingford road between home and the railway, where several steam engines could be seen at least twice a week loaded with bricks or tiles and occasionally a few well loaded showman's engines.

There was by now, a whole lot of machinery to be kept in repair at Basildon, so it was decided that Blandy's Farm, at Upper Basildon, should be turned into workshops so that everything could be repaired there. This was about central for all of the Estate. Apart from two teams of horses, all the livestock from this farm was moved out to other farms and the barns and other buildings were made into some very nice workshops and storage places where the ploughing engines could be under cover for the winter months. There were also drilling machines, a hacksaw machine and a large Drummond lathe fitted into one of the barns with overhead shafting driven by a Blackstone oil engine. There was, of course, no electricity around in those days, so a model-T Ford engine was stripped out, bolted to the floor and harnessed up, from its flywheel, to the shafting to generate light for lead lamps etc. A new blacksmith's shop was built with two forges to deal with shoeing and repairs, operated by Bill Kirk and Harry Ford who were kept busy most of the time.

My brother Bert was now spending most of the winter in the workshops doing a few jobs to the ploughing engines. He also helped the new fitter who had been brought in to do repairs to the lorries and all the farm petrol and oil engines, plus the three model-T Fords that were chauffeur driven for Major Morrison to travel around the Estate. The Major could often be seen stood on the back seat or sat on the fold down hood with his double-barrelled twelve-bore shotgun ready to have a pop at a rook or pigeon while on his travels.

With the long winter evenings now with us, Bert and I would sit round the fire and talk about engines. He would tell me different things like how the slide valves worked over the steam ports and with a few rough drawings, I soon had it all weighed up. Also, how the injectors worked and things like this were pushed into me and I was all the time eager to find out more and more. Like my father and brother had said, if you learn something properly when you are young, it sinks in so much quicker and you never forget. I often think now how right they were.

Photograph: Rural History Centre, University of Reading.

'Pictured above are young ploughmen being trained at Turner's Court, near Wallingford. Unless you were an experienced plough man, this could be very hard work, as a single furrow plough using two horses is not easy to handle when turning at the ends of a field. However, for those with years of experience, it was relatively easy, as the horses did most of the work. Nonetheless, a ploughman would walk many a mile during a day's work behind a plough ...!' **JOE CHALLIS**

Chapter 2

'Steam Arising'

One evening, Bert came home with some pieces of brass that he had turned up on the lathe that day. These were a cylinder and piston for a model steam engine, one of the oscillating cylinder type. A very simple design that was fairly easy to make, so for a few evenings (if it was not too cold) we would be out in the shed fitting the pieces together and soon, with a few odd pieces from the workshop, the engine was ready to go.

We now needed a boiler, so Bert hunted around the workshop for something we could use to generate some steam to drive our new project. The best he could find was a very heavy five gallon drum which must have been well over $1/16$in. thick. So, a fitting was soldered into the top of the drum for the steam pipe to be connected to. This was all ready for the weekend when we would be trying our new engine.

The drum was half filled with water through the screw-in cap, but we had no pressure gauge, water gauge glass nor safety valve, so we would have to take great care not to overdo it. We figured that if it made just enough steam to turn the engine over, we would be happy. Behind the brick built woodshed that we were using for our workshop, was the fireplace where the pigs' food was cooked up. This was three six-foot sheets of corrugated iron bolted together to form the sides and back, with a short piece for the roof, some bricks were placed round inside with two bars across the top for the pot to stand on, with a wood fire underneath.

On the Sunday morning, the fire was made up and our boiler stood on the bars in place of the pig food pot. The steam pipe was disconnected and the tap turned on, so that we would know as soon as steam was being produced. We would then make up the fire, just enough to keep it on the boil and making sure not to overdo it. As soon as steam started to blow from the pipe, it was connected up to the engine and the tap turned back on and we were away, but not very well, as there were several modifications to make, one of which was a bigger flywheel.

This was the first of a whole string of engines to follow (some bigger and some smaller) and we now needed a lathe and drilling machine as it was not always easy to get use of the lathe in the Estate workshop. The latter was often in use and set up for some job or another concerned with the Estate.

A two speed breast-drill was purchased from Sarjents Tool Stores, a very small shop in West Street, Reading, very different from their later huge

Oxford Road store. The drill was bolted down onto a piece of flat steel bar with the drive wheel lying flat on the top. A home made slide rest pushed along in both directions by long $^3/_8$in.-set screws, then tapped back, with a soft hammer, ready for the next cut - not at all easy to operate. The cutting tools were pieces of hacksaw blade with a strip of $^1/_8$in. flat steel underneath them. This was not very accurate but we could turn up a piston for one of our engines or anything else that could be held by the $^1/_2$in. drill chuck. There was, of course, no tailstock but we got by for that winter hoping that a small secondhand lathe could be found ready for the next winter.

Our lighting in the woodshed, come workshop, was a carbide generator which had been taken from the German lorry (which had by now been fitted with electric lighting). Rubber tubes ran from the generator taking the acetylene gas to cycle lamp burners fitted to brackets on the wall, with pieces of polished brass behind the lamps as reflectors. Not a bad light really for those days and much safer than oil lamps.

Every Sunday at around mid-day, it was my job to walk down the lane to the main road and wait for the paper man who came from Reading with his two sons on bicycles loaded with papers. I would bring back the *News of the World* and a comic for my younger brothers and sisters. One Sunday afternoon, my brother was looking through the paper, which always had plenty of adverts in it, the two main ones for the Great Universal Stores and Graves of Sheffield. These two big mail order firms sold just about everything and if an item was more than a couple of pounds it could be had on hire purchase.

On looking through these adverts, Bert spotted a picture of a lathe, the offer of the week in the Graves advert. It was a 3in. back-geared screw-cutting lathe, just a plain bench job with no stand and nothing to drive it. It was listed as a Portass model-makers lathe and the price I am pretty sure was around £17. This was quite a fair sum of money in those days when you think about it, a steam plough engine driver's wage was twenty-seven shillings and six pence (about £1.37). So, with a few quiet words with father, as Bert was under 21 and would need father's signature as guarantor, it was decided that he should send to Sheffield for both order and H.P. forms.

As soon as these arrived they were filled in and, along with a deposit, posted off and we awaited the day for it to arrive at Pangbourne Station. This seemed weeks, as we were both eager to see what it was going to be like so that a stand could be made up for it. As Bert was working until five o'clock and the goods shed closed at five, we had decided that, when it arrived, I should cycle to the station on my way home from school to see just how big and heavy it was.

When I reached home one night from school, mother said that the letter had arrived to say that our lathe was at the station. So, off I went to see what it was like. All the way to Pangbourne, a distance of three miles, I was saying to myself that if there is any chance of getting it on my bike I would bring it home. On reaching the station, I went to the station master's office with the letter, which I suppose was the delivery note or something of that sort and explained who I was and what I was after. He said "How are you going to carry it?", and when I asked if it was too heavy to put on my bike, he just laughed and said that it was at least 1½ cwt.

We walked along to the goods shed and there it was in a heavy wooden crate which must have been nearly as heavy as the lathe. I looked at the crate then at my bike, which was not a full size one as I was still under 11 years old. Should I try to get it home, as three miles is a long way to walk even without a load as it was by now becoming dusk, or should I bike back home and we would have to make some other arrangements. Then, I suddenly remembered that I had no lights with me so I would have to walk as the police were red hot on lights in those days.

It was now getting on for five o'clock, so I had to make up my mind quickly, so I said I would try it. The crate was stood on end on the right-hand side pedal then roped up to the crossbar and saddle. It was nearly up to my shoulder and my bike had to lay at a pretty crazy angle to get it balanced and so I set off. That three miles seemed endless. My tyres were not that special and I was sweating all the time about getting a puncture or breaking the spokes of the wheels as they were running on the sides of the rims. I had not got halfway home when my brother arrived, as they had wondered where on earth I had got to and was I glad to see him. My shoulders were aching and I was dog tired, so he took over while I pushed his bike home and we eventually made home by about 7 o'clock.

A quick cup of tea, a bite to eat and we were out in the shed to unpack the lathe. The crate was carefully pulled to pieces and the contents taken out and placed on the bench. All the protective grease was removed and it now looked very nice, but we had still to make up a stand and something to drive it. A few rough drawings and measurements were sorted out, so we knew what materials to look for. Our stand was made up from steel angle from old bedsteads with a piece of 2in. thick oak timber bolted to the top. A shaft with a crank on the end and a large wheel from some shafting for a flywheel, plus a pair of ball-bearing plummer-blocks taken from the Estate workshop lathe, together with parts of the treadle (for power was taken from the overhead shafting) and we were ready to go. A few odd pieces of brass were turned up to get us used to our new toy and we were ready to make some real steam engines.

Bert ordered a set of castings for a vertical single cylinder high speed marine engine, from Stuart Turners of Henley-on-Thames and within a few weeks this was completed and ready to be tested. Our oil drum boiler had by now been fitted with a safety valve and pressure gauge, the latter was from a car foot pump and worked quite well. We had no water gauge glass, but two taps were fitted, one just above and one just below the halfway mark. Using these we could see if steam or water came out when they were turned on. We decided that 10 psi was about the safe maximum and at this pressure our new engine ran very nicely, so we were very pleased with it.

Our next project was a much bigger scale beam-engine, which took much longer as there were so many more parts to be machined. Before we had got very far into it, the longer days were with us again and the ploughing engines were out, so Bert was working much longer hours and very little was being done in our workshop. By now, I could use the lathe pretty well and wanted to get down to something all on my own. I had words with Bert and he was happy to let me use the lathe to have a go, but what was I going to make?

I had already made up my mind that it was going to be a 1in. scale model of father's 8 hp Fowler traction engine. At the meal table we were talking this over and father was more than delighted as he loved his old Fowler and thought it would be nice to have a model of the old girl in the family, but Bert was a bit concerned. I thought he was trying to put me off. He started bringing up some of the snags that I was up against, such as there were no castings available, no drawings and how could I cut the gears and things like this. I said drawings would be no problem as I would make my own. I would go with father every Saturday morning armed with paper, pencil, rule, calipers and anything else that I needed, and could then come home to draw them out properly with all the measurements. He could see that I was not going to be deterred and wished me luck, telling me that he would help me all he could. Again, I was determined to tackle this myself, so I said that I did not want any help and would like to tackle this all on my own, though a bit of financial help would be very much appreciated. So, that is how we left it and he would give me a few bob when I had to go and buy something.

My first job was to make the boiler, so I took a trip into Reading where there was a big scrap merchants yard. Here I managed to find a piece of copper tube the correct diameter for the boiler barrel and some copper sheet of about the same thickness for the firebox, hornplates, etc. Some pieces of oak were found and shaped to flange the firebox plates on after the copper had been heated and softened on the kitchen range.

Within a couple of weeks it was taking shape and very nicely riveted together with rivets from Stuart Turners. I was spending every minute I could on my new project, getting up in the morning with father and Bert and having a session before getting ready for school. Then, I would dash home after school and into the workshop again to get as much as possible done before the good weather arrived. There was no way that I was going to miss my steam ploughing.

I was not seeing quite so much now of Charles Openshaw's big Fowlers with their loads of bricks. They were using the A329 very little by now, so we were lucky to see one or two a week. I suppose that lorries were beginning to take over for long distance heavy haulage but I had but very little interest in these things. Steam was in my blood and I thought of nothing else.

There were always a lot of beech trees being felled every winter at Basildon and most of this was going to the Star Brush factory at Stoke Row in Oxfordshire to make their brush backs. Most of this had been drawn by horses, then one day they turned up with a new Scammell lorry to start clearing several hundred beech trees that had been cut close to my home. The trees were cut into shorter lengths than they were for the horse drawn timber wagons. A tripod was set up over the road and one of the horses that had been used to drag the trees out from the wood walked across the field harnessed to a cable. Thus, by the use of pulley blocks the timber was loaded onto the Scammell in a very short time, sometimes two loads a day.

About half a mile from home, was a large beech wood known as Harley Wood. This was a steep hill about half a mile long where some of the finest beech trees you would ever find had grown. That same winter, all the best of them were felled and we expected them to be taken away as usual by the Star Brush factory. However, it was a different team of horses and two Yorkshire men who turned up to start drawing the trees out from the wood. We thought they were very clever, one of the men would be up on the hill and would put the chains on to a tree then send the horses off with their load, often at a gallop to keep away from the trees. Once started, they came down the hill at a fair pace, then across a meadow and out to the side of the road where the timber was cut into standard lengths. These lengths were much longer than the brush factory Scammell was taking, so we guessed that something different would be collecting them when the time came.

I came that way home from school most evenings and watched the trees being spread wider and wider over the field. Then to my great surprise, one evening on my way home, in the meadow alongside the rows of trees was a big Fowler road engine with two timber wagons and a steam plough living van behind it. They had just pulled in and were sorting out a place to park the van, which was to be their home two or three nights a week. I parked my bicycle against the stack of trees and made my way to the big Fowler to have a browse round it. To my great surprise, on the motion side plates was the name *Big Ben*. She was one of the engines that I had seen so many times loaded with bricks or tiles. Now, instead of bearing the Openshaw name

21

along the cab it was Samuel Hester of Stokenchurch, Buckinghamshire and they were going to take the timber to High Wycombe for furniture making.

I dashed off home to get my tea but, instead of going to the ploughing tackle for the evening, I made my way back to the timber hauling gang and was soon chattering to them and helping clean the engine which looked immaculate. This was the first time I had ever stepped onto the footplate of a three-speed Fowler road locomotive and my first thought was how on earth do they see where they are going. I could not see anything less than about ten yards in front of the ploughing engines, but this was even worse. From the steersman's seat, however, it was not too bad, as I could look along the side of the engine. The cab sides seemed to come down very low and I felt terribly shut in. Just behind the steersman's head (bolted on the cab sideboard), was what looked like a giant bicycle bell and attached to this was a cord trailing back to the end of the load where the third man had to sit. If anything wanted to pass, he would pull the cord and ring the bell. This was the law in those days.

I stayed with them until nearly dark before making my way back down the lane to home, to tell my parents what I had been doing and what a wonderful engine *Big Ben* was. I had seen it pass through Lower Basildon many times, but had never had a chance to even 'touch it', let alone stand on the footplate. The rest of that evening, father was telling me different things about the three-speed Fowlers, as he knew just about all there was to know about this type of engine. He had spent over four years on one of the very same engines for the Binfield Brick & Tile Co., between leaving Thomas Baker & Sons of Compton and coming to the Basildon Estate.

I had heard little about this part of his life, so out came a cutting from a paper and a few not very good photo's. The paper cutting's picture showed him stood by his engine at Addlestone in Surrey, with three truck loads of tiles with their wheels nearly buried. They had broken through the road surface and had brought the big Fowler to a standstill. As far as I could gather, the police had turned up and had pinched them for being well and truly overloaded. Father said that it had cost his firm a lot of money.

The next afternoon I came the same way home from school and was surprised to see *Big Ben* and the gang still there, but they were coupled up to the timber wagons ready to be away in the morning. I didn't stop too long, as I had been told to come home and change into different clothes. As I always went back to the ploughing engines, these clothes were always washed with father's and Bert's overalls. Within an hour, I was back with the timber gang and soon learned that they would be away as soon as it was daylight the next morning. High Wycombe was a full day's haul, as they had to go a long way off their route to get across the Thames. There was only one bridge between Reading and Clifton Hampden that could carry the weight of this giant and its load, at Shillingford. This was a place I had not yet heard of, as Shillingford was about twelve miles from my home and I had not yet ventured that far on my own. I had plenty to keep me more than happy on my doorstep.

While I was chatting with the driver that evening, he had told me their route was the A329 through Streatley, Wallingford and over the Thames at Shillingford, then turning off right and away over the Oxfordshire hills through Benson into the Chiltern hills to High Wycombe, where there would be a gang to unload the timber. The loading timber gang were far from youngsters, but were a very happy gang and always ready for a lark and a joke. I was there chattering with the driver and doing a bit of brass polishing. I had already told him that I could drive the plough engines and that both my father and brother were drivers. He seemed quite interested in what I had to say, as I had told him that I would be leaving school in just over two years time and would be going to work on the plough engines.

His two mates had gone for a stroll up into Harley Wood, from where their trees had been felled and as they reached us, he took out his pocket watch and said that it was time to get the kettle on for a cup of tea, then get to bed as they would be away early next morning. So, they made their way up into the living van to light up the stove to boil the kettle and soon had smoke coming from the chimney. Alongside the van were several sacks of coal which I suppose they had brought with them for the return journey. There were also a few empty sacks, so he picked one of these up, gave me a wink and then threw it up over the van chimney. In anticipation of the pandemonium which then ensued, he then dashed off to hide behind the stock of trees that were lined up ready for their future loads.

I stayed and had a cup of their tea and was ready to leave for home, when the driver said "How often do you get a baker call at your home?". He was a bit surprised when I said "Every day" (this was a pony and cart from the bakery at Streatley). The question then was "Would mother collect a couple of loaves every other day for us?", as this would save them looking for bread while on their journey. This was fixed up and they were to stop and pick it up from home on their way through, which would be late afternoon or evening every other day, it being a full days trip each way. The next morning, it was hardly daylight when I could hear *Big Ben* on its way down the lane and almost instantly I was out of bed and standing at the window to see them go by.

What a sight it was. The flywheel was turning fairly slowly, but the engine and load were moving at a more or less running pace. As she ambled into the distance, I could see but very little of the engine as the timber was

23

piled high above the cab. How I wished I was on board with them. The third man was sat on top of the rear timber wagon with the communication cord, ready to ring the bell if anything was wrong, or someone was trying to get by. He must have had a grandstand view of the countryside as they made their way to the furniture factories of High Wycombe. My next evening would be spent with the plough engines as usual. *Big Ben* was spending the night at High Wycombe and would be ready to leave at the crack of dawn for Basildon for another load of our beech trees.

The afternoon that the timber gang was due back arrived, I could hardly get home quick enough. I would have hated to miss seeing this beautiful engine come into sight and pull up outside our home in order for the crew to collect their bread which mother had taken for them from our baker. It didn't take me many minutes to get changed into my engine clothes, as I would be following them back to Harley Wood when they eventually reached us. It seemed hours before they turned up. I had long got the fire lighting wood ready for father to boil the kettle in the morning (this was my job every day). I had had my tea and was standing at the garden gate with my eyes glued in the direction of the A329, where *Big Ben* would be turning off into Hook End Lane and up to our home.

Sure enough, eventually I could see the smoke coming through the top of the tall elm trees which lined both sides of the lane. She came to a halt outside the house and the driver came up the path and had a word with mother, saying how he hoped that she didn't mind doing this job for them. She assured him that it was no trouble as we were a steam engine family and every possible help would be given to them as long as they were coming our way.

They had a short chat, the bread was paid for and more ordered for two days time. Mother said to him "If this young rascal gets in your way send him home with a flea in his ear", or something like that. The driver just gave a little grin to himself and, with his oily hands, ruffled my hair (which was then a head of fair curls) and said "We will see you later on then". Mother said "He is ready to come now and has been waiting for the last couple of hours", so he got hold of my hand and said "Come on then", and off down the path we went.

The bag with the bread was handed to the chap on the last timber wagon (they had got three wagons behind them this time). I thought that I was going to have a ride with him and was all set to jump up onto the wagon, but was marched off up the front and bundled onto the footplate. The engine was blowing off like mad and you could hardly see anything under the cab. Most of the excess steam was going up through the oval brass tube which covers the safety valve, then up through the roof. But, there was still plenty that wasn't getting away, so the injector was put on and she was soon quietened down.

A few shovels of coal on the fire and we were ready to travel the half mile to Harley Wood. I perched myself on the front of the coal bunker so that, as I thought, I would be out of the way but to my great surprise, I was hauled up to the front by the regulator. This was a double lever lying at an angle crossways and could be pushed, pulled or both to open it, but it was way above my shoulders. The driver stood behind me and said "Right we are now ready to open her up". I stood on my toes and could see that the high pressure crank was in the wrong position for starting with the lever forward, so I gave the brass button a push and gave a yank on the regulator at the same time and we were away.

A few hundred yards up the road, there is a fairly steep slope up through some beech trees and as we started up the slope, she began to turn over a bit slower, so he gave me a dig and said "Give it a bit more", which I did. This did not seem to make much difference, however. She was in top gear and I had let it die down too slow, so I opened it right back and still she was only just about making it. With nothing else left, I gave the brass button a push and we were away again. She sounded really nice under the trees, but was nearly lifting off the ground in front each time the crank turned over. It was at times like this, when you realised how highly geared these engines were.

On reaching the gap in the hedge, which had been cut for the timber to be taken out, we stopped to get into low gear. This produced a problem for me, as I could not reach the pins which held the gear change levers into position. There are three levers with links connecting them to each other so that two gears cannot be engaged at the same time. The gears were sorted out for me and away we went out into the field, circling round to come back alongside the stack of trees with the first wagon lined up ready to be loaded. This was done by the horses that evening, the second one was loaded the next morning and the third one during the day after the engine had pulled out with the first two wagons to make her way to Wycombe. While the horses were loading up that evening and the engine gang were having their meal, I sat on the van steps watching the two horsemen at their job and thought how wonderful they were. The horses knew every word that was said to them, moving just an inch at a time if needed.

Their meal over, the engine gang were on the move to coal up the bunker and clean the engine down. The driver unhooked the poker and clinker shovel from under the footboard and said to me "Would you like to clinker out for me?". I immediately clambered up the steps onto the footplate. Using the poker, I pushed the remaining fire to one side and poked any lumps of clinker to the front of the firebox. This clinker was then shovelled out and the fire pushed back onto the clear side of the grate. After the other side of the grate had been cleared of clinker, the fire was spread over the bars and with a few small pieces of coal added she was ready to be banked down for the night. During all this time, I had been carefully watched by the driver and, when I'd finished, he said "I can see that's not the first time you have done that".

I had gone to school by the time they had pulled out the next morning, so I would not be seeing them for a couple of days. However, I would be with the ploughers next evening and hopefully get a drive on *Big Ben* the following evening. When that evening came, I had had my tea and was waiting for the timber gang to call for their bread, but, as they were very late, I spent a couple of hours working on my model. They came in sight just as it was getting dusk. I went down the path with the bread and waited for them. I was not going to miss my drive up the lane so, as soon as they arrived, I clambered up the engine steps and we were on our way. This time I was not going to let her die down too slow. It was quite dark under the cab as we went up the hill through the trees. The banks at the side of the road were thick with ivy so, as the damper was open, I could see the glow from the ashpan shining on the ivy leaves and I thought that this was great.

I walked back home in pitch darkness, it was only half a mile and I knew every inch of the road, as I had walked it many times before, although never before in the dark. On arrival mother's words were, "Where on earth have you been? It's time you were in bed". She did not worry too much as she knew exactly where I was. By now steam engines were to me the same thing as drugs are today to many of the younger generation. I was well and truly hooked on steam engines and nothing would keep me away from them. As I look back over the years, I realise how good my parents were to me. They never once tried to keep me away from the things I loved. My older sisters always said that I was mother's blue-eyed boy and could never do anything wrong in her eyes.

Throughout the summer holiday, I spent as much of the day as possible with the ploughing engines. The evenings, when the timber gang were not about, gave way to working on my model. Nearly every Saturday I was with father and the old Fowler traction engine, which was now beginning to give a few problems. Age and hard work were beginning to take their toll, problems such as leaking tubes or stays were regularly cropping up. Father had been told by the management to keep her going as best he could until his new engine would be ready. He was not too keen about the new engine, as it was to be a Wallis & Steevens. Father had never liked their engines, reckoning that they were noisy and down on power compared with the Fowler.

One evening, father came home and told me that he had had a big problem with the Fowler. One of the tubes had burst, quickly putting the fire out, with the result that boiling water had poured from the smokebox. He said, "When something like this occurs you don't open the firehole door to see what is happening, that's asking for trouble". I was interested to know how he was going to solve this problem. Since the Wallis was being built as a one off for the Estate, and so would not be ready for at least another month, the old Fowler would have to last out until the Wallis would be ready. He explained that the burst tube would have to be blanked off.

I was up early that Saturday morning to ensure that nothing was missed. When the Fowler was cold, the ashpan was dropped down, the firebars taken out and exact measurements of the tube's inside diameter were taken. Two steel bungs were turned up in the workshop and a long drawbolt made. The drawbolt was passed from the smokebox end through the tube and one bung was screwed onto the drawbolt at the firebox end. The front bung had a hole through it, so that when it was passed over the drawbolt, and a copper washer and nut were pulled up tight, the bungs were drawn tightly into both ends of the tube thereby blanking it off. Everything had gone to plan, so by mid-day she was ready to have her boiler filled and checked for leaks.

The hose pipe was put into the filler plug hole and soon the water was up to the level. The firebox end was checked first, this was OK, then the smokebox end, unfortunately there was a slight leak round the nut, but I was assured by father that this would dry up as it heated up. True enough, it did and by mid-afternoon she was blowing off and raring to go once again. He nursed the old girl along until the Wallis arrived, then the Fowler was run out under the trees at the back of the sawmill where she waited for the scrap man to come along. At least, that is what everyone thought.

The new Wallis was delivered to Blandy's Farm and parked outside the workshop and we went back after tea to have a look round her. I was more than surprised as she was nothing like a farm traction engine, more like a showman's engine being very nicely painted and lined out. Father said that she was not the sort of thing to take around muddy farm yards with a set of threshing tackle behind her. She looked altogether wrong for a hard working engine. With her full length cab, 6ft 6in. rear wheels and being very short she looked almost as high as she was long. She had three gears and the only thing that ruled her out as a road engine was that she did not have a belly tank.

The very first job for the Wallis, was to take two truck loads of coal from Pangbourne station to the brick yard. She tackled this pretty well in second gear as far as Brick Kiln Hill, where low gear was engaged to tackle the climb and here the first snags cropped up. By the time the top of the hill was

27

reached, the fork on the gear lever, which holds the gear in or out, was red hot. She had also become very difficult to steer as the front wheels were hardly touching the ground. This problem was caused by the coupling on the tender being far too high from the ground, the drawbar was pulling the back of the engine down and so lifting the front end. The fault with the gear lever was plain to see.

The normal Wallis gear layout has the low gear next to the crankshaft bearing and the high gear outside it. But this Wallis had all three gears on the same side of the shaft. The high gear by the bearing and the low gear on the outside, which must have been at least a foot from the bearing. This caused the shaft to spring away from the load on the gears every time it pulled hard in low gear. The oil that was poured over it, produced a catherine wheel effect. How long could this go on without serious trouble?

In less than a week, while they were drawing coal from Pangbourne to the lime kiln, a real big snag had cropped up. On reaching the skew bridge (where the A329 crosses the railway), they had problems getting round the corners, she wanted to go straight on. It was obvious that something had gone wrong with the differential gear. She had never gone round corners very well, but with a load behind her she had more or less refused to turn at all. They had great difficulty turning into the road leading to the lime kiln, so she was coaxed into the chalk quarry and parked away for the night. The Basingstoke mechanics were called in the next morning.

My father was by now just about fed up with what he reckoned was the biggest heap of rubbish that ever left the Wallis & Steevens factory. He knew that the Wallis was going to be off the road for a few days, so while this was to be sorted out, he went back to the old Fowler and brought her out of a very short retirement to carry on where she had left off.

I kept a close watch on how the seized wheel was removed, by calling in to watch them every afternoon on my way home from school. They first used chains fixed to the seized wheel with a big screw jack which pushed between the end of the axle and the chains, but this had very little success. Things were at a standstill for a couple of days as no one turned up from Basingstoke. They were busy making up a special puller and when they returned with it, they looked as if they meant business.

The puller was as much as two men could carry and looked like a massive tuning fork (just like our school teacher used for singing lessons). It was made to fit onto the centre of the wheel and reached far enough beyond the end of the axle to take an even bigger screw jack than the one that they had first tried to use. It had a big steel block where the jack pushed against it, so that it could be bashed with a sledge hammer to jar it. Two days went by and we could sit indoors listening to the sledge hammer at work, but they were getting nowhere fast. When two pieces of steel this size pick up and seize together you are in deep trouble.

On Saturday morning, I went with Bert to the ploughing engines. When we reached home at mid-day, the sledge hammer was still at work, so we had our meal and walked across the field to the lime kiln to see what progress had been made. They were using a huge paraffin blow lamp, the same type that was used at that time to heat the cylinder head of the big oil engines before starting. They had been heating the seized wheel and it had started to move, by late evening it was finally pulled off. There, plain enough for everyone to see what the problem was, there was no sign of an oil hole or an oil way having ever been cut into the bearing. Somebody had slipped up.

On the Monday, the bevel wheel was removed and the whole lot taken back to the works to be machined and have a bronze bush fitted. This time with oil holes and oil ways, they had learnt their lesson. With the job completed, the Wallis & Steevens' fitters made their way back to Basingstoke and the engine was ready to go into action again. Father had seen enough of the Wallis and had told the management that he wanted no more to do with her, saying that she should be sent back to Basingstoke as a complete failure. The management would not admit that they had made a mistake and so decided to give her another try (father had told them they should get another Fowler, but they thought they should support a local firm). It was agreed that George Johnson should take her over.

George was a fairly new employee on the Estate, having previously worked as driver's mate for a farmer by the name of Saunders at Purley, near Reading. Saunders owned a set of threshing tackle, powered by an eight horse-power Wallis expansion engine which were occasionally hired by the Estate to help out while the rush was on. George was quite a nice chap and had spent a bit of time with father doing a bit of threshing and had also helped with the ploughing tackle. He thought that he was being highly honoured by taking over the new engine, especially as he liked Wallis & Steevens machinery, having spent several years with the Purley firm's expansion engine.

It had been decided that there was enough work around Basildon to keep the two steamers going, as a result a new set of boiler tubes was ordered for the Fowler, so that she would carry on for a few more years. She was working at the sawmill when the tubes arrived, so that is where she was re-tubed. I helped to draw out the last few old tubes on the Saturday morning. I was spanner man at the smokebox end while father used the short sledge hammer in the firebox.

I was shown how to use the expanders and how far to tighten the tubes. A tube can be ruined, as can the firebox and the tubeplate, if you overdo it

(I still have my father's tube expanders among my souvenirs, including the sets that did this job). I was surprised what little effort it takes to expand a tube enough to make it water tight. Usually if the joint holds with cold water, you can bet your life it won't leak when hot.

As the summer came to an end and the days were getting shorter, the ploughing engines were mostly pulling the plough, the cultivator having been laid aside until the spring. I was now getting plenty of practice as a plough man whilst still doing a fair share of driving. I had two more years at school and was longing for the day when I could be earning my living as a steam plough man.

All through the winter, my evenings were spent working on my model. Bert was now well on the way with his beam engine and he would be finished long before I had my boiler ready. I did not mind, as I had all the time in the world in front of me and as I'd always been told "Rome wasn't built in a day". The ploughing tackle was parked away for the winter, so my spare time on Saturday mornings was spent with father on the Fowler. She was still doing most of the hauling from the station, as the two lorries seemed to be in the workshop as much as they were out.

The new Wallis was busy doing most of the threshing, which she did very well once the threshing machine and elevator, or the baler, or the chaff cutter (whichever was being used), had been set to the corn stacks. The Pickering governors that she was fitted with seemed to have worked extremely well whilst on these tasks. She was a compound, and must have been at least eight horse-power, but seemed very quiet after being used to the crisp bark of the Fowler single.

Now that I was a bit older it was my job most Friday evenings, to go to Goring to do the weeks shopping. This I did by riding my bike with two bags of shopping on the handle bars. I set off one Friday as soon as I was home from school and reached the Goring bridge, where it crosses the Thames. I could see something unusual on the river close to the bridge, it was a big barge with a tall gantry on one side and a huge vertical boiler in the centre. This was a massive pile driver that was being used to make a start on building both the new Goring and Streatley bridges. The old bridges had long been restricted to a two ton limit. I would now have something else powered by steam that I could go and watch working.

The timber gang had now finished their contract and it was a sad day when the last load of beech trees passed by home on their way to High Wycombe. I had enjoyed a good many hours with the Stokenchurch men and their beautiful Fowler engine *Big Ben*. I had helped to clean her many times and had spent a lot of time at her regulator whilst (about three times a week), doing the half mile trip from home to Harley Wood.

I came home from school one afternoon and mother said that she had heard the pile drivers at work, or at least there was a lot of banging coming from over the hill in that direction. True enough, next morning before I left for school they had started up again, with an almighty thump about every half minute. That evening, I had a quick cup of tea and was away to Goring to have a peep at the pile driver before darkness fell. By the time I reached the bridge, it must have been about half-past four and they had already called it a day. However, I could see how the pile driver must have worked, there was a flexible steam pipe from the boiler to a block of metal, which must have weighed well over a ton. This block was somehow lifted up the rails of the gantry using steam power then, when it reached the top, a cord (which was attached to the hammer) was pulled. The steam was thereby released and down came the huge lump of metal onto the top of the pile. Each pile was about 18in. square and every bit of thirty feet long and the steel point was being driven into the river bed. These piles were for temporary bridges to go alongside the old bridges, but they would then be demolished once the new concrete bridges had been built in their place.

Photograph: Rural History Centre, University of Reading.

'An early photograph of ploughing on the Basildon Estate, taken close to my home at Lower Basildon, shows my elder brother Bert in charge of the engine. Normally, there would only be two members of the gang on the plough, but if there was a lot of 'trash' on the ground, more help was needed to help keep the plough clear ...!'

JOE CHALLIS

Chapter 3

'Earning a Living'

W e were now getting some pretty hard weather and both of the backwaters, that powered the water wheels which drove the generators at the Goring and Streatley mills, had frozen over, a sight that I had never seen before. The corn grinding machinery in both mills had been taken out and dynamos installed to harness the power of the water wheels to supply electricity to the two villages.

Father was now busy drawing gravel from the pits just off the A329 near the skew bridge, as all the drives to the Basildon Park house were being resurfaced. On the Saturday morning, as usual, both father and I set off before six so that we would be at the pits in good time. We pulled up outside the hut and went in to have a cup of tea with Jack Richings before loading our trucks. Jack already had steam up in his crane and so, as the grab must have held a couple of yards, we would soon be loaded. I put the Fowler into low gear, circled round the yard and pulled up with the first truck across the ends of the rails which the crane travelled on. There were about two hundred yards of rails laid down with a few spare lengths laid alongside, ready to join on as the pit grew longer. Jack fired up his boiler and said "Come on, have a go here". I didn't need asking twice. I had watched him many times before, always hoping that one day I would have a drive. Now my turn had come.

The crane, which had been made by Stothert & Pitt, was powered by a twin-cylinder horizontal engine. The engine had no flywheel, although the crankshaft had fairly large discs at each end and to these the connecting rods were attached. The rails were in an unusual layout as the crane had four wheels on each axle, the inner wheels were about four feet apart and the outers about ten feet, thereby enabling the crane to lift a fair weight from either side. There were four levers in a bunch, one each for travelling, swivelling, winding in the rope and raising or lowering the jib. I had watched Jack operating these levers many times before and so knew which one to use for travelling. Off Jack and I went fairly steadily down to the end of the track where Jack took over. Jack swivelled the jib round and dropped the grab through the ice with a bang. Then, fishing up a grab full of gravel we were away back to our truck, where the grab was lowered down and the cord that opened the grab was pulled then, away we went for another fill up.

Within a very short time, we were loaded and on our way up the steep slope to the main road where we had to turn sharp right. Without the use of the bank by the railway cutting, we would be struggling to get round, as the front wheels were nearly off the ground. I am sure the new Wallis would never have coped here. We crossed the skew bridge, over the railway and turned left towards Park Farm, through the lodge gates and up the drive towards the mansion. Here we stopped to unload the trucks as they would have been frozen solid by Monday morning (this task had to be done by hand as there were no tippers in those days). Afterwards, father had told his gang to make their way home, whilst we made our way up to the sawmill where John Fowler would stand until the following Monday morning. I had engaged 'big wheel' and was ready to go but father said that, as we had to pass right by the front of the mansion, I should make up a fairly big fire so that it would be burning brightly and smoke free by the time we reached the house. We climbed the hill, gently by the house and so away to the sawmill where she was parked away for the weekend.

It must have been three or four weeks before enough gravel had been hauled in to resurface the four drives which run from each side of the park to the mansion. I would think that there were about four miles of drives altogether and throughout the time that the resurfacing had gone on, I had spent each Saturday morning with father. I had also put in quite a bit of time on the steam crane which, by then, I could handle pretty well. With the resurfacing job finished, the Fowler went to the sawmill as more gate posts and fencing were needed. Father had persuaded the management to leave the big Robey portable at the brickyard for the winter, as it was far too dangerous to keep transporting it backwards and forwards. He had explained to them the damage that could be done if the portable happened to sink in and turn onto its side on the soft clay of the brickyard road. So a shed was built over the portable which sat on its concrete pad.

At the northern end of the Estate was Kiddington Farm, consisting of a big barn, a few smaller buildings, a pair of cottages and hundreds of acres of good fertile soil which grew some very good corn. The big snag was getting to the farm in the winter as there was no surfaced road to it. There was a cart track to it from the Streatley to Aldworth road, just a three-ply track which could only be used by horses and carts. The track was very steep and narrow, having been cut into the chalk hillside with a bank on one side and a steep drop into the woods on the other. When wet, it was as slippery as ice and would have been suicide to try to take any steam engine down it, even in the summer. Kiddington Farm laid right at the end of a valley and the track was at the steep end. There was, however, another cart track running the full length of the valley, about one and a half miles in length, but again it was just a chalk track, very slippery when wet and not the route to travel with threshing tackle in winter. The usual thing was to take the tackle in from

Streatley up this track in the harvest time and thresh all the corn straight out from the fields and then get everything out while the weather was still good.

The ploughing tackle had spent a lot of time at this farm a couple of years previously, having cultivated a big area of the downland on the western side of the existing fields. As a result of this, some good crops of oats and wheat had been produced, so there were two long rows of corn ricks at the farm as well as a full barn. None of this crop had been threshed out during the harvest, which had always been the drill, but, as some of the corn and straw was needed, somehow the threshing tackle had to be got to Kiddington Farm. We were still in the grips of a severe winter and they had missed the boat, the hard frosts had finished and we were now getting snow and rain. The uphill track from Streatley was in just about its worst possible condition. It was quite obvious that whoever dropped in for the job was in for a tough journey, but, if they could get there, they would be able to make it back as it would be all downhill, although fairly steep in places.

In the field at the end of our garden, stood two big ricks of oats and these were to be threshed out to tide them over until Kiddington Farm could be reached. On the Friday afternoon, just after I arrived home from school, George Johnson with the Wallis & Steevens pulled in to tackle this job. We had a very nice garden hedge which was always kept beautifully trimmed and in the middle of this were about six strands of wire, which I suppose were there before the hedge was planted. At the end of the garden, in the corner of the hedge was a big post about 9in. square to take the strain of the wire pulling along both sides of the garden. It was getting dusk as I stood at the garden gate to watch them go by to the end of our garden, here they would pull off left into the field and up to the ricks ready to get set to them next morning. They had behind them the Marshall threshing machine, a Ruston baler and the fold-up Roberts elevator. All this made quite a long load.

Unfortunately, they had misjudged their distance, resulting in them cutting the corner a bit short, this had caused the front wheel of the elevator to hit the post, pulling it over at a crazy angle and taking our gate post with it. The worst was to come, the rear wheel ran up the post and almost tipped the elevator over onto its side. The sheet that covered the threshing machine at night, was spread along the top of the elevator for travelling and sat on this was an old chap by the name of Billy Downham. Billy was the communication man and had a cord which went to the steersman's arm. Billy had worked on the Estate for many years, having travelled many miles with my father doing the same job. In the accident, poor old Billy was thrown off his perch, complete with two or three pedal cycles, breaking a leg in the process and that was the end of the old boy as a threshing man. He passed away a few months later.

35

Next morning, I was out there to see the tackle being put into position, ready to start threshing on the Monday morning. It was a pathetic site, the fields had been ploughed by horses up fairly close to the ricks and the baler had to be pushed up between the ricks first, then the threshing machine up behind it. The ground was fairly wet, it was slightly up hill and there was a fair bit of wet straw lying between the ricks. A full set of spuds were put on the wheels and they were ready to go, but without much luck. The wheels of the baler slid, pushing the wet straw in front of them and they were soon at a standstill with the front of the engine slewed round sideways, but they still had at least another ten yards to go. Going home time had arrived and they were still struggling with the baler, so they decided that they would give it a miss until Monday morning. By now the space where the threshing machine was to have stood (and be levelled up) was well and truly chewed up. When father walked up and had a look in the afternoon, he said it looked as if they had been in deep trouble, but he reckoned that his old Fowler would have coped far better than the Wallis was ever likely to. I did not see the performance on the Monday as I was at school, but it took them all day to get the threshing machine jacked up and stood on pieces of timber for levelling up. (If the thresher is to do its work properly it must stand almost level in all directions.)

With the two ricks now threshed out and the straw baled up, the Wallis was taken back to the sawmill to take over the sawing, whilst father, with the Fowler, would tackle the dreaded trip up Streatley Valley to Kiddington Farm. (There was no way that they were going to chance it with the Wallis.) It was decided that he should take the Marshall threshing machine, as this was much lighter than the Clayton & Shuttleworth that he normally used, although they both had 54in. drums. This, with the elevators, would be as much as they could hope to make the journey with, even then the load would almost certainly have to be roped most of the way. We had been sent home from school for a few days whilst plumbers replaced some radiators that had burst at the weekend. This was a godsend to me, as I would be able to go with father on his forthcoming mission.

The day before this journey was to start, father brought home his Fowler with a light farm wagon, which had been fitted with a drawbar, the wagon carrying a closed-in water filled tank and about half a ton of coal in bags, which he hoped would be sufficient to see him through. By the time things were sorted out and everything coupled up the next morning, it must have been nine o'clock, so father, his two mates and I walked down the garden path to the house where mother had got a pot of tea made ready to help warm us up before we left. With the communication man perched comfortably on the coal wagon, the steersman in position and myself

36

perched on top of the coal bunker, we set off. We had soon covered the two miles into Streatley village and were away up the slope to the fork in the road, here we went left, up the Wantage road for about a quarter of a mile then left again up the narrow road leading to the Streatley golf links, where our track to Kiddington forked right and the trouble was to begin.

A full set of spuds were fitted to each wheel, then father and I walked a short way up the track to see what we were up against. We didn't have to go far to find out that we were in for a real picnic, the low places in the ruts were full of water and the chalky mud was as slippery as glass. The burning question was, should we keep to the tracks or straddle one of them, thereby keeping the wheels on the high ground. We could see that there was no hope of getting along with our load coupled to the engine, so the rope was untied, pulled through the guide rollers on the side of the tender and shackled to the drawbar.

One of the advantages of the Fowler over the Wallis, was that the rope drum was in two pieces, the centre boss (which had the holes for the drive pin) was keyed to the axle, the rope drum being free to turn on this boss when an oblong spring-loaded block was lifted out from its socket on the centre boss. This way, you could put the drive pin in, travel the length of the rope, then take out the drive pin, engage the oblong block and were then ready to pull in the rope. The Wallis did not have this ability, so each time the engine was moved the rope had to be pulled in from the guide rollers and tied to the drum, then after the engine had moved forward, the rope was man-handled back to the load. This was not easy as the axle has to be pulled round all the time this was being done, often the engine had gone a bit too far and the rope would then not quite reach. The drive pin, for the differential side rear wheel, was placed into position and kept pushed in until one wheel had slipped enough for the holes to line up, thereby letting the pin go right home and so lock the 'diff'. The cotter was pushed in and wired up and we were now ready for a painful one and a half miles.

The daylight was beginning to fade and it was time to call it a day. We had not yet covered a quarter of a mile, so it was going to take about another day and a half to complete the journey. The engine was banked down for the night, our bicycles unloaded from the top of the elevator and we were soon on our way towards Streatley and home. The next morning father went off on his own. I was going to walk across country (which was less than half the distance that it was by road). There were several footpaths that the gamekeepers had made which cut off a lot of corners and I loved to wander over those hills. I often take a drive back to Basildon now and take a walk over those hills as I did over sixty years ago, what memories this brings back.

As I walked over the top of the hill, to make my way down across the fields to the engine, I saw the smoke but very little activity. They had been filling the engine's tank using buckets of water from the tank on the wagon at the rear end of the tackle, which was safer than trying to get the engine backwards down the soft field to pull the water out with the lift pipe. It was now time for a bite of food and a drink before setting off, but I had eaten a good breakfast and so was not ready for food yet. I was too taken up by the task that was in front of me. Father had told me that I could drive the engine to pull in the rope with the load on its end. This was something that I had not yet done and so I hoped all went to plan. After a few pulls my turn had come, we had made good progress because the ground seemed drier and harder as we went gradually higher. We had passed the lowest part where the water laid and it seemed that the worst part was behind us. It was decided that we should try moving without the 'diff' locked, so the gear side pin was left out, the scotch blocks picked up and loaded onto the coal bunker and we were ready to go again. I started off and to our great surprise she made the grade quite well. We ran with the right-hand side wheels on the track where horses had always walked and so straddled the deep cart wheel ruts. This was done as there is a vulnerable place on the threshing machine, which can easily be smashed if the wheels drop in a rut. This is the cup box, being the lowest point on the machine and is where the corn is taken to and from. The corn is collected by steel cups attached to a belt and taken back to the top into the awner, then finally, onto the screen and into the sacks.

I kept the front wheel in the middle of the track while father walked up the left-hand side, keeping his eye on the rope drum, ready to give me a shout when the rope had nearly run out as I could not see both sides myself. The scotch blocks were put in place again, the drive pin taken out, the drum drive block placed in position and we were pulling again, but of course, it is geared very low. I stayed on the engine for nearly all the rest of the day and had a wonderful time and I think everyone went home more than happy with the day's progress. We were within a few hundred yards of the farm as things had gone better than expected. Next morning, we had to cross to the opposite side of the track as there was a drop of about two feet onto the field for about one hundred yards, this bank was riddled with rabbit holes and to risk this would be asking for trouble. So, a few wheelbarrow loads of flints were collected from the field, the ruts filled in enabling us to cross without much trouble and so we were outside the big barn by midday. The first job was to clear the barn as it would be needed to stack the sacks of corn until such time as they could be taken to other farms. With the barn empty, the elevator and threshing machine were taken to the far end of the two rows of ricks, the machinery could then be pulled back as the ricks were cleared and so leave one row of huge straw ricks to be used when needed.

By this time the first tractor on the Estate had arrived. It was a weird looking object called an 'Overtime' and I am pretty sure that it was made in the USA. It had iron wheels, each of the rear ones having two rows of triangular spuds (which must have been at least 5in. long). For travelling on the road, there was a steel band bolted on in sections to keep the spuds clear of the road, but the bands gave just about no grip at all, so it was dangerous for going up and down hills. Its first job was to draw the corn down the track to Streatley where it was transferred onto the Seldon lorry and then delivered to the farms around the Estate. The chap who drove this lorry was Bill Baker. He had spent quite a bit of time with my father on the threshing tackle and had been looking after the Robey portable at the brickyard all the previous summer, but it was now retired for the winter. As Bill lived in a house, called 'The Rest', which was at the top of Streatley Hill (on the Streatley to Aldworth road), this job would be on his doorstep, all that he had to do was walk down over the hill to Kiddington, a distance of about a quarter of a mile.

A few days went by and the sacks of oats were beginning to pile up, then along came the 'Overtime' tractor, followed by the Seldon lorry with about a couple of tons of coal in sacks, to feed the Fowler during the two or three weeks that it would be at Kiddington. On reaching the start of the track, the road bands were removed from the tractor's wheels and it was ready to make its first trip up the track to couple up to the wagon which had been brought in behind the Fowler as a water and coal tender. With nothing behind it, the tractor trundled along up the valley without much effort, the wagon was coupled up and taken to the barn where it was about half filled with sacks of oats, not much more than a ton, I would think. This it made fairly light work of, as it was all down hill to the end of the track where the lorry stood, the sacks then being transferred to the lorry. There were two tons of coal to go back up the hard way and the tractor had not gone far before it was in trouble. There seemed to be enough power there, but not the weight and it soon started to dig itself in. Half the coal was unloaded and then it just about made it, but let's be fair about it, the old Fowler with her full set of spuds had left her mark.

One of the main problems was that the coupling on the front of the wagon was too high and was lifting a lot of the weight from the tractor when it was pulling hard. At the workshop a new drawbar was made up and was cranked down so that it was now pulling in a straight line with the coupling on the tractor. The drawbar was delivered to Streatley by the lorry and Bob Goddard, the Estate fitter, had come with them to fit it as he was interested in seeing how the tractor was going to cope. Bob was a hundred percent internal combustion man and admitted he knew nothing about steam and didn't want to know. He had been brought in to look after the lorries, the many barn engines and the model-T Fords at the big house and also to supervise the many repair jobs that crop up on an estate of this size. The new drawbar was fitted and a full load of corn put on board and away she went down the track with no problems. So Bob was highly delighted and told my father what wonderful things they were and that with a few more years of development, they would push out and replace the steam engines. Father said that they had no hope (all the steam men then thought the same), but make no mistake about it for steam engines the writing was on the wall.

With the threshing at Kiddington completed, the journey back down to Streatley went off far easier than the uphill one had. I did not see this as the radiators at school had been repaired, so we were back at our lessons again. I was more than happy with what I had done on the uphill trip, as I had learnt a lot and it is something I shall never forget. Many years later, after I had been married a few years and my two sons were aged four and two, I made this very same trip with a Morgan three-wheeler car. We went to see my aunt who had for many years lived at Westridge, a small hamlet on the Streatley to Aldworth road (near the top of Kiddington Hill), until her old thatched cottage had been condemned and she had moved to one of the farm cottages at Kiddington. If you have ever driven a three-wheeler car, you will know that it's not the thing to take up a three-ply cart track. What memories this brought back to me as the track was still just about the same as when I made my way up with the John Fowler as a school kid.

I was still soldiering on with my model of that wonderful old Fowler, but progress was pretty slow as the winter evenings were so cold and, all through the spring and summer, I had wanted to spend as much time as possible with the ploughing engines. I would be leaving school in less than two years time, so I wanted to gain as much experience as possible before then, so that I would be able to take my turn at driving right from the start. I had already been told by Jim Smith (the steam plough foreman) that if I could grow a bit taller and put on a bit of weight, I would be as good as my brother or any other member of the gang and that there would be a job there waiting for me.

Activity at the Goring bridges was at its height, the temporary bridges were now in use and the old ones were being demolished. Another big pile driver had arrived, this was even bigger than the first one and worked on a different principle. The barge that it was on had a vertical gantry at the side, the same as the first one, but instead of the massive weight being lifted directly by steam, it was hauled to the top each time by a steel cable. This cable was pulled by a winch, powered by a twin-cylinder horizontal steam engine running all the time at a constant speed and was coupled to the

40

winch by a clutch (that was engaged by a man pulling a big lever). The weight was pulled to the top, where it lifted a lever with a small cable attached to it that disengaged the clutch, sending the weight onto the interlocking girders which were being driven into the river bed. The girders made a big oval dam that would be pumped dry, so that they could lay the concrete base for the new bridge footings. I spent a few hours each week watching the pile drivers, as I could stand on the new wooden bridge and look straight down on to them. I got a good view of what was going on and enjoyed the smell that comes from every steam engine, be it big or small.

As the summer drew nearer and the days lengthened, I spent a lot of late evenings with the ploughing engines, becoming a pretty good driver and was being encouraged more and more by both my brother and Jim Smith. I was longing for the day when I could leave school and earn my own living as a steam plough driver.

Bert came home one evening saying "We are fitting a new length of rope to my engine on Saturday so you had better come along and see how it is done". There were three hundred yards of rope to go on as the old one had begun to give trouble. When a rope is getting worn out, an odd strand will break and start to unwind. If this breakage is not noticed in time, the strand will go outside the pulleys at the 'monkey head' and before you know what has happened, a good few yards of rope are ruined and the damaged length will have to be cut out and the rope respliced. That evening, the Fowler book, that was supplied when the engines were new, was dug out and I spent a few hours the next day browsing through the pages on rope splicing. The book gave a rough idea how it is done, but both my father and my brother said the instructions were very hard to follow, some of it being very misleading, but never the less I would know a bit more about it when the time came.

When Saturday morning came I went off with Bert, not too early, as normally a good gang of three can, with no effort, splice a rope in half an hour and that was all there was to do that Saturday. The job was to be done very slowly for my benefit, with each operation very carefully explained as we went along. The new piece of rope was pulled out and laid alongside the old length that had to be cut out, then the tools were taken out to the end of the new rope. These tools were two spikes, a three cornered file, a sledge hammer, a hand hammer, a length of tar twine (this is string that has been treated with tar) and the heaviest piece, one of the wheel spuds. The file would be used to cut the rope, this I had been told about but had never yet seen. The spud was hammered into the ground with the flat side up, the file laid on it, then the rope laid across the file with two members of the gang standing on the rope either side of the file to keep the rope held tight down onto the file. With about three good smacks on the rope using the sledge hammer, we had two pieces of rope. The tar twine was used to bind the rope about eleven feet from the end to stop it unwinding as the strands were laid in or out and also bound the ends of the strands that were being tucked into the centre of the rope with the spikes. The hand hammer was used to knock the rope back into shape once it had been spliced (a soft hammer is best for this). The old piece of rope was rolled up ready to be dumped once the eye had been removed. They were using the type of eye that was machined from a round steel bar and had a hole bored to take the end of the rope. The eye was held in place by a round taper cotter driven into the end, this expands the rope into the eye so that the harder the pull on the eye the tighter the cotter goes. This type has the advantage of being able to be pulled much closer to the pulleys, as there is not that long overlapped length of rope that you get with a spliced-in eye of the normal type. Also you don't have that long piece of rope and eye hanging out from the 'monkey head' when travelling on the road. The eye was removed by heating it to red heat in the firebox then cutting it off. The cotter was driven out and the strands of rope pulled out one by one with a pair of pliers.

To me the whole job appeared far more simple than I had expected, but it had been done in very slow motion, so that I could take it all in and had been very carefully explained as we went along. The method had well and truly sunk in, as over the years I have helped splice many steam plough ropes and it always came back to me as if I had just had the lesson.

The second tractor had now arrived on the Estate, this time a 'Titan'. There was also a new plough to go with it. This tractor would also be used to pull the binders for cutting the corn, so reducing the hard work for the horses and removing some of the ploughing work from the engines. For pulling the binders it was a big step forward, as this was a killing job for horses but, as for ploughing, it was not so good. The tractor only pulled two furrows and was very slow, doing no more in a day than three horses, also the headlands were almost as wide as those that the steamers left behind but, of course, the tractor could plough its own headlands whereas the engines didn't.

Whenever the steam and tractor men got together, there was a lot to be heard about how much could be done in a day by each type, such as what one man could do in a day with a tractor against a gang of five with the engines. Then there were always the carters with their horses and single or double ploughs, they reckoned their work was far superior to that of either of the tractors or steamers, which it no doubt was as far as finish was concerned. Most of their ploughing was just about as straight as a gun barrel with every furrow exactly the same as each other. Now, with a single or double horse plough, once it is set right, every furrow has got to be the same, but when you start using a balance or anti-balance steam plough you are dealing with ten or twelve furrows. This is a far different kettle of fish, but if a ploughman really knows his job and is prepared to spend a bit of time on the adjustments, of which there are many, a steam plough will turn out just as good a job as any horse or tractor plough.

The engine drivers can also play a big part in this as the speed at which the plough is pulled along can make a lot of difference to the finish of the work (depending on what type of soil is being ploughed). For instance, if the soil is light and you pull too fast, it will be thrown far and wide and won't leave a very good finish. Also, if one driver pulls a bit faster than the other it will show. If a driver keeps his engine turning over at the same speed all the way across the field, he may not realise that by doing this the plough is travelling very much faster at the end of the pull than it was at the start. This is because when a full drum of rope is being used, the centre of the drum is not much more than half the size of a full drum, therefore, at the end of the pull the speed is nearly doubled if your engine is going to be kept turning over at the same speed all the way. This does not matter much when cultivating or harrowing as it does not show up in the finished job as it does with the plough.

We were having a very good summer with many weeks of hot dry weather which was surely making up for the hard winter we had just experienced. The ploughing tackle had been kept busy and we had everything well in hand and were waiting for the harvest to be gathered in so that the plough could be brought out of retirement (but this would be two or three weeks before the first field would even be cut). Now was the time to break up more of the downland beyond the Kiddington valley, the fields and hills were now nice and dry, so there would be no problem getting to the Downs. The engines, cultivator, harrows, living van and water cart travelled the same route as the threshing tackle had the previous winter, plus at least another half a mile beyond the farm across the fields (which are quite steep), but as it was very dry, there were no problems.

Every schoolboy, over twelve years old, whose father worked on the Estate could spend his summer holidays in the harvest fields, leading the horses from stook to stook while the corn was being loaded ready to go to the ricks. For this he would be paid about seven shillings (35p) a week which was a lot of pocket money for a schoolboy in those days. I had to make up my mind which I should do, go leading horses (which I did not like) or spend time with the iron ones and get nothing for it. The seven bob a week would have been very handy to buy material and tools for my model making, but I was not doing too badly as both Bert and my parents were giving me a few shillings every week to take care of this. So I decided that I would go with the things I loved most and this is where I spent most of my seven weeks holiday.

The downland was covered with Hawthorn and Juniper bushes. Not very big ones, but enough to make things awkward, as they kept blocking the cultivator up, so causing a lot of turning round to be done, thus producing a lot of big heaps to be levelled off. This was just up my street, I wanted to get used to this sort of thing as I would no doubt come up against these types of problems in the near future so now was my chance to gain some experience on this sort of going.

A patch about twenty chains square was now cultivated both ways, but it was littered with heaps of bushes which would have to be cleared before harrowing could be done. So a few farm labourers were sent in to do this while the engines moved on to do another area the same size. This piece was marked out with posts (with a piece of cloth or something nailed onto them) and Jim Smith said "Now is your time to set out the engine ready to start a new field". This task was normally done by the driver with no other help and it was my brother's engine that was to go to the far side of the new plot to be worked. I had all the room in the world to play with, but Bert said "Treat the marking posts as a hedge or fence and keep close to them but do not go outside them". He walked alongside all the way in case anything went wrong. The rope from the other engine was coupled to the back of my engine so, with the fire made up, I was ready to go.

As the ground was pretty rough, Bert reminded me about the steering wheel. He had always told me to start with the engine set at a reasonable speed, stick your toes into the hole in the coal bunker (where the coal is shovelled out) and hang onto the wheel good and tight. Bert said "If you don't let it go you don't have to stop it, but if it does take over never try and stop it as this is asking for trouble". I started off at a pretty good pace, following the posts up to the corner where I circled round so that the engine was at right-angles to the direction that I had just come from, then stopped to uncouple the rope from the back ready to couple my rope to it. If you don't want to roll down a lot of the field unnecessarily, you have to pull out a few yards of your own rope to couple onto the one you have been pulling out from the other engine. This is not easy to do single handed if you don't know what it's all about. You must remember that a drum filled with rope must weigh well over a ton and is not started off very easily, also there is the drag of three bronze bearings. If these bearings are fitted as they should be, it takes quite a lot of starting. The main offender is the pinion bearing which is of big diameter and fairly long; inside the pinion is another bearing that the vertical shaft runs in; the third one being the main drum stud bearing.

Also the brake band pawl has to be held up, as there is no way that the drum can be turned by even three men with this down.

So, here is a tip for the would be steam plough driver. The brake pawl is normally fitted with a long chain link attached to a spring on a small lever which is pivoted in the middle and rests under the band round the clutch that is operated by the clutch lever. When the clutch lever is lifted and the clutch dropped down into the engaged position, the brake pawl is lifted and when the clutch is moved out the pawl is dropped onto the band brake. The drill for this, when single handed, is as follows; swing the coiling lever round so that the 'monkey head' is close to the front wheel then carefully drop the clutch and pull the rope eye close to the pulleys. Jump down out of the tender, lift the brake pawl and turn the long chain link that is attached to it crossways and this will hold the pawl clear of the brake.

If you are driving the right-hand engine, walk round to the other side and catch hold of the 'monkey head' which now has the rope eye close to it. Put your foot against the front wheel and give a good pull. The coiling lever and drum complete, can be pulled round fairly easily and once started is no problem, so you just keep pulling at the rope eye until you have enough loose rope out to reach the rope from your mate's engine. Couple the two ropes together then, most important of all, go back and turn the link on the brake pawl to its normal position, otherwise you are in dire trouble. A couple of short blasts on the whistle and your mate will be pulling back the rope while you are reversing back into the corner of the field, then fire up ready for the first pull of that field. Yes, I did this at the age of thirteen and I was not very big for my age. It's just the know how that counts.

I spent the rest of the day driving Bert's engine, so I went home dirty and tired, but very happy as I had spent nearly a full day in complete charge of the K7 with no help from anyone. Bert had spent most of the day on the cultivator and Jim Smith had been for a stroll over the Downs to view the beautiful countryside. You can see for miles on a clear day if you climb to the top of the hills and look across the Berkshire Downs to the Vale of the White Horse.

With the cultivating finished, we moved back to the piece where we had started and hooked up to the harrows. The heaps of bushes had been burned, so we had to harrow the land over to get the rest of the rubbish out and break down the clods of earth so that the carters with their horses and light harrows could get it ready for planting the winter corn. The harrows are fairly easy to pull as you don't go very deep, so the faster they are rattled along the better they do their job and the rubbish doesn't seem to block up too much. It's a rough ride for the guy that's steering the harrows, as you have only a flat wooden seat to sit on and can go home after a long day in the saddle with a sore backside. However, it's good fun for the engine drivers.

I loved to hear the hum of the bevel pinions on the vertical shaft and crankshaft which you don't get when pulling harder and slower. To me it was wonderful to stand on the footplate, open the regulator and see the smoke from the chimney going high into the sky. Also, looking at the short stroke, perfectly balanced crankshaft, half hidden with smoke from the oil on top of the boiler and a bit of dust from the field, there appeared to be just a red blur, whilst the flywheel looked as if it had no spokes. This is something you don't get with the older single-cylinder engines.

I spent at least four weeks of my summer holiday on this patch of the Downs and how I enjoyed every minute of it, this was a few weeks that I shall never forget. I had gained a whole lot of experience and was now a very good driver and reckoned that I was ready to take on any job where steam plough engines were concerned. I had still another year at school and this would surely be a long boring twelve months, but unlike most school leavers, I would not have to go looking for a job.

I often go back to Basildon to drive round the back lanes and look across the fields, thinking of the wonderful times I spent as a boy with those Fowler K7 ploughing engines. There were very few fields on the Estate that I had not travelled over, either on the engines or the implements. When I travel the Streatley to Aldworth road and look across to the Berkshire Downs, I think of the wonderful time I spent there (well over sixty years ago) helping to transform those hundreds of acres of wild scrubland to what it is today. I recently travelled down Hook End Lane, by Harley Wood and noticed that the gap (where the bank and hedge were removed for the Stokenchurch timber hauling Fowler to get into the field), is still there with just a few stakes and strands of wire to fill it. The hedge was never replanted and that was sixty-four years ago. Perhaps, it was left for the next generation of beech trees to come out.

The harvest was well on the way with many fields cut and carted (the tractors made life a bit easier for the horses), so the engines were getting to work with the plough. I wanted to spend as much time as possible on the plough to make sure of all the adjustments and handling of this monster, so that I would be as good with this tool as I was with the other implements or the engines. I had made up my mind that I needed to be a first class all round steam plough man as this was how I wanted to earn my living. Every evening, whenever possible, I would put on my working clothes and was away to wherever the ploughers were working, usually coming home with Bert, often in the dark.

I would spend a few evenings on the plough, a few driving the engine and was able to pull the plough within inches of the engine, be in gear and moved forward in seconds. This process is most important when ploughing, as it makes it so much easier for the gang on the plough. It is all to easy to pull the plough down and be ready to jump on only to find that the rope is up between the last two ploughs. This means that you have then got to stop the other driver from starting his pull, lift the plough and sort out the rope before you can get going again. This wastes time and also makes hard work which is the last thing that you want to do. However well things are going, when you have spent about twelve hours hung onto a five or six furrow plough, often with a press hanging on the side, you will go home tired. I know I have had some.

I was still spending most Saturday mornings with father and the Fowler traction engine, so I was keeping my hand in on the single-cylinder job, she was a wonderful old engine and I enjoyed every minute spent with her. Sundays were my pile driving and bridge building days, as they were now working seven days a week as the bridges were to be ready by the next August. There was also another gang on the scene, they were going to rebuild the lock at the same time. This was to be much bigger than the old one, a double instead of the old single. So there were now three steam pile drivers and two steam cranes at work within a few hundred yards and so the racket was deafening.

The winter was not as cold as the previous one, so I was doing a bit to my model which was now beginning to take shape. The boiler shell, tender, smokebox, front axle, chimney, rear axle, axle bearings, and some gears were now ready and together were beginning to look very nice. I was really chuffed with my handiwork, as were the rest of the family, but I·had still a long way to go as I had yet to tackle the firebox, wheels, several more gears and many more small things such as the pump, drain taps, check valves, etc. These fiddling bits always take longer than the bigger parts and I had still had to get a cylinder and a flywheel cast somewhere.

The winter seemed to pass by fairly quickly and it was soon time to clean up the K7s and to get them ready for another season. I was very much looking forward to this as it would be my last turn with them as a schoolboy, so I wanted to spend every possible spare hour with them. Father had always drummed into me that no matter how much you know about any job there is always something else to learn. He had always told me "When you go out in the world to earn your own living, take notice of what you are told by your elders. Keep your eyes and ears open and your mouth shut and you won't go far wrong".

There was a new manager on the Estate. His name was Chesterton, and he was soon very unpopular with most of the workers as he started cutting down on everything. He had obviously been called in to curb the spending. For many years, at all the agricultural shows around the South of England the Estate had swept the board with their prize cattle, pigs, sheep, poultry, etc but this was now going to stop as most of the prize beasts were sold off. It became cut down on this and cut down on that. There had no doubt been millions of pounds spent out and not enough had come back in to cover it.

Major Morrison was seldom at Basildon, he had divorced his first wife several years previously and had married an American actress, so most of his time was spent abroad. There was a lot of uneasiness amongst the workers, many of them feared that they would lose their jobs and, as almost everyone of them lived in an Estate house, thereby lose their homes. Things were not quite as they had been for many years but, without a doubt, plenty of the Estate's workforce had been drawing a pretty good wage for doing just about nothing and they also lived rent free so these were the people who were about to catch a cold.

The ploughing engines started working again as soon as the fields had dried out enough to carry their weight, but Jim Smith said that we would have to be a bit careful if I was ever with them in the daytime, as I had done in the past during the holidays, etc. The new manager was red hot and probably would not go much on it to see me driving the engines, but Jim said that it would be all right in the evenings as no one would be around after normal working hours. I was still getting quite a few hours on the engines every week and this went on to about the middle of the summer. But then disaster struck, several of the outlying farms along with much of the equipment was put up for sale. Many of the horse and tractor drawn implements, the Wallis & Steevens traction engine and, worst of all, the complete set of Fowler ploughing tackle were taken to a field at Home Farm, which was at the Pangbourne end of the Estate, where they were lined up and a sale was called. There was obviously something wrong, far more serious than any of the workers knew anything about and this was the start of the big crunch. I was just about heart broken as I would now have to find another job of some sort.

I was to be fourteen years old in a couple of months time, but had to carry on at school until the Christmas (which was the end of the term), so I had five months to look around for something to do. I wanted dearly to go somewhere with ploughing tackle, but if I could get any job with any steam engine I would take it. From then, until the end of the year, I had made out a list of every firm for miles around that we knew had got steam engines and this was a pretty long list. Most of the ploughing contractors were a long way from home. These were Wrights of Alton in Hampshire, Watson & Haig of Andover in Hampshire, Baisleys of Warminster in

Wiltshire, The Oxford Steam Plough Co. and nearest R J & H Wilder of Wallingford, Berkshire. Father explained to me that working for any of these would take me a long way from home, so I would be lucky to get home every weekend, but although I was prepared to accept this, mother was not very happy about the idea. Father told me that it would be no good thinking about this until the spring and that at the end of the season I would almost certainly be put off, as not many cookboys were kept on through the winter.

The bridges at Goring were nearly complete, a month or two late, but they would be in use long before the end of that year so I waited for the big day. Some wonderful news reached us, the bridge was to be tested and opened on the coming Monday and some steam engines were to be driven over them before they were to be opened to the public, so I took a day off from school to see this. On the Sunday evening, I took a bike ride to Goring so that I could have a chat with Peggy Deacon, a chap with a wooden leg who had been the night watchman all the time the bridges were being built. He told me that there were to be four of Charles Openshaw's engines, each with two truck loads of bricks from the Tilehurst brick works and they were to pass on the Goring bridge which was by far the highest and longest span of the two bridges. It had been arranged for two engines to come in from the Oxfordshire side to deliver their load to Smallbone & Sons, a big building firm at Streatley in Berkshire, whilst the other two engines came in from the Berkshire side to deliver their load to Thomas Higgs, the building firm at Goring in Oxfordshire.

A couple of weeks previously, we had moved house as Primrose Cottage, our old home, was going up for sale with all the surrounding land. We were now living at No.11 Lower Basildon right on the side of the A329, the Reading to Wallingford road and this would be on the route of the two engines that were to go over into Oxfordshire. I could stay at home until the engines arrived, then follow them to Streatley, get onto the temporary wooden bridge and have a good view of those four marvellous three-speed Fowlers.

The engines came in sight about mid-morning, so I followed them to the notorious Crown Hill where they stopped to screw on the brakes on all the trucks, get into low gear and edge their way down. This I had seen many times before, but never two loads close together. With the first one safely down and on its way up Grotto Hill, still in low gear, the second one moved off. I followed close behind, something I had never done before as I had always been going in the opposite direction, on my way to school. There seemed to be a lot of hanging around and time wasting going on, but the opening was to be at mid-day and they were a bit before time, so I perched in a good spot on the wooden bridge so that I could see both pairs of engines just waiting for the word 'go'. Off they went, very slowly, nose to tail, from both sides and the bridge was full from one end to the other, a wonderful sight.

What a beautiful picture that would have made, but a camera of any description was a real luxury in those days. Nowadays, when I pass over those bridges I think of that day, and wonder what weight there must have been on them and would it be safe to risk the same thing today. Those bridges are just about sixty years old and a lot of water has gone under them in that time.

Photograph: Rural History Centre, University of Reading.

'This lovely photograph shows an early Fowler engine and a typical steam plough gang outside the Cross Keys Inn at Fovant in Wiltshire about 1910. Scenes like this could often be seen when ploughing engines were in their heyday ...!'

JOE CHALLIS

Chapter 4

'Men of Iron'

My fourteenth birthday had come and gone, but those two months to Christmas seemed to drag. I had made up my mind that when the time to leave finally came, I would take any job for the rest of the winter and hope that some job with steam engines would turn up in the spring. My first day of job hunting was spent in the Pangbourne area and I came home that same night with a job which I was to start after Christmas.

In Horseshoe Road at Pangbourne, there was a big sawmill where they had a Garrett tractor (which was used for timber hauling) and their sawmill was powered by a huge Lancashire cotton-mill engine. I had called in to see if there was any chance of a job with the engine, but, of course, the answer had been no! However, they said that I could have a job making boxes and as this was something to do for the time being, I took it and would be there to start at 6.30am after Christmas.

The boxes were made from green beech and elm and were used for packing sheets of tin. They were made in various sizes but none of them was more than 3in. deep but, when filled, weighed several hundredweight. The frame of the box was very thick (somewhere around $1^1/_2$in.) but the bottoms were only a $^1/_4$in. thick. How I hated this job, the boards were stacked out in the open and so they were frozen together in the mornings and had to be banged onto the bench to part them. They were placed out and nailed to the frames with 1in. wire nails (with no points to them, as with pointless nails you don't split the thin green beech boards). So, with fingers half frozen all day, I soldiered on always glad when five o'clock came, all the time hoping and praying that an engine job of some sort would soon turn up, but I knew that it would be April before the ploughing tackle started to move.

Most of the farms and fields around us had been sold, so we wondered if any of the steam plough contractors would make their way into the Basildon area to take over where the Estate K7s had left off. One person, who had already weighed things up and was into this, was Albert Wickens, an oldish chap well into his sixties. Albert had spent many years travelling round the farms on a pedal cycle getting work for the ploughing sets of Baisleys of Warminster in Wiltshire.

Albert had retired from Baisleys and moved to South Stoke, a small village in the Thames Valley, where he had taken over a pub, the 'Perch and Pike'. He had his eye to business and saw that there must be work for a set of ploughers as there had been more than enough for a set while it was Basildon Estate. He knew most of the steam plough contractors over the south of England and had been in touch with the Gloucester Steam Plough Company, who had a set of Fowler BB1 engines waiting for a job, so Albert was ready to come out of retirement and was looking for a gang to work them.

He contacted the people that had worked the Basildon set, but they were all a bit reluctant to take up this offer, as they might be taken too far from home and this was something that they had not been used to doing. My brother said he would try it as things at Basildon had become very shaky and the engine men were doing farm labourers work or anything else that they were detailed to do. Bert wasn't happy with this situation, so he handed in a weeks notice and on the following Monday went to Gloucester to help bring the set of BB1s into Berkshire and, when they arrived, if a cookboy was needed here would be my chance.

Bert left home early on the Monday morning to get into Reading where he caught the train to Gloucester. Mother did not relish this very much, but for her, there were worse things to come. That same morning, I made my way into Pangbourne to make a few boxes and all day long wondered how Bert was getting on. He had never been away from home in his life, so I knew mother would be thinking the same and would almost certainly be very downhearted for a few days. When I reached home that evening, I could hardly believe my own eyes. We were not far into March and there, in the field opposite our house, was a set of ploughing tackle which had pulled in only a short while before.

They had come to plough the big field that runs from the A329 to the railway, running from the village through to the river Thames. I didn't stop for any tea as I wanted to see where they were from and how they were fixed for a cookboy. It was a set from R J & H Wilders of Wallingford, who had come in and were set out ready to start ploughing the next morning. The engine near the road was one of their twelve horse-power singles with the old fashioned tank steerage. She had an Oxford chimney and smokebox door and to me looked more like something out of the ark than a ploughing engine. I had never seen a single-cylinder ploughing engine before.

The gang were in the living van having a meal, so I had a good browse around the engine and waited for some of them to come out. I could see that the engine had not got its damper on and therefore would have to be banked down for the night. As soon as one of them appeared, we got chatting to each other. I was asking a few questions about the engine and he said "I can see you are interested in steam engines". I told him that my father and brother had worked with the engines on the Estate and that had they still worked there I would have been working with them. He straight away said "You can come and work with us if you like. We are looking for a cookboy". I didn't need asking twice, so I told him straight away that I would like to go with them, but I would have to go back to the sawmill the next day to hand in my notice. He said "Go and have a word with your parents and see what they think about it".

It was getting dark as I hurried back across the road to home. Once there, I broke the news. Father was full of it but mother didn't seem so happy. As I sat eating my meal, I saw that she was a bit upset. Father explained a few things to her, such as the fact that if I missed this chance it might be a long time before another one came along and that we were not sure about the Gloucester job. I finished my meal and was sat chattering about this job, when father said "Let's go over and have a word with them". The gang had cleaned themselves up and were sitting in the van taking a rest when we arrived, but we were soon invited into the van to talk things over.

The chap that I had been talking to was the foreman. He was around the sixty mark, but the two drivers and the cultivator man were all about half his age and they seemed a very nice little crowd. I was sure that I would be happy with them. They told us, the same as father had told me earlier on, that I would not be kept on through the winter, but this didn't matter too much as I was fed up with the box making any way, so there was no way that I was going to have another winter of that work. We stayed chattering with them for a long time.

Father told them how the Estate was folding up, although this was something that they had already heard. He told them that I could do most of the jobs with ploughing tackle, so would be able to take my turn on the plough or cultivator and that I was a pretty good driver, so they would find me very useful. We were told that I had got the job and could start as soon as I was ready.

I didn't get much sleep that night as I was too full of my new job. The next morning I was away to tell Bill Flowers, the sawmill owner, that I was leaving that night. It seemed an endless day and I couldn't get away quick enough when five o'clock came. I was on my bike and home in record time and after a quick meal I was out with the ploughers. They had not ploughed much as it was the first day out after the winter lay off, so there were a lot of adjustments to be made. This is quite normal at the beginning of the season as there is always the odd bearing that will give trouble after being cut back and adjusted up during the winter check over. A bearing that is a little bit on the tight side, will not cool down properly during the day once it has run hot.

I jumped on the plough and had a ride across the field to the other engine, even before the plough had stopped I saw that this engine was different to the one on the other side. As this was the last pull for that evening and it was getting dusk, I didn't stop to look round the engine, but I was told on the way across the field that this was the one and only Wilder piston-valved engine. They were not too impressed by it, as there were a lot of small problems still to be ironed out. We were stood by the engine nearest to home, having a little chat and I was told the names of the other four members of the gang (they already knew mine).

The foreman was George Parks, the driver of the Fowler was Charlie Jefferies, the one on the Wilder engine was Wally Ilesdon and the cultivator man Fred Jones and they seemed to be a very nice gang. As this job was on my doorstep I went home to sleep, so I asked George "What time do you start in the morning?". The answer was, "Soon as it's daylight as we don't go by the clock, the only b—- clock we keep an eye on is that one up there" and pointed to the steam gauge.

Next morning I was there before it was daylight. They were on the move but had not come out of the living van, so I went in ready to light the fire and boil the kettle to make the tea (as this would be my job from now on). To my surprise, George said "We will see to that, while you walk across the field and take the damper off and poke the fire up", this was just up my street and I was soon on my way. It was still dark, so I could not see much of the engine to weigh up the differences in the two engines, but I could see that they were very much the same.

While I was waiting for the fire to draw up, one of the Great Western engines came thundering through. Many times in the past I had stood on the wire fence (which the ploughing engine was running alongside) so that I could watch those beautiful old engines pass through, but never before in the dark. As soon as the gang had gone out of the van to start work I did the washing up, tidied up generally and was soon out on the engines. What a difference they were to the K7s that I had been used to working with. Everything seemed so big and clumsy, they turned over so slowly compared with the compounds, but the crisp bark of the exhaust was sweet music to me.

By about 9.30am they were ready for a cup of tea, so I was detailed to go and boil the kettle. When the tea was made I had to carry it across the field, by way of the plough, to the engine on the far side by the railway. Meal break was about 1pm and they stopped for about half an hour for this, so the kettle was boiled and the tea made as soon as Wally had put the damper on the Wilder and jumped onto the plough to come across to our side of the field. A quick snack, a couple of cups of tea and they were ready to move again.

Wally was away first, as he had to walk to the other side of the field ready to make the first pull, the others soon followed on their way. I then got on with the washing up and was soon out on the engine with Charlie. After a few pulls I got on the plough and had a few rides across the field chattering to George about the plough and pointing out a few of the things that were different to the Basildon Estate plough. That plough had been quite a bit more modern than the one we were on, George said "They all have a few little things that are not the same as each other but they all seem to do the same job". I found this out over the years as, although I worked with a good many Fowler ploughs, I never found two exactly the same.

The afternoon was ticking away, when out of the blue George said "Come on get behind this wheel for a few pulls as it will soon be time to brew up again". I had been waiting for this and I think they were all a bit surprised at the way I could handle things. While they were drinking their tea George said, "Do you think you can manage the engines?". I said "Just try me, they look a bit awkward but I would love to have a go". So while the plough was on its way to the other side of the field, Charlie said "Have a go and get used to the regulator".

I could hardly believe how easy and docile this big single-cylinder engine was compared with the old Fowler traction that I had been handling for so long and which had been as quick as lightning. I had got the plougher ticking over at a nice speed to drop in the clutch, but running in the wrong direction, then when the plough was pulled down I just pulled the reversing lever back, lifted the clutch lever, dropping it in nice and quietly and was soon hustling the plough across the field at a nice speed. Charlie was looking over my shoulder, ready to take over when the plough was within a couple of dozen yards from the engine, but I steadied down, pulled the plough within inches of the cylinder, pushed the lever forward, out with the clutch, in with the road gear, forward about the width of the plough and turned round to Charlie and said "How's that?". With a little grin he said "That was b——- good, just like a veteran".

From that day on I was taking my turn on the plough and both engines, I think they were all more than surprised at how well I did. I had been told they were far more difficult to handle than the compounds, but to me it just seemed to come naturally.

By mid-afternoon the next day the field was finished and both engines were together by the gateway ready to pull out the next morning on our way to Appleford for our next job. On our way through Wallingford, we called in at the works to pick up the other Fowler engine which had been steamed up ready for us. The Wilder was going back to have a few little problems sorted out. At the meal table that evening, I was chatting with my parents and telling mother that I would need enough food packed up to last me a couple of days as I wouldn't be home until Saturday afternoon. I saw that she was not taking it too well.

We had not heard anything of Bert since he left home on the Monday morning and now I was off, her two eldest sons (who had never been away from home for a single night before), both leaving in the same week. I had tidied myself up and went back across the road to the engines for an hour before turning in for the night. I saw that father was already there talking to George, I expect he was telling him to look after me, because as my older sisters had said many times, I was mother's blue-eyed boy.

The next morning, soon after dawn, we were ready to pull out and my job was to sit on the plough seat, which was coupled to the living van behind the second engine. I held the communication cord which was tied to the steersman's arm, so that if anything was trying to get by and we were out in the road a bit too far, I could let them know (this was the law in those days, but only for the last engine). We reached Wallingford in fairly quick time as this is only seven miles from Basildon, the engines changed over and we were on our way to Church Farm, Appleford. There was a big field to be double-tined both ways, so the tackle was set out that evening ready for an early start next morning. As we sat in the van that evening, I was asked all sorts of questions about the Basildon Estate engines, did I know this, that or the other and as I told them the different things that I had done, I think they were a little bit taken back. George said "Not many fourteen year old boys know even a quarter of what you do about this job, you have certainly been well trained, you should go a long way".

Next day I took my turn on the cultivator and the engines while the rest of the gang had their meals one at a time, so keeping the wheels turning, non-stop, all day long. This was the way all steam plough sets operated in those days as it was all done on a piece work basis, with each member of the gang drawing a small weekly wage plus the acreage money, drawn at the end of the season when the tackle was taken home for the winter. On the Saturday morning, George said for me to have a look round the hedgerows of the field to find enough dry wood for lighting up the two engines on the Monday morning. He seemed surprised when I told him that there were a couple of bundles all tied up ready in the locker under the living van (I had collected these from a copse on the opposite side of the A329 to where we were working at Basildon). About mid-morning George said "You might as well make your way home for the weekend, you have around twenty miles to go, the rest of us are fairly close to home, and don't bust yourself to get back for Monday morning, ten o'clock will be plenty soon enough".

By the time I had tidied everything up, had a couple of trips across the field to say cheerio to the drivers and got myself ready, it was getting on for mid-day when I got on my bike and was heading for home. I had planned my route which was from Appleford to Didcot, then across to Blewbury, follow the Berkshire Downs to Streatley where I would pick up the A329 and soon be home. It was a glorious day so I took my time, I travelled across beautiful countryside and it was late afternoon by the time I reached home, tired but extremely happy.

I just loved to be with steam ploughing engines and was now earning my living with them, which to me was all that mattered. Bert had beaten me home, he had arrived before mid-day, his gang had brought the BB engines and tackle from Gloucester. They had started working the engines at Hampstead Norris but did nothing on the Saturday as they all were home for the weekend and as Bert had no bike with him, he had to make his way home the best he could. There was a good cooked meal waiting for me, for which I was just about ready, as I had not eaten anything since breakfast at about five o'clock that morning and I had peddled my bike some twenty miles over pretty hilly country.

Mother had already had a good chat with Bert about his job and the gang he was working with, so now it was my turn. I was able to tell her that I was getting on fine, they all seemed to think the world of me and George was acting just like a father to me. One question was "How do you sleep?" and another "What is the bed like?". I just laughed and said "The beds are nothing like we have at home, they are a bit on the hard side but our nights are pretty short and when we turn in we are all dog tired so getting to sleep is no problem".

All the weekend Bert and I had plenty to talk about. He was telling me about the BB engines, which had done very little work, so were still in prime condition and how much faster they were on the road than the Basildon K7s. The driver of the other engine was a Gloucester chap and Bert was getting on well with him, but he could not make up his mind about the chap that was in charge. He was a Yorkshire bod and seemed to want to rush everything, wanting a field finished before it was hardly started.

We went to bed that evening, chattering steam ploughing engines for half the night and were still ploughing for breakfast next morning and for most of the day. I think the rest of the family were about fed up with us, but we were both dead keen and thought of nothing else. After we had finished tea, Bert got ready to make his way back to the engines so that he could be there to light up early on the Monday morning, he had only about six miles to go against my twenty but I was not going until early Monday morning.

I was up with the Basildon larks next morning and on my way soon after dawn. This time I was to take a different route. I kept to the A329 to

Wallingford, turned off left through Brightwell towards Didcot, then right for Appleford. This route was about the same distance but not quite so hilly. I was fresh from a good night's sleep, the day was cool and I had the journey covered in about half the time it had taken me to come home on the Saturday. I was there in time to make the tea for the mid-morning break, a cup of which went down very nice after a twenty mile bike ride.

We had double-tined the field one way, changed round and started crossing it in the other direction, when my turn came to take over the engine in the corner of the field nearest to the farm. Charlie had gone for his meal break, but after having a couple of pulls I saw that the rope was not running quite as it should. The headland was sloping up towards the hedgerow at the side of the field, therefore the engine was leaning towards the field. This arrangement is something that you try to avoid as the rope does not turn properly at the top of the drum if the engine is leaning into the work. The system always runs better when leaning slightly away from the work.

Mr. Pullen (the farmer) and George were stood close to my engine having, I suppose, a chat about the job (they knew each other well as George had been there to work many times before). After I had pulled the cultivator up to the engine and moved forward stopping a bit short, I jumped down with the firing-up shovel and put a few shovel fulls of earth in front of the wheel, then pulled up onto it so levelling her up (something I had been shown a few years previous). I couldn't miss hearing the farmer say "You've got a good one here George" and George replied "That's our wonder boy, they don't come like this one every day".

Our next field to be cultivated was about half-a-mile away on the other side of the farm and to reach this we had to cross the main Great Western line. There was no bridge so we would have to use the level crossing. The crossing was very narrow being designed for horses and carts only, so the man in charge at the crossing gates would not let us cross until there was a long enough break between trains to allow us to cross in safety, this took about one and a half hours.

Our next job was at Steventon, a village a few miles away on the Newbury to Oxford road, but the soil there is a very heavy kind of grey clay and with the cultivator well down the old singles could be heard a long way off. There is a strip of this type of soil stretching from the Berkshire Downs through to the river Thames, running from Blewbury to way beyond Wantage. It lays very wet through the winter but grows some wonderful crops.

From here we moved a few miles further on to a village called Hanney, still the heavy soil and our nearest point for drinking water nearly half a mile away by a pair of farm cottages that stood at the side of a farm track.

There was no mains water laid on, the only supply was a hole about four feet across in the corner of the field behind the cottages, which was covered over with a part of a wing from a World War One aeroplane. There were dozens of aeroplane wings around the farms here, where they were used for sheep and cattle pens. They had been sold off at the end of the war from nearby Milton (a big army ordnance depot). I got out the yoke, hooked up the two buckets and made my way across to this water hole, lifted up the piece of aeroplane wing (which was very light as it was only a thin wooden frame covered with fabric) and there was this hole filled nearly to the top with very clear water.

Lying on the bank around the hole were about a dozen lizards, but they hardly moved as I dipped up the water. I had never before used water for drinking other than that from a tap and when I told George about the livestock around the hole he said "That will be perfectly all right when it's boiled" and I suppose it must have been OK as the cottages had nothing else to use.

I had learnt that Wilders owned seven sets of ploughing tackle and that each set had its own area that it worked, year after year, but surprisingly they were all within a radius of about fifteen miles from Wallingford. Our set was the odd one out, we travelled around tying up all the loose ends of the sets. If they happened to be too busy to get to a farmer that was waiting for them, ours would be the set that would take over. As a result we could be fifteen miles one side of Wallingford one week and the same distance the other side the next week, which meant we did a fair bit of travelling.

We finished our job at Hanney but our next move was a long one, we were going away into Oxfordshire to a place called Chalgrove, almost a full days run (even with the best of luck), so we would be away at the crack of dawn next morning. I don't remember the exact route we took from Hanney, but we crossed the Thames at Clifton Hampden, this was one of the few bridges that would carry us in those days. This bridge was built of brick and had a toll gate, so on arrival we stopped while George walked across to pay the toll-keeper. Then he came back to tell me that I would have to steer the plough across the bridge, which was fairly narrow and had a pretty sharp corner at each end. (A ploughing engine, living van and plough is a rather long outfit to get round such corners.)

Normally the plough wheels are set on a straight course and the steering wheel then tied to the seat with a piece of cord, so this was untied. I was on the seat behind the wheel, ready to go and George said, "When the plough reaches the corner steer it out round the corner as far as possible and when we get to the other side we will stop and tie the wheel again". We went onto the bridge from the Berkshire side with no problem, this was a left-hander and the shape of the plough is ideal for going this way, but it's a different story when you turn right as the tail end swings over to the left and is out over the top of the hedgerow or whatever happens to be there. I was perched on the seat, looking back to where we had come from, because when you are tucked in behind the living van there is no way that you can see what is ahead of you. As the plough reached the corner, I did exactly as George had said and steered the plough out as far round the corner as possible.

I could see the tail end of the plough coming nicely round close to the wall of the bridge. Then out of the blue there loomed up a big white post, with the toll gate hung on it and I could see that it was too late to steer back the other way and so miss it. The plough share of the last plough hooked into the post, pulling it away from the brickwork, leaving the gate and post laid in the road with a few bricks scattered around. Charlie could see what we had done and gave a blast of the whistle to stop Wally with the leading engine.

By the time George had reached us I was in tears because I thought that it was all my fault and so I would probably be sacked as this was going to cost the firm a lot of money. The gate was picked up and placed against the wall, then there was a lengthy conversation with the toll-keeper before we were ready to press on again. George could see that I was really upset, so he came over to me and said that I should not worry about what had happened as I had done exactly what he had told me to do, so it was really his fault and not mine. But I was still in tears.

Fred Jones was steering our engine but he was not too reliable, always seeming a bit frightened so Charlie had to keep a constant eye on him, often having to grab the wheel himself to avoid going into a ditch. We still had a long way to go and so, as we had lost a lot of valuable time, George was telling us that we would now have to press on if we were to reach Chalgrove in daylight. I had just got the plough wheels lined up and tied the steering wheel, when to my great surprise George came back to me and said "Come on, you can drive the engine and let Fred sit back here".

George had weighed things up and he knew that I was capable of driving the old girl, so with Charlie on the step (hanging onto the steering wheel) we would be able to push on and try to make up some lost time. Wally and George set off at a pretty good pace and we followed on keeping them in sight. I thought this was great as they must have had a lot of confidence in me and I wondered how many other fourteen year olds there were in the country doing the same as I was. Now, as I think back, I realize that I must have been one of a very small few.

We crossed over the Wallingford to Oxford road near Nuneham Courtenay and within a few hundred yards Wally stopped by the stream that crossed under the road. He was waiting for us as we had the lift pipe in the van, this was screwed on in quick time and they were soon filled up and pulled forward to let us hook up to the pipe. With our tank full, the pipe was put back on the hanger on the van, carefully strapped up and we were ready to go. Wally had by then disappeared round the bend in the road and was out of our sight, but we would soon be with them again, or at least that's what I thought.

We started to pull away but I suppose Charlie had pulled a little bit too hard into the side when we stopped to pick up our water so, as soon as we moved, the side of the road broke away and she went full lock straight towards the ditch. With the old type tank steerage when something like this happens three men would never be able to hold the wheel, let alone just one. I had managed to stop in time with the rear wheel still on the road. I gave a long blast on the whistle which they heard on the other engine and so George came hurrying back to see what had gone wrong.

This was about the only time I had ever seen him get rattled about anything, he was always so calm and collected, but this time the air was a bit blue for a few minutes. He had a look around, weighed up the situation and went storming off to bring back the other engine (which was nearly half a mile up the road).

They reversed the other engine back to us and were well over onto the right-hand side of the road with the rear end across to our wheel. The big chain was put round our front axle, which was by now nearly onto the road, this way (with the chain coupled up short) they would be lifting us as well as pulling. Charlie was now at the regulator with George at the wheel, while I was taking care of Wally's steering wheel so that he could be looking back to see what was happening. They had not changed their gear wheels and when all was ready Wally gave it a big handful, but bang went the chain, which did not please George one little bit. He jumped down off the step and said "That's a b—- good start in top gear" and he grabbed the chain off the other engine and changed them over while Wally changed the gear cogs.

This time everything went to plan, meaning that we were soon ready to go again, the 'big wheel' put back on and off we went to where Fred was waiting with the cultivator, harrows and water cart. George came back to us and said "You go on in front and we will follow on, but push it along or we are going to finish up in the dark". We pulled out round the other tackle and were soon ambling along at a good speed. It was getting dusk, so I kept a sharp lookout in front in case anything loomed up in front of us. Suddenly Charlie gave me a swipe round the back of my neck with his cap, he thought I was pushing it a bit too much and told me that he had been shouting at me for the last half-mile, but there was too much noise going on for me to

63

hear him. As I was close to the reversing lever he could not reach me from the step, leaving his cap as the only answer.

We had travelled at least three miles after normal lighting-up time and it had become really dark. We were within a mile of our job but, as we could see that the verge on the side of the road was wide enough to take us, we decided to stop, so Charlie and I walked along to make sure that there were no deep water outlets cut across it. By this time the other engine was with us and George was soon off the step to have a look. He decided that this would be our best bet as it would be out of the question to try and get into the field in pitch darkness.

We pulled up over the bank, which was about a foot high and made our way along the grass verge to the end of the wide strip, leaving enough length for the other engine and implements. Unfortunately, we had slipped up, we should have let Wally go on first as we finished up leaning towards the road with the living van leaning at a pretty crazy angle, but we were off the road and that was all that mattered. We had all had enough for one day, as we had been up early in the morning, on the road by six o'clock and had not eaten anything all day, so were just about ready for a meal, but could not really enjoy it as our cups and plates would not stay on the table.

There was not much said by any of us that evening, I suppose they were all a bit fed up and I was still thinking about what was going to happen about the toll-gate. As we sat there that evening, it crossed my mind several times, "What would have happened if the police had caught up with us?", we had been travelling in the dark with no lights for about an hour and a fourteen year old boy was driving one of the engines.

We had not been in bed long when it started to rain and as the night went on it just got heavier. It was still pouring when we got up in the morning and it was almost certain there would be no cultivating done that day. So after breakfast George put on his overcoat and walked off down the road to see what the gateway into the field (which we were to cultivate) was like. When he returned, and told us what it was like, we knew that we would be staying put for the day.

There was a steep pull up into the field and water was pouring off the field, out of the gateway and into the road. We sat in the living van for a couple of hours and the rain seemed to ease up a bit. Both Charlie and Wally went out and got the pick-axe out of the locker, then they started digging some holes to drop the van wheels into in an attempt to level it up a bit. They went down about a foot so when the wheels were dropped in we were almost level and what a treat this was. As we sat eating our mid-day meal there were, as was usual when all were together, a few jokes going round and it seemed that everyone had settled down to normal again. We were the happy little gang that I had known for the past few weeks, George was chipping Charlie about his new driver and between them they reckoned I was the cat's whiskers. Charlie was telling them how he had kept an eye on everything from his step but had not needed to remind me about anything. The water glass was at about three-quarters full all the time, the steam gauge kept near the red mark but not once on the whole journey did she blow off and that is what he called good driving and George agreed.

When Friday afternoon arrived, the boss came round to bring the wages and he had a long chat with George. The toll-gate disaster was talked over and after the boss had gone I was told once again to just forget all about it, as it was something that could happen any day and I was certainly not to blame. George handed the wage packets round to all of us and said that, as we would not be doing any more cultivating this week, we would stay where we were until Monday morning, I could be away as soon as I wished next morning. He realised that I had a long way to go and that there was no rush for me to be back on Monday.

We were in bed in good time that evening and, as our van was on an even keel we had a better night's sleep. Everyone was up early next morning for breakfast, then I got everything ready for Monday morning meaning that all of us would be making for home in good time. I was away first and, because I was in strange country, I followed the route that George had drawn up for me the previous day. The sun had come out and it looked as if I would get a good journey home so, as I had got all day in front of me, I took my time. I was the happiest boy alive and what a story I would have to tell when I reached home.

We had about two weeks work at this farm, then we moved on to Wheatley, which is fairly close to Oxford. I said to George "Surely we are now in the Oxford Steam Plough Company's country", to which he replied "Our firm has an agreement with them not to poach each others territory, unless either firm is overworked and cannot make it". We had cultivated two big fields on this farm and there were more fields to do, but they would not be ready for us to start for about a week. As we would be standing idle for a while and we had no other farmer waiting for us, both engines were placed side by side in the farmyard so that the boilers could be washed out.

We steamed one engine and used it to wash the other one out with a high pressure hose from the injector pipe. Then we changed over engines and did the same again with the other one. It was perfectly safe to blow down the boiler then start washing it out as soon as the other engine had raised enough steam to work the injector, as the boiler is being washed out with boiling water, but you never blow it down and wash out with cold water from a tap, this is a bad thing for the boiler.

Next day was Saturday again and I was on my way home early, I had well over twenty miles to do that weekend. Monday morning we were all to meet at the Wallingford works at 7am where we were all to spend the week in the foundry. I was home well before midday and asked mother if she knew where Bert was working, she had no idea exactly where, but knew he was somewhere fairly close. He had been home on the Wednesday evening and he thought that he would be late home for the weekend and that he was not too happy at the way things were going with his gang. When he reached home we had tea and talked steam ploughing as usual, I told him what I had been doing and what a nice little crowd they were to work with. However, Bert had a far different story to tell, some of the farmers they had done work for were complaining that the work was being skimped and that Jack Griffiths, the foreman, was moody being all rush and tear. Their cookboy had only stayed with them for a few weeks so they were now without one.

The cultivator man, Barry Wickens (the son of the old boy that was getting their work) was bone idle. The only one that Bert had any time for was the other driver, Gerald Gooch from Gloucester. He was a good driver, worker and an excellent mate and they were hitting it off well together. This was no good for a steam plough gang as if it is to be successful, you must be all in the same mind, work together and be prepared to work hard and long. There is always the odd wet day or two when you could all take it easy.

I left home on the Monday morning at 6am and was at the work's gate (long before anyone else arrived), waiting for it to open. I had not seen the works before and was eager to see what it was all about. When we eventually got inside, I could see what a big place it was and the work force was big to go with it. There was a long queue waiting their turn to clock in, which was something that we did not have to do as the steam plough gangs didn't have a clock card until the winter, when they worked full time at the works.

Our gang was detailed off to the jobs that they would be doing for the week and I was went with George into the foundry where we would be making cultivator points and reversible plough shares. George said "You have helped to wear out a load of them, now you can help make some to replace them". I was really chuffed as this was something new to me, my father had told me how he used to do the same thing when he was at Bakers of Compton, so I had a rough idea of what it would be like. There were heaps of black sand everywhere and piles of moulding boxes of all sizes but the ones that we were to use were a little bit different to the others. Half of the moulding box was a big cast iron block shaped to make one side of three plough shares whilst the other half was a normal box with sand. A wooden pattern was placed onto the block, located by two small pegs, then the cores for the socket of the shares were made up in threes and had a small spike on each to form the hole for the small wooden peg which held the share onto the plough body.

The cultivator heart-shaped points were made in the same way, but were made in blocks of four at a time. Making the plough share pegs was usually the cookboy's job and I have made a few hundred of them. I used to try and get hold of as many rick pegs as possible, these are the wooden spikes that were pushed into the corn ricks to hold the thatch down. These pegs were usually made of hazel wood, and were ideal for plough pegs. I have travelled backwards and forwards across the field on the plough seat for hours while using a sharp pocket knife to cut and point these pegs off, so keeping a good supply always at hand in the plough tool box.

We spent two days making the moulds, so by Tuesday evening we had two long rows across the moulding shop and were all set for Wednesday when they would all be filled with molten cast iron. I was eager to get to work next morning as this was something I had not seen, but had been told by my father that it was heavy and hot work and I soon realised this when the action started, but it was very interesting work. There were many moulds of different sorts to be filled that day, most of them were completed by mid-day. Ours were to be completed after the meal break and then everyone would be able to take it quiet for the rest of the day. Next day it was my job to help remove the boxes, knock out the sand and plough shares, break off the runners and risers, then wheel them across the yard to be stacked in an open fronted shed. This shed held thousands of plough shares and cultivator points of various shapes and sizes.

When these jobs were completed, the moulding boxes had been stacked away and the sand shovelled into tidy heaps, George took me for a look round some of the other parts of the works. The first area being the boiler-shop where I was introduced to Fred Saunders, the boiler-smith, he had been busy drilling a side of a firebox on a big radial drilling machine. I said to George "That looks like a part of a big firebox" and he said "You are right that is for the other Wilder piston valve engine, if it ever gets finished". In the boiler shop with Fred there were two old ploughmen, both past retirement age, just doing a few light jobs and keeping the place tidy. George told me how they had both worked with him as drivers many years before, one was 'Bandy' Jack Edwards and the other 'Jip' Quatermain and from what George was telling me Jip had been a right character as a younger man. They were once working together in the Abingdon area, unable to go home for the weekend, so they decided to go into town on the Saturday afternoon to do their shopping. They had left it a bit late to get a decent joint so the butcher was showing them what he had got left (which wasn't much). Jip said to him "That looks more like a bit of rhinoceros than beef", anyhow they agreed on the joint, the butcher wrapped it up and said "Shall I put it in a bag for you" to which Jip piped in "No tie a bit of b—— string on it and I will lead it".

We went back through the machine shop, a huge building, with a row of forges (for the blacksmiths) along one side and the rest filled with lathes, shapers, milling machines, a huge planing machine, several drilling machines and pneumatic hammers. A very interesting place just humming with machinery. We spent the rest of the week sifting the sand that we had used for our moulds and generally tidying the place up. I thought that this would be a good chance to have a word with the head moulders about getting a cylinder cast for my model Fowler. (I had not touched the model for several weeks.) I showed him the shape that it needed to be by chalking it out on a moulding box. He explained to me how to make the pattern and said that he would be happy to make it for me the next time we were in the works.

The following Monday morning, we all met at Wheatley to carry on our cultivating as the farmer was ready for us. This job took about four days and we then moved on to Sandford, where the soil was sandy with a lot of sandstone scattered everywhere. Our van was pulled into a disused stone quarry at one corner of the field and there must have been hundreds of rabbits in this quarry. As we sat having our meal that evening we could see the rabbits running up and down the stone ledges. Charlie said "I am going to have a couple of them to take home tomorrow". Just before dusk we went out with some snares (which were in one of the van's lockers) and a hammer from the engine, the pegs were driven in between the slabs of stone and the snares set. Sure enough next morning there were six rabbits hanging on the quarry wall and I had one of them to take home to Basildon.

We spent the rest of the season around that area and, each time we moved from one farm to the next, Fred Jones would make sure that he was going to ride on the plough. He seemed frightened to death of getting on the step to steer the engine and, as George had said many times, he was not a very good cultivator or plough man. George reckoned that I should have been drawing Fred's wages and Fred drawing mine, but I was happy as we were going. I was doing a lot of driving in the fields on both engines and driving Charlie's engine on the road every time we moved. I was not complaining but George was not happy with it all, he said "When we get back to the works you will be stood off while Fred will be kept on. Worst of all I shall be going out with a set of threshing tackle and Jonesie will be my mate for the winter".

Our last job for the season was at Harwell for a farmer by the name of Cauldwell. The farm was on heavy grey clay soil, it was getting late in the year and the fields were wet, so it was really hard slogging. I would think that those old 12 hp single-cylinder engines could be heard barking back at Wallingford, where the other six gangs were all back home, greasing up their engines and draining everything off to leave them safe for the winter. Ours had been the first set out that year and we were the last ones back. I had spent a wonderful summer and had enjoyed every minute of it, but this had now come to an end. I must look for another job for the winter but would almost certainly be back in the spring.

We left Harwell on the Thursday morning to make our way back home, there was no hurry as we were not more than about eight miles from Wallingford and we reckoned on getting there for our mid-day meal. We stopped at Brightwell to pick up water and before we left, I said to George "I suppose I ought to get on the plough and let Jonesie be in his proper place before we reach Wallingford". The answer was "You will stay where you are and let them b—— that end see who should be drawing the cultivator man's wages". I found out later that he had tried to get a few more shillings for me each week but with no luck. We made our way round the back streets of Wallingford which brought us to the A329 where we had to go straight across and into the wharf. Here the other sets of ploughing tackle, along with several sets of thrashing tackle were lined up, a very impressive sight and would be even more so today.

The wharf is several hundred yards long and stretches from the A329 to the river Thames. The wharf looks, to me, just about the same as it did sixty years ago when I first saw it, but sadly today it is lined with tractors and other farm machinery instead of those beautiful old Fowler steam engines that I loved so much. As we crossed the main road we looked down from the engine into the Wilder office and there, watching us from the window, was Mr. Little. He was head man in the office and more or less ran the firm, being the boss when the Wilders were out. Had he seen me driving the engine or was I too small to be seen when up on the footplate? We pulled down the wharf until we were clear of the main road then boiled the kettle, made a cup of tea and had our meal. We were soon surrounded with steam ploughing men of all ages and sizes, some old, some young, some big and some small but from what I could see, I was the titch of them all as the other cookboys had been laid off.

It was now time to get our tackle lined up with the other six sets and it looked as if we were going to be a bit pushed for room. Seven full sets of ploughing tackle and about the same number of thrashing sets take up a lot of room, so they were parked as close as possible together with just room to walk between them. All the engines were together at the end of the wharf nearest to the road, then the living vans, next the thrashing tackle and all the ploughing implements lined up at the river end. There were somewhere around thirty ploughing men around so all our implements were manhandled into position with very little effort and Wally's engine was then backed in alongside the other ploughers. This left our engine with the van and the plough behind it, the last to go in.

Charlie pulled his engine down the wharf until the van was in line with the other six, it was then uncoupled and pushed into position. The plough was then coupled to the engine and pulled down to the bottom of the wharf where there was just about room for it. With our plough parked away, everyone walked back up the wharf to size up how much room was left for our engine. They all agreed that it would be a bit tight, but George stepped it across and was certain there was plenty of room. At the back of the wharf there is about a ten foot drop down a steep bank to a stream, so care has to be taken not to go back too far. They were all stood there having a natter (I don't know how many acres they had ploughed between them), when George walked across to me, smiling all over his face, and said "Come on sunshine, show 'em how it is done". Nobody else moved, I was to back our engine up the wharf and in between the other engines, with very little room to spare either side.

I walked off down to where the old girl was standing and realised that she was still in top gear, so the first job was to change the cogs. The fast speed wheel on these engines must have been at least a hundredweight, I had to take it off the crankshaft and place it over a peg on the footboard. I had not had a go at this before, but now was the time to have a go. I had seen it done many times and knew what I was up against. The pin was taken out and put in the tool box, where there was a leather boot lace used to tie around the keys in the crankshaft. These keys were loose in the shaft and would fall out when the gear wheel was removed, so I slid the wheel halfway off then tied in the keys and I was then ready for the tricky bit. I looked back up the wharf and saw that they were all looking, but no one was coming to help, so I thought here goes. To my great surprise I lifted it off, laid it on the footboard and got it over the peg with no problem. The 'small wheel' now on and connected to the lever, I dropped it into gear and made my way steadily back back up the wharf to where they were all standing. There, with them, was Mr. Little from the office, so I locked the wheels round to make the first shunt back into the space left for us. It was the first time that I had felt a bit nervous since the time I got on that engine to drive it away back at Basildon several months previously. I had two shunts and was just about in line, then I edged my way back between the other engines, stopped just about in line with the row of front wheels (which were all within a few inches of each other). As I slipped her out of gear, George said "That will do fine" and a big cheer went up from some of the other drivers and foremen. I had surprised them all, as well as myself. As I stepped over the wheel, onto the footboard, to put the damper on the chimney, I could see George and Mr. Little walking up towards the office, talking something over which I was to hear all about a bit later on.

The day's oil was wiped from the boiler lagging and the drain holes round the top of the rope drum well cleaned out, so that when it rained the top of the drum would not fill up with water. The motion bright work would be greased over the next day and the boiler, all valves and pipes would be drained off to leave them safe for the winter.

While talking of the drain holes in the drum top, I have stood by a good few ploughing engines at different rallies and noticed that the holes have not been cleaned out for many years. These holes can hardly be seen so, without a doubt, the people that are looking after them have never worked them for a living and just don't know that they are there. This was one of the most important things for a driver to look after, especially after a wet night or weekend as, if these holes are blocked, the cavity round the top of the drum between the brake and the gear ring would fill up with water. This could be a few gallons, taking a long time to mop up with a piece of rag and you must never start working unless this has been taken care of.

Most ploughing engine owners will know that the brake must be kept oiled, but will also know that oil and water mixed is as slippery as ice, so when this happens you are in dire trouble. If the brake is not working properly the drum will spin freely, often resulting in as much as a whole bed of rope dropping all over the place, the coils will get crossed and tie themselves in knots, losing valuable time. Most ploughers have a brake on the drum pinion which is operated by the clutch lever. I have seen drivers sit on this lever with very little effect, as it is steel to steel and nearly always well oiled. For those who don't know where to look for these drain holes, they are slots in the base of the brake drum where the band rests on it and are cut horizontal so that the water can run out into the open part at the inside of the drum. This part of the drum can be kept spotlessly clean with no problem, we always used cotton waste for cleaning and a piece of this about the size of your fist dropped into the cavity that collects the oil and water, ie between the brake and the gear ring. This will roll round and round as your rope is running out, keeping it perfectly dry and clean, but it will also help to block the drain holes which must be cleaned out occasionally.

Wallingford was only seven miles from my home, I decided that I would not go home for the night as I was finishing up the next night, so I would spend the night with George in the van. He had been so good to me that I hated leaving him. I had spent the whole summer with him and, had I been his own son, he could not have treated me any better. I knew that I owed him a great deal.

The rest of the gang had gone home, as they all lived within cycling distance from Wallingford and George and I were having our meal, chattering about some of the things we had done through the summer and what we would be doing through the winter. I was telling him that there would be no hopes of a job back on the Estate as they were paying off a few more each week and there was very little to do for those that were left. He just smiled at me and said "You don't have to worry, you are coming threshing with me. I have had words with Georgie Little and, as far as he is concerned, you will be my mate for the winter, but we still have to meet Mr. Wilder tomorrow as he is the boss, but I am sure that I can fix him".

I could hardly believe my luck, I was sure that I would be finishing the next day as, until then, not a word had been spoken about a winter's work for me. When I had started with them, I had been told that the cookboys were not kept on after the tackle was in the yard for the winter.

The Friday was spent round the engines greasing everything up to protect them from the winter, the plough mould-boards had already been done when we finished our last ploughing job. I was plastered with grease and oil so, about 3.30pm, George said to me "Get cleaned up, we have got to be up at the office by 4 o'clock". We walked up the wharf and across the main road into the office, this was the first time that I had been in there. Sat at their desks were Mr. Little, Mr. Wilder and two or three other office staff. I suppose I was a bit shy, so I stood behind George as he was chattering to the two gaffers.

Mr. Wilder was telling him that a new Ransome clover seeder was on the way from Ipswich and he would be going out with it as soon as it arrived. Then he said "I understand you want to take this lad with you". A few more words were passed and I could tell the boss was not too happy about it. He looked across to me and said "How old are you?" and I said "I shall be fifteen tomorrow". Straight away he said "But George, we can't have boys of this age on our engines" and a few sharp words were exchanged. George said to him "If he can't come as my mate, Fred Jones certainly won't, as he is just about useless. Here we have a youngster that is worth his weight in gold, he is a born steam ploughman and there is very little that I, or anyone else, can teach him about steam ploughing. All the summer he has carried Jonesie".

George then told him how I had been driving the engine every time we moved from one job to another and said "Apart from his size, he is as good a driver as any in the firm and should certainly be looked after". Then Mr. Little had a few words to say about how he had watched me put the engine away for the winter and agreed with what George had said. I was told to go back to my work and, as I walked back to the engines, I wondered what the outcome would be. Was I going to lose Jonesie his job?

By now the other steam ploughmen were getting ready to go for their wage packets, several of them stopped chattering to me and asked what I was going to do for the winter? What could I tell them as George was still in the office ironing things out. It was after five o'clock when George came back to the van, where I was getting ready to go home. (I could not see things going his way after hearing what Mr. Wilder had to say.)

As George made his way up the van steps, I could see he was all smiles and he soon poured out the whole story. "Yes, your job is safe. You will be my mate for the winter, meanwhile Fred Jones will be given a job at the works". George handed me my wage packet, all eighteen shillings (90p) of it, then he told me that, after a lot of hot words, he had got them to see sense and he gave me another wage packet. "That's some acreage money for you" he said (this was something that cookboys never got).

I had put the kettle on ready for a cup of tea before I left and this was now boiling so the tea was made while George told me of some of the jobs that were lined up for us as soon as the new machine was with us. I would not be going home that night as we were to get our engine ready next morning, or at least make a start on it. This was a six horse-power single Fowler, called *Little Mary*, a wonderful little engine George reckoned. We had finished our tea and I was still thanking him for what he had done for me when he noticed that I had not yet opened my second wage packet which was still on the table. He said "Have a look and see what they have dished up". I was speechless, in the packet were two five-pound notes, the old type of course, which were about 9in. by 6in. I had seen only one of these before and ten pounds in those days was a lot of money, especially for a fifteen year old.

As we were sat there chattering, it suddenly dawned on me about the journeys I would have to do every day. George said "Don't worry, we will have a van with us as we shall be covering a lot of Berkshire and Oxfordshire and clover seeding is a slow job". This job was another one that I had not seen yet.

We started cleaning up the little Fowler the next morning. It seemed so small after several months on the ploughers, but George was telling me that it was a wonderful little engine for power, although she was not too good at holding back while going down hill. I left the wharf at twelve o'clock and made my way home to tell my parents the good news, they thought that I was finishing that weekend. They would, almost certainly, be expecting me to be coming home with a long face and be down in the dumps. Instead I was just the reverse, I was as happy as a king and when I showed them the five pound notes they could hardly believe it.

Now Bert had not been home for two weeks, his gang had taken their tackle back to Gloucester and it was a bit too far to come home every weekend. I was hoping he would be home this week, as I had got so much to tell him and he would no doubt be in the same position. I spent most of the afternoon splitting up wood for lighting the fire (a job I had always done while I was at school) and by the time it was all packed away in the shed it was time for tea.

As I was washing my hands Bert walked in, he had travelled by train from Gloucester to Reading, then by bus from there to home and was ready for a cup of tea. As we sat there round the table he was telling us that he had now finished for the Gloucester Steam Plough Company and would be starting for a different firm on the Monday, this time on a steam roller for the winter.

A few days before they started their long journey back to Gloucester, Albert Wickens, the old boy that had cycled around to the farms to get the work for them, had told Bert that the Gloucester firm would not be doing any more work for him, as he had taken so much stick from different farmers about the quality of their work.

Albert had signed up with another firm for the next year, so he wanted Bert to take over a set of tackle that would be sent into our area and so he would come to talk things over with him on Sunday. We spent the evening round the fire talking about steam ploughing as usual and I told Bert how George had got me a job with him. Bert reckoned that I was dead lucky, as not many cookboys were kept on, least of all to become second man on a set of threshing tackle at only fifteen years of age.

We were up quite early the next morning, as father expected a load of wood to be delivered from the Estate and we had to get most of this cut up during the day. Bert and I were busy with the big crosscut saw, whilst father was splitting up and stacking the wood in the woodshed, then Albert Wickens arrived. We went in for a break and a cup of tea while Albert was telling the story of the new firm that Bert would be working for. It was A J Ward & Sons of Thorpe-Lea, near Egham in Surrey. They had got a set of K7 Fowlers that had been stood idle most of the year, partly through lack of orders, but chiefly because they had nobody to work them.

Most of their steam plough men had retired, whilst the younger ones were not interested in the long hard days and I suppose steam ploughing was already on the decline. Albert had been told that this had been a spare set for several years and had been operated chiefly by threshing men, if ever a job had come up for them. Bert was to report to Egham next morning to get the tackle ready to bring down to this part of the country where it would be parked away ready for spring. The tackle would stand at Great Lea farm, near Three Mile Cross (a small village on the Basingstoke road just out of Reading). This farm was being farmed by Jim Hayes (his wife and Sidney Ward's wife were sisters). It was a big farm with plenty of room (the yard at Egham was a bit loaded with rollers and their other two sets of ploughers) and so, as they would be working in our area, this would be ideal as a base to work from.

We both left home on the Monday morning round about the same time, I had to cycle to Wallingford by 7am whilst Bert had to catch the bus into Reading for the train to Egham. George and I spent the day cleaning up *Little Mary* and getting her ready for the day when the new clover seeder would arrive, so that we could start our winter round. I was looking forward to this job and, I think, George was also as he had told me that he would much rather be working outside than in the works. Next morning my first job was to remove the brake band so that it could be fitted with new blocks as the old ones were a bit worn. The brake on this little Fowler was on the third motion shaft, consisting of a drum about 12in. diameter by 3in. wide, situated just over the fire hole door and fitted with a hand wheel to screw it on.

I had removed the band and had cleaned it well when George said "We will take it up to the carpenter's shop to get some new hardwood blocks fitted. Then I can show you round the woodworking machinery, but first of all we had better take the diameter of the drum so that they can get the blocks about right". So he wandered off up to the fitting shop, where he borrowed some big callipers and we took the measurements then set off to the woodworking shop. There were lathes, planing machines, vertical spindle and woodworking machinery of all sorts, most of which were being used. They were making the wheels and all the other wooden parts for their steel frame farm wagons, for which they were famous in those days. Some of these wagons were fitted with roller bearing wheels and some were fitted with half-round steel tyres, but these were more for road use rather than farm work.

We had spent a few days round the engine and had her fired up to make sure all was well, when down the wharf came Mr. Wilder to tell us that our new machine was at the station ready for us to collect. Off we went to unload the clover seeder. This did not take us long, but George had twigged something that would have to be done before we moved out from the works. This machine did not have lock chains fitted to the turn carriage and these are most essential when a machine has to be pushed between ricks (this was fitted as standard on all Marshall and Clayton threshing machines).

We pulled it into the wharf and a few things were compared with their old Marshall clover seeding machine, which I gathered had seen better days. The blacksmiths and carpenters were to fit a set of lock chains so that we would be ready to go the next day. Meanwhile, the living van was sorted out, a bag of cotton waste for cleaning and a few drums of cylinder and machine oil were put in the locker along with about half a ton of coal, which we would have in reserve for any long journey we might get.

Our first job was at Radley, a village close to Abingdon and George reckoned that this trip would take us most of the day, as we had a fair load for a small engine (there was the new machine, our living van and a Roberts folding elevator). I had noticed that on the oval brass plate on the side of the boiler, which carries the engine number (as all Fowlers did), she was under nine tons and I would think our load was more than twice that. We were all coupled up and ready to go, but as it was Friday morning, George said "We will wait until the office is open, go and draw our wages then be on our way".

While George oiled round the engine I made sure that all the wheels had been oiled (we hadn't missed any), there was one more thing, our bicycles were in the van, but had not been tied, so I did this and made sure that our stove was safe as we had used it to boil the kettle for our morning cup of tea. While I did this, George made his way up to the office and collected our wage packets, so we were then ready to go. The 'big wheel' was engaged and we were away. Our journey was all pretty flat country with very little hill climbing to do, so we did not have any problems. We stopped for our first pick up of water and while the tank filled, I walked back to have a check on everything but, as I came back to the engine, she seemed smaller than ever. She looked almost like a miniature in front of her load, but as George had said there was no shortage of power and she seemed to make light work of it all.

We arrived at the farm in good time and were shown where the clover rick was, about a couple of hundred yards along a farm road. The rick was a big one, so George reckoned that it would take best part of a week to clear it. We had all the Saturday morning to get everything set up, so we got our van ready for the job and, while George banked *Little Mary* up for the night, I boiled the kettle and made a pot of tea. This drink was very welcome as we had not stopped all day, so we were both thirsty and feeling a bit hungry.

While we were having our meal, George told me some of the do's and don'ts of clover threshing. The one that surprised me most was that if there is even a damp atmosphere, you don't open the rick as a clover seeding machine will not get all the seed out properly if it is the slightest bit damp and clover seed is very valuable. A clover seeding machine has two drums, instead of just the one that a corn threshing machine has, the top drum just takes off the heads (this has beater bars almost the same as on an ordinary threshing machine). The bottom drum has short beaters, set at right angles to the drum, these rub the seeds from the heads, which have been taken off and passed down to the bottom. The drums on a clover machine must be driven faster than a threshing machine and if my memory serves me right it is 9,000rpm for the top and 11,000rpm for the bottom. There was a short 6in. wide flat belt (which coupled the two drums) running on a pulley about 10in. diameter at the top and about 8in. at the bottom.

We set up on the Saturday morning and were all ready to go by about ten o'clock, so the belts were put on, then the machine and elevator were kept running for about half an hour to make sure that all was well for Monday morning. This was when Jack Saunders (who was head man in the fitting shop and brother to Fred the boilersmith), would be out to us with a rev counter to make sure that the governors on *Little Mary* were set about right.

We were sheeted up, ready to go home before twelve, but I had a long way to go and the weather was not too special as winter was almost with us. Before we left I said to George "I will be back on Sunday evening as the weather could be a bit uncertain to leave early on Monday". It was cold, so I pedalled pretty fast to keep warm and was home by about 2.30pm, I found that Bert had already arrived home, his gang had travelled from Egham to Three Mile Cross with the K7s and parked them away for the winter.

He had come home on the Friday evening and was to go back to Egham on the Sunday evening, then he would be going out with a roller on the Monday. He had no idea what roller it would be or to where he was going (this was typical of Wards as I found out a few years later). Over the weekend, I was telling my father about our new machine and *Little Mary*. I explained what a nice little engine she was and how she looked very much the same as his 8 hp Fowler on the Estate, although quite a bit smaller. He said the same as he had told me many times, "Give me a Fowler for power and a Marshall for governors". He then told me a few things about clover seeding as he had done quite a bit of it while at Bakers of Compton. The thing that struck me most was the weight of clover seed. He said that "If it is good quality seed you will have no problem getting 5 cwt into a normal corn sack which normally holds 2$^{1}/_{4}$ cwt of wheat.

By 7 o'clock on the Monday morning we were ready to start. The few workers from the farm were there to start pulling the thatch off the rick, but the weather looked a bit doubtful, so only a small part of the rick was opened, a hay cutting knife was used so that it would be easy to cover up if it did come on to rain. A slice about eight foot wide was cut down and we were ready to go. George had opened up the governor valve a bit and *Little Mary* was ticking over quite fast as we started putting the clover through the drum. I could tell that it was going to take a lot more driving than an ordinary corn threshing machine (I had spent many hours with the Basildon Fowler and driving a threshing machine was a playgame to that old girl).

Our little engine was making quite hard work of it, it seemed that she was working hard for about half a minute after I had stopped feeding clover into the machine and I could tell that it was the bottom drum that was using most of the power. We stopped for our ten o'clock break and a check round the bearings on our new machine, some of which were fairly hot (which we had expected). The farmer seemed quite happy with the seed we were threshing out, as it was of very good quality and quantity and was a purple brown colour and this is always the best. During the break Jack Saunders arrived with his rev counter. On checking he found that we were running just a bit too fast, so the governors were shut down just a bit and all was well.

We did several jobs around the Oxford area, getting as far out as Witney then back to Thame, where we spent two whole weeks, then a long journey back to close to my home, Wood Green Farm at Upper Basildon, which was one of the Estate farms now under new ownership. Our job here was a bit of a disaster. The seed was so poor that after a day's work the new farmer decided it was not worth going any further, as the cost to him was going to be more than the seed would be worth. The next job was at Hampstead Norris, about ten miles away. George was now in strange country, but I knew every inch of it well. I explained to him that we had some hill punching in front of us which ever way we went, some up, some down, but the worst was Buckhold Hill which we would have to go down (to miss it would mean going miles round).

I told George that my father had been up and down this hill many times, but his engine was bigger and he did not have a living van behind. Since the time when father last travelled that way, the hill had been resurfaced with 3in. granite which was very slippery and just like some of the old cobble streets that could be seen in a good many towns around the south of England at that time. This was not the route to take with steel-shod steam engines, as I found out myself several years later and will tell you all about it as time goes on. It was decided that we would take this route and if need be we would take our tackle down in two lots although this would take up a lot of our valuable time.

We set off that morning and on reaching the hill, George walked off to see what he would decide to do. While he was gone, I put the injector on to fill the boiler and this pulled the steam right down, *Little Mary* had a habit of pumping herself up fairly quickly when being held back down hills. He came back with a bit of a grin and said, "You are right, it is steep and b—— slippery but the camber is in our favour. If we keep tight into the side we will be all right" (there was a fairly high bank on each side), "We will take a chance".

The 'drug bat' was put onto the threshing machine (this was a big cast iron shoe which the wheel was pulled up onto and was attached by a chain, fixed to the main frame of the machine, this chain pulled it along while under the wheel and so acted as a brake). The brake on the living van was screwed hard on, the shunting pole put through both elevator wheels and off we went at a crawling pace. We had not gone more than twenty yards over the brow of the hill, before I could see we were in deep trouble.

We were getting faster and faster, but the engine wheels were going slower, they had started to slide and it was a long way to the bottom of the hill. George had seen what was going on and had dropped the reversing lever forward, hoping that she would stop sliding, which she did, but by then the crankshaft was turning over far faster than I had ever seen it running before. We were completely out of control, but were still tight into the bank. I don't mind admitting I was getting a bit scared and I think George was too.

The lever was by now nearly right back again, but this seemed to make very little difference. The gears were making a humming noise, the crankshaft was spinning so fast it looked just a blur, the third motion shaft brake (which I had screwed on tight while the boiler was being filled) was on fire, there was blue smoke coming from the piston rod gland and to top it all, she had started to blow off. We were being sprayed with boiling water from the safety valves and could see just about nothing for steam. I looked back as we rounded the right-hand bend at the bottom of the hill, the elevator was still coming sideways and, where our shunting pole had dug into the bank, there were cart loads of turf and soil all down the hill.

We reached the bottom of the hill OK, but we were both looking a bit pale. We sorted ourselves out, took off the brakes, etc and were ready to go on our way. George had a little grin and said "We had better let that be a b— —- lesson to us and steer clear of this hill in future". He changed back into top gear and we were away towards Ashampstead where we had a long, pretty steep hill to climb. We stopped to pick up water at Bottom House Farm and, while we were filling up, George screwed the nuts on the piston rod gland up a few turns as it was blowing badly where the packing had burned out coming down the hill. This made very little difference, so while we were punching up the hill through Ashampstead village, we had a job to see the sides of the road for steam and this would almost certainly be our first job the next morning.

It was getting dusk when we reached Haw Farm, so we pulled into the farmyard and called it a day. As we sat eating our meal, we talked of our high speed trip down Buckhold Hill and George was telling me how he had heard of a ploughing engine getting out of control many years before when they were going down a steep hill causing the piston rod to break. This was caused by over revving and this could well have happened to us as I have never seen a steam engine spinning round like *Little Mary* was that day.

We finished our job here but, as there was no more clover threshing for us to do for a while, we went back to the works at Wallingford for a while. I was sent into the boiler shop with Fred Saunders, he was putting a new firebox into a Tasker tractor belonging to Snows of Wallingford (who did a fair amount of hauling). I would think that the driver of this engine was not one of the best, as the boiler had not been kept washed out properly. On his way back from Didcot, his gauge glass had blocked but, as there was so much mud and scale on top of the box, the fusible plug did not melt out. She had got so hot that her boiler had expanded enough to cause the pistons to hit the back cylinder covers and this eventually stopped him.

Most of the plates had been flanged and drilled, my job was to dolly up on the rivets. They used a pneumatic riveter, the noise was deafening and, even with my ears bunged up tight with cotton wool, the noise was ear splitting. As I rode my bike home in the evening, the racket was still ringing in my ears. With the box completed and pushed into position, we then had to deal with the rivets for the foundation ring. The racket from this was even worse as my head was inside the firebox, thereby getting the full benefit, but it was a very interesting job and I was enjoying it very much. With the riveting completed and the tubes fitted, our next job was to fill it with water to give it a hydraulic test. The working pressure was 200 psi so Fred said that he would push it up to 400 psi and it was kept at this pressure for about thirty minutes, so the next day we would be steaming her up.

It was my job next morning to drain the water down to about half a glass full, light the fire and get steam up. The safety valves had been removed and replaced by a piece of boiler plate with a gasket. We had to be a bit careful with the fire, so as not to overdo it, as there were no safety valves. During the afternoon the gauge went up to 300 psi and was kept at this for about two hours before letting the fire go out. We then had to more or less rebuild the thing as just about everything had been taken off, as is always the case when a new box is to be fitted. I really enjoyed doing this, it was a dirty, heavy job, but it was something new to me and was just up my street.

I had about three weeks in the boiler shop with Fred Saunders and, after the Tasker tractor was finished, we switched over to the second Wilder ploughing engine. This stood at the end of the shop and was only worked on when there was no other boiler work to be done. The boiler was partly built, but there was still a lot of riveting to do so, again, I was holding the dolly for a few days. I would cycle from Basildon to Wallingford in the morning in freezing cold weather and light up the furnace for heating the rivets. Before any rivets were heated up, a couple of big lumps of steel were put in the furnace and, when well heated through, they were put into the boiler (for about half an hour) to dry it out. I would then crawl into the boiler with the dolly and the rivets were handed into me with tongs, not a very pleasant job whilst you are head first inside the boiler with red hot rivets being handed in from behind you. One false move and you've got one down your neck.

The rivets were $3/4$in. diameter, in a double row and although the boiler had been dried out, it was still pretty cold for a while. By the time a dozen rivets had been fixed, the plate began to glow red and I was glad to get out for a breather, but it was something I would not have missed for the world. As far as I can gather the work was all in vain, as she was never finished but scrapped instead and to think what that boiler would be worth today.

During our stay at Wallingford, I had made a few trips across to the moulding shop and so I had a cylinder, a set of wheel hubs and several other small castings for my model Fowler. When I would have time to machine them was a different story, as I only had weekends at home through the summer and it looked as if the winter was going to be the same.

Photograph: Rural History Centre, University of Reading.

'Most of the ploughing was carried out after the harvest was finished and went on through the Autumn until the fields became too wet for the engines to travel on, when they would be drained out and packed away for the Winter. Torwards the end of the season, when the cold weather began to bite, you could sit on the plough as it went to and fro across the field and almost freeze to death, as there was nothing to do, other than to walk the length of the plough and pull the other end down, then jump aboard again and back to the other engine, then do the same again. No time was wasted with a good well trained gang, the plough was never more than about 10 seconds before moving in the opposite direction ...!' **JOE CHALLIS**

Chapter 5

'On the Move'

There seemed to be no more clover threshing for us for some time, but some of the threshing sets were getting a bit behind with their jobs, so we were sent off to bring *Little Mary* back to Wallingford. Once there, we picked up the spare Marshall threshing machine to help out, this again meant that we would be travelling far and wide, which suited me down to the ground as I enjoyed long journeys. Our first threshing job was fairly close to Wallingford, at a farm by the side of the Oxford road at Dorchester. The farmer's name was Mr. Shrubb, he was a nice old boy, but he had one habit that George did not reckon much to, he was a heavy pipe smoker and every time the threshing tackle went to his farm he would come out with a box of pipes to blow them through on the cylinder drain taps. The black treacle that came out of them would run out onto the footboard and down onto the boiler, the smell being terrible for days.

True enough, the second day that we were there, out came the box of pipes. There had been a sharp white frost that morning and the old boy was stood on our short ladder (that we used when oiling the drum bearings), he had it resting against the footboard. George had opened the drain taps slightly for him and, after only a few had been decoked, the smell was coming up to me. I was feeding the corn into the machine, so I dropped a sheaf into the drum without cutting the string, this made *Little Mary* cough up and that was the end of Mr. Shrubb's pipe, shattered into bits and pieces.

He looked up to me a bit annoyed, but I was shouting across to the men on the rick making it look as if they had thrown a sheaf a bit too far and it had gone straight into the drum, or at least that's how I meant it to look. We travelled around Oxfordshire for the rest of the winter helping out the regular threshing sets, some good jobs and some bad. Spring was just around the corner and time was getting close for us to be out again with the ploughers, the job I loved most. I lived for steam engines, but the ones with a rope drum underneath them were my favourites.

We had taken the threshing tackle back to the wharf and parked it away for the summer. The ploughers were cleaned up ready for the big day, the implements were checked over and a crack was found in the frame of our cultivator where two of the zig zag frame bars were riveted together. I clicked for the job to saw the cracked piece out, this was a steel bar 4in. wide and $5/8$in. thick and it was riveted onto another bar the same size, so I had to cut the cracked one out without cutting into the good one. Any one who has used a hacksaw will know that sawing something 4in. across is a slow job especially when you are kneeling on a cultivator frame and sawing straight up and down with just room for the saw frame to be worked between the two bars, a real knuckle shining job, but I won.

I had not seen much of my brother Bert for a few weeks, as he had been working one of the Ward's rollers in the Portsmouth area and this was a long way to come home for just a few hours. Mother had received a letter from him saying that as soon as a driver could be found, he would be coming home to get his ploughing engines ready to be on the move as soon as the weather was good enough. The Fowler K7 compounds, *Darby* and *Joan*, were at Great Lea Farm, Three Mile Cross, where they had spent the winter.

George and I had our set of tackle ready to go and were waiting for the day when we would be rolling out from the wharf to start the new season. On the Saturday morning, George Parkes came to me with some disappointing news. He said "Lad Walters is going out with his tackle on Monday and they want you to go with him until they can find a cookboy". This was their oldest set, they were 10 hp single-cylinder Fowlers with the vertical shaft just behind the smokebox driven by a horizontal shaft running along the top of the boiler. This shaft had a pair of bevel gears at each end and the rope clutch was on the crankshaft.

These were some nice old engines, but made a loud ringing noise when the rope was running out. This came from the bevel wheels as they were in constant mesh all the time the rope was going in or out and so were known to everyone as the 'Jingle Bells'. I was not too happy about this, as I had spent a wonderful summer with George the previous year and was looking forward to another season with him. Once I was away from Wallingford, I would more likely than not have to stay with Lad and his 'Jingle Bells'.

George had told me that Lad was a nice enough bloke, but everything had to be just so, also I would not get much time driving the engines. His two drivers had been with him for many years and they both worshipped their engines so were not too keen on letting anyone else get on them for long. They were both in their sixties, as was Lad and his cultivator man, but they were quite a nice gang to get on with. They all lived within a few miles of Wallingford and so cycled home every night as this set was never more than five or six miles away from base. Their area was from Crowmarsh to Goring on the Oxfordshire side of the Thames, a distance of about five miles and was farmed by three farmers.

If you have ever travelled the Crowmarsh to Goring road, you will have noticed those big rolling corn fields stretching from the River Thames far into the Chiltern Hills and there are not many of these that I have not travelled over many times on a Fowler implement of one sort or another, as

I ended up staying with this set for the whole of the season. Most of this land was then (and no doubt still is) Oxford College property. Most of the Crowmarsh end of our patch was farmed by Charles Keen. The Goring end was taken care of by William Bullock and higher up, in the hills towards Woodcote and Ipsden, was Walter Hatt. All three of them were real good farmers who grew some wonderful crops of corn. The soil is light, chalky and very fertile, so it does not have to be cultivated too deeply and the fields are big making it steam ploughing country at its best.

We had done only a few days work when the weather set in bad. It rained day after day and so we left the tackle in the field and went back to Wallingford to wait for it to dry out. George Parks had not yet taken his engines out and the firm had bought a nearly new Marshall threshing machine from a farmer at Woolhampton, a village on the A4 near Newbury. So George and I were to get *Little Mary* steamed up to go and bring the threshing drum back to Wallingford. We got everything ready for an early start next morning and Jack Saunders would come out with the van to pick us up and bring us back again next morning.

We arrived at Woolhampton soon after mid-day, got the threshing machine coupled up ready to go next morning and were waiting for our transport for home, when we could see a steam roller coming up the road from the A4 towards the farm where we were. We walked out from the farmyard to see her go by, but instead she pulled into the farm as they were going to work on the road by the farm and would make this their stand.

This was just about the most impressive engine that I had ever seen, she was a piston valve compound Marshall, supplied new to the Newbury District Council and this was her first job. We stood by her, sizing up a few of her luxuries, it was hard to believe that she was powered by steam. She was as silent as the grave with not a whisper of steam from anywhere and as she moved all that could be heard was the crunching of stones under the wheels. The gears were in an oil bath, as were the steering worm and wheel. She was fitted with a full length cab and painted a kind of purple-maroon whilst the boiler bands were polished stainless steel. She looked almost like a showman's engine. She was supplied as a ten-tonner, but looked much more than that. As we travelled back home in the work's van, George and I talked about this wonderful engine, thinking what a great job it would be to drive and look after her. (A few years later it was my luck to do just that, which I will tell you all about later in my story.)

I went home most nights as my longest trip was not more than seven miles. I was, therefore, up with the Basildon larks, on my bike and away into the Oxfordshire hills to spend another long day at the job I dearly loved. I was mostly on the cultivator or plough, but I was still doing about a couple of hours a day on each engine while George Newman and Guss Becket had their meal breaks. These old engines were very much the same to drive as the 12 hp singles, but the rope clutch was very different and to drop it into gear quietly was a work of art. The clutch on an engine with a normal crown wheel is geared down to a ratio of about three to one and so is fairly easy to drop in nice and quietly but, when the clutch is on the crankshaft, it is a different story. However, I soon got used to this and a few years later I worked on a pair of ploughing engines that were fitted with an even more crude rope clutch than the 'Jingle Bells' set, but I will tell you more about as time goes on.

I had spent a full season with this set and had picked up a few useful tips. One of these was how to fit a new socket on a steam pipe without pipe grips. George Newman had for several days been working with a leak on the steam pipe to the injector, the socket had worked loose and was getting worse by the day, so with the first wet day this job was sorted out. A new ³/₄in. socket was sorted out from the living van, but there were no pipe grips with the tackle, so how would it be done? There were plenty of old Fowler open-ended spanners, so one that was a bit wider in the jaw than the diameter of the socket was sorted out. A piece of broken file was placed in the gap between the spanner's jaw and the socket and this worked as well as any pipe grips.

At the end of the season, we took the tackle back to the wharf and to my surprise there were three of the Basildon Estate steam drivers working for Wilders. They had been paid off from the Estate during the summer, but no one had seemed to know where they had gone. Jim Smith (the steam plough foreman), Don Cresswell and George Johnson had all three found a job at the Wallingford works but, as they were all still living at Basildon, I would have some company to bike with to and from work through the winter.

We had been back at the works just a few days when George Parks came in with his set of ploughers. He soon fished me out, wanting to know how I had been getting on all the summer and to say that he would not be going out with the threshing tackle that winter. He was due to retire early in the next year and intended to have a quiet winter, but would do one more summer ploughing if he was needed.

Like myself, he lived for his ploughing engines and had done for most of his life. We had a long chat about the following summer and what we would do. He seemed to think that he might not be needed now that another foreman and two drivers had joined the Wilder firm. I had told George that I had been fairly happy all the season, but it was not quite the same. But that if he was going out next year, I would go with him and no one else, unless Jim Smith took over George's set as I would willingly go with him. My brother had told me that he could almost certainly get me a driver's job at Wards and this was what I would do if things turned out wrong for me. We still had the whole of the winter in front of us, so I would hope for the best.

I spent a few weeks in the workshop with one of the blacksmiths making water cart axles and the angle steel frames for their famous steel frame farm wagons and really enjoyed it. It was hot heavy work, but was very interesting and using a seven pound sledge hammer all day soon builds up your muscles. I was really enjoying the change, when the workshop foreman came round and said to me, with a little grin on his face, "You are going home tomorrow. George Johnson is taking *Little Mary* and a set of threshing tackle to Basildon as there are several weeks work in that area and he has asked for you to be his mate".

We had cycled to and from Wallingford together for a few weeks and George had not said a word about all this. He had kept it as a surprise and had said that he was sure I would be pleased to join him. We set off next morning for Basildon with the Marshall threshing machine (that George Parkes and I had collected from Woolhampton a few months before), a Ruston baler and a Roberts folding elevator, a fair load for *Little Mary*. It was low gear up all the hills, but we made it in good time to Lower Basildon. Here we turned off right for Upper Basildon, where we had two miles of low gear as it is quite a climb all the way, pretty steep in places and the road in those days was not very good. By the time we reached Blandy's Farm, the smokebox and chimney were almost red hot.

A few weeks were spent around the Basildon area and we then moved on to Ashampstead, (this time steering clear of Buckhold Hill), where we spent about another three weeks. Our last job here was down a cart track about half a mile into a valley. This track was quite steep and narrow with banks and hedges on either side. As we made our way down, George said "God help us if we get a lot of rain while we are down here". Our job here was two big saffron ricks. This is something that you see very little of today. It is similar to clover with long cone shaped pink blooms and the seed is very much like nasturtium seed and fairly light.

We spent a few days on these ricks, hoping to get them finished and get the tackle back to the top of the hill by the weekend, while the weather was still good. Unfortunately, time ran out on us and, by Friday night fall, we still had about couple of hours work left, so it was agreed that we would all be there early next morning as there was a big football match in Reading which some of the gang were going to see.

We left home a bit earlier than usual and reached Ashampstead soon after six. It still being dark, as we wheeled our bikes down the track there was an unusual smell of something burning. As we turned into the field where the tackle was, we found *Little Mary* about twenty yards back from where we left her the evening before. She was almost blowing off, the water was almost out of the glass, the threshing machine and baler were just a smouldering wreck, but somehow it had not reached the big stack of bales.

We were there weighing up the situation, when one of the farm workers turned up. He lived in the village close to the end of the track and had seen the glow in the sky during the night. He had rushed down the track to see what he could do. He had somehow got *Little Mary* into gear and pushed her back down the slope to safety but *Little Mary* had blown the damper off and he had forgotten to replace it. Our first job was to notify the management at Wallingford and as there was no phone anywhere near, I volunteered to cycle back to the office and break the news. This took me about forty-five minutes and on reaching the office I was asked all sorts of questions. Was it arson? Had we left it with a hot bearing? No one ever knew!

There was panic in the office. This machine had been purchased in the spring of that year and somehow had not been insured and would be a total loss, so someone would have a lot of explaining to do. While the conflab was going on with the office staff, I had put two and two together and could see a way out of this, but would I be speaking out of turn? I listened to what was going on for a while, then I thought here goes and said "There is a way out. Why not switch the plate from the burned out one with the one on the old worn out Marshall machine that stands down the wharf?" and after a while they agreed.

Every Marshall threshing machine had a cast iron plate about 12in. by 9in. which had Marshall's name as makers, a sheaf of wheat and the machine number all cast in it. So, I was to take a screwdriver, go down to the wharf and remove the plate from our old machine, take it up to the blacksmith's shop (where it was to be put in the forge to burn it off) then take it back to Ashampstead, find the plate from the burned out machine and very carefully change them over. This seemed all very good, but I said there is almost sure to be eyes looking around when I get back.

It was decided that nothing would be done over the weekend, so on my way back I left the plate that I had collected at home, then went back to tell George what was to be done. I went back at crack of dawn on the Sunday morning and switched the plates, the genuine one I kept for many years. I never knew whether the insurance was paid out, however a new Marshall machine was delivered to Wallingford before the winter was over.

We took the baler back to the works to be overhauled and repainted, this took about two weeks, then we set off with it and a spare Clayton and Shuttleworth machine to Ewelme in Oxfordshire, where there were a few ricks of corn to be knocked out and that would be the end of the season for us. Ewelme is getting towards twenty miles from Basildon and, as we had no living van with us, it was pedal our way there in the morning, get steam ready to start work at seven, do a day's work then pedal home at night. This worked out at around fifteen hours a day. I can't see any of the present generation sticking something like this for long, but for us it was that or nothing as there were a lot of unemployed people around. The big depression of the thirties had already started to bite. They were long tiring days and this was the dead of winter. More than once I reached home, had a wash and fell asleep at the meal table, so we were glad when that job was finished.

All through that winter, the A329 (Reading to Wallingford road) was littered with broken down Foden steam wagons. The firm of Fry & Sons from Southampton had bought a fleet of ex-WD Foden overtype wagons and trailers for shifting hundreds of tons of World War One shells of all sizes from the Bramley ammunition depot near Basingstoke. They were taking them somewhere up in the Midlands for scrap. Along that road, every few miles apart, almost every day, could be seen a wagon and trailer, well loaded with scrap shells, stood at the side of the road with something or other wrong with it, chiefly broken drive chains. I expect that they had all seen service in France during the war and so were all well and truly worn out.

We were on our way to Ewelme early one morning (there had been a sharp frost so the roads were slippery) and as we made our way down Shillingford Hill to the bridge, we could see that someone had met with an accident. There were lights and police everywhere. As we reached the bridge we could see what it was all about. One of the Fry steam wagons had got out of control on the slippery hill and had not made it round the right-hander onto the bridge. He had hit the bridge wall, knocking it into the river and the wagon was hanging head first over the River Thames, dangling on the trailer drawbar with his load of shells in the river. I suppose the masonry of the wall had steadied him enough, so all that was stopping him from plunging into the river was the trailer load of shells, which was still on the bridge. There she was hanging on the drawbar, another few inches and it would have been a cold morning for the crew.

We had made a good show on the row of corn ricks which were on both sides of a field road or cart track. On the Saturday morning, George walked back up the track to collect some lighting up wood ready for Monday morning. He had collected a bundle of rick pegs and was on his way back when, about 200 yards away, *Little Mary* started to bark and very quickly picked up speed. She was getting faster and faster. The governors had stopped and she was running flat out. I was stood in the feeding box facing up the track and could see George running, but he had a long way to go, so I dropped in three or four sheaves without cutting the strings hoping to fetch the driving belt off, but it didn't work. The threshing machine was getting up to a rock and the baler was nearly jumping off the ground.

I had learned many years before that if you run a threshing machine too fast, the drum expands and the beaters will hit the concave bars and rip them off the drum, so I would have to work fast. I didn't even think about going down the ladder, I just jumped onto the rick - which must have been a jump of at least six feet - then down to the ground and dash back to the engine, which was by now really humming round. I scrambled up into the tender and slammed the regulator off, but it was too late. Now, anyone who has seen a Ruston baler at work will know that it has two rams, one for pushing the straw down into the press and one to follow up by pushing it forward. The one that works up and down is spring loaded to allow for any overload when it is pushed down onto a steel plate. It is also sprung loaded for pushing back up and it was these that caused the trouble that Saturday morning.

As I shut the regulator off, I heard this almighty bang. The 'horse's head' as we always called it had gone down, but was running so fast that the springs were working overtime and did not go back up quick enough, causing the main horizontal ram to get caught. What a mess it was. It looked almost as if a bomb had dropped into it and there was hardly a bit of the whole machine that wasn't damaged. It was a complete write off. It is hard to say, but no one will convince me otherwise that it must have been the heat from the fire a few weeks previous that had taken the temper out of those springs and they were now softer than they were in the first place.

It was hard to believe, but the governor belt was still on its pulleys and had not broken, as was usually the case. As with most Fowlers, the belt pulley on the crankshaft was a slightly raised part between the two gear wheels so, when the second motion shaft double wheel is in neutral, it is not far away from the belt and as the belt has to be removed for road work it is joined by a buckle. It was the odd piece of belt sticking out from the buckle that had caught in the double gear wheel and, as the belt was a bit slack and oily, it stopped. The joint in that belt had passed by those gear wheels millions of times over the years and decided to catch up just at that crucial time when no one was near at hand. It just wasn't our day. We finished the other ricks using the elevator to replace the baler. George had told the farmer that if he needed the straw to be baled up, the firm would have to bring a baler out later and do it free of charge, as at this time there was no spare in the yard at Wallingford.

We took the tackle back to Wallingford and parked it away for the summer. The baler was pushed into a corner of the wharf never to turn again and I was sent back to the blacksmith's shop to help make a few more water cart axles and wagon parts. This time I was with a different blacksmith. He was an oldish man, very skilled and knew all the answers about smithing and was always ready for a joke. He was always playing jokes on just about everyone in the workshop, especially the apprentices that were working on the lathes and milling machines.

Every lunchtime, the apprentices would swallow their sandwiches, take off their overalls and go out into the square outside the works with a football and that's where they would stay until the bell rang. While they were out there, Jack would nail their overalls to the bench or put a big lump of grease into their pocket, he always had something weighed up. One of the lads was a tall chap named Bob King. He was an apprentice moulder and, when they all filed back in after the bell had gone, if there was anything on the floor that he could kick he would boot it. Inside the main door to the workshop, was a big steel plate which was used by the blacksmiths to level up any parts (such as the turntable rings and wheel tyres) that had been made for the wagons.

The workshop lights were gas and there were always a few gas-mantle boxes around. So, one day, Jack picked up one of these boxes and walked over to the hacksaw machine, where there were a number of 2in. square steel off cuts from the lengths of bar that were used to make the water cart axles. He found a short piece that just fitted into the mantle box and placed the full box on the levelling plate and sat, waiting for the bell to ring. As the apprentices filed in 'Kingey' was first through the door. He spotted the box and bang! It hardly moved and Bob King was off work for a few days.

The guy that worked the big lathe was Jim Perry. He would often come over to us for a little chin wag and always carried a pair of tongs with a lathe tool in them, so that, if any of the management walked through, he would put it in the forge as if he was going to harden it or reshape it. We were making turntable rings for the wagons one day, when Jim strolled over with his tongs and lathe tool, but this time it was a genuine trip, as he wanted to harden it. We had our length of steel in the forge, which was about $1\frac{1}{2}$in. by $\frac{3}{4}$in. and were about to cut a short piece off, as it was about an inch too long.

Normally we used a piece of an old copper firebox (from one of the old engines that had been scrapped) to place on the anvil so that when the cutter went through the hot metal it would not be damaged by the hard anvil. Jim had heated his lathe tool to the required heat and had gone across to his lathe with it - where he had a bucket of oil - and was bent over towards us,

91

watching the colour come up as he carefully dipped it into the oil. This time we had not used the copper plate, so I was being very careful with the sledge hammer. Jack said "Go on hit the b—— thing or it will be cold". I gave it one big swipe, the piece of steel came off and went soaring across the workshop, straight down Jim's neck. He rolled over on the floor. He nearly stood on his head, but the piece of steel still stayed put. It was laughable at the time, but really was quite serious.

I had some wonderful times in that workshop and learned a whole lot. I had the odd day in the boiler shop or with the moulders and all the time I was as happy as a sand boy. I had spent a couple of wonderful years with the Wilder firm and was looking forward to another season of steam ploughing (which would be starting any day now). I remembered what my father always said, "Give me the time when the sun shines both sides of the hedgerows".

The steam ploughmen were down the wharf, getting the engines and implements ready for the big day (which was not far off). Every lunchtime I would eat my sandwiches, then wander off down to them to see what I could find out about who was going out first. I was almost certain to be sent with the first gang to go. I was hoping and praying that it would be George Parkes or Jim Smith, either of these and I would be more than happy.

For several days, I just couldn't seem to settle at anything and at the weekend when my brother was home we talked most of the time of what I should do if I did not get with George or Jim. Bert seemed convinced that he could get me a job as a driver at Wards, because several of their ploughmen had retired or gone onto rollers. The hours were far less on rollers and so the ploughmen were a bit reluctant to go back to the ploughers. We were having our Sunday dinner and were still deciding what was the best move, when father (who had been listening, but saying nothing) butted in and said to me "Look my boy, there is no harm in giving it a try. We all know that you are quite capable, the only thing against you is your size". I was still pint-sized and looked more like fourteen years old than sixteen and a half.

By now, I had made up my mind that if I was detailed to go with any gang, other than the two that I knew so well, I would pack it in at Wilders and go to Wards. Bert said that he would be going to Egham in the week to get a few things for the set that he was getting ready at Three Mile Cross and that he would have a few words with Sid Ward to see how the land laid. He said "I shall be needing another driver and can no doubt get you in my gang" and I thought this would be great, both together again and working in the area of which we knew every inch.

I went back to Wallingford on the Monday morning, as usual and into the blacksmith's shop. At lunchtime I went and found George Parkes. He was in his van having brewed a pot of tea which he shared with me. I told him what I had in mind and he said "Good luck to you. I am sure that if you don't like it there you will always be sure of a job back here, you may not know it but they think the world of you here, which you will find out if you do decide to leave". I went back up to the workshop a little happier, but was still waiting all the time for someone to come in and say we want you to go out with so and so tomorrow.

Sure enough, on the Thursday afternoon, the workshop foreman came in and said "You are going out with Lad Walters tomorrow, he is going to South Stoke to get ready to start cultivating on Monday". I just didn't say a word. I was choked, so he said "You don't seem too happy, what's wrong?" All I could say was "I would much rather go with George Parkes or Jim Smith, but anyway I will go, but I won't be stopping" and he walked off.

In a very short time, Georgie Little (from the office) walked in and came over to me, as I was measuring up a piece of 2in. steel angle for drilling and took me across into the corner of the workshop. He started to talk to me about going out with Lad Walters and said "Is there something you don't like about him or what is the problem?". I had to think fast. I said "There is nothing wrong with him, he is a very nice bloke. Last year I got on fine with him and the rest of his gang but I get very little time on the engines. They all go home every night so there is not much fun for me sitting in the van on my own all evening, so I have to bike home but I have much farther to go than they do". Georgie said "Give it a try and go out with them tomorrow and we will see about changing you back when the others go out". I told him exactly the same as I had told Jack Saunders, the workshop foreman, a short while before. I said "I will go but I won't be stopping", to which he said "Don't be silly of course you will stop".

I turned up at my usual time next morning, just before seven, and the 'Jingle Bells' were raring to go. Our bikes were loaded into the van and we set off for South Stoke. If you have ever been through Wallingford you will know that the streets are very narrow and the corners very sharp. So there is no way that you can get a set of ploughing tackle round the corners at the crossroads in the middle of the town where the A329 crosses the Crowmarsh road.

In order to get onto Wallingford bridge, to take us into Oxfordshire, we had to make a detour right round the town, a distance of about a mile. Our job at South Stoke was on the side of the Crowmarsh to Goring road and we were soon set out ready for Monday morning. Lad paid me my wages and said "Take the morning off tomorrow, there is no point in coming all this way for nothing". As we were talking I thought that I had better break the news a bit gently so I said, "I doubt if I will be staying with you long as I

93

am thinking of trying for a driver's job". I could see he was taking it a bit hard and he said "I am sorry to hear that, but good luck to you if you do get a job as a driver, but I think that you are still a bit too young".

I waited for Bert to come home on the Saturday to see what the verdict was about starting with Wards and he started playing about with me and said "There is no hope of a job at Egham as they are full up with drivers, so you had better stay where you are". I could tell he was just having a joke and then he reeled it off, "You can start as soon as you like, but I don't know yet which set will be going out first so we will have to hope for the best. I will try my hardest to get you with me but you will find it much different to Wilders. Sidney Ward is a hard man and expects the last ounce from his men and machinery". Bert had told me many times about Ward's BB1 set and how hard they were working, most of the time on the market gardens around London where the cultivator was nearly always down to its full depth and was still not deep enough for some customers. He hoped that I did not get landed with one of these.

On the Monday morning, I set off a bit later than usual as the office would not be open until eight o'clock. I was calling in to give a week's notice and so I would be finishing on that Friday evening. That morning when I reached Streatley, instead of turning right over the Thames to Goring and then on to South Stoke, I went straight on keeping to the A329 to Wallingford. I walked into the office and told Mr. Little what I was there for and he just couldn't believe that I was going to finish working for them. He said "I think you are foolish as we were going to sort something out for you. Why don't you go back and wait until we can work something out?", but I told him that my mind was made up and that I would be in for my wages on Friday. All that week Lad Walters and his drivers were trying to persuade me to change my mind and stay with them for another season, but I was hell bent on taking charge of one of those ploughing engines, just like the ones I had grown up with.

About half past three that Friday afternoon, Lad and I were going across the field on the cultivator and he looked at his pocket watch and said "You will soon have to be going or the office will be closed", so I shook hands with all of them. Lad said "I am more than sorry that you are leaving us but I know that you will make the grade and good luck to you in your new venture". I got on my bike and as I left I looked back at that wonderful old pair of engines and have never set eyes on them or anything else like them since that day.

I walked into the office and who should be sitting there, but John Wilder himself. He looked up from his desk and beckoned me across to his corner. He said "Sit down I want to have a chat with you. I haven't seen much of you while you have been working for us but I have heard quite a lot. I am very sorry that you are leaving us but I will not stand in your light, I wish you every success. If ever you think you would like to come back we will be pleased to have you".

I came out from the office and made my way down the wharf to see if I could find George Parkes, I had to have a few words with him before going home. He was just getting his hands cleaned up as it was nearly five o'clock. There were several plough engine drivers and a few foremen there, including George's brother Alf (he was in charge of one of the BB1 sets). They all had a chat with me and were all surprised that I was leaving. They were all saying that I had settled in so well and had been the only cookboy on the firm to be kept on through two winters and they thought that I, like most of them, would be there for life. One by one, as they left, they wished me all the best, then George said "Lets go and put the kettle on and have a cup of tea before you go".

We sat in the van chattering over our cups of tea and George was giving me a few bits of advice. One thing that he said to me I never have and never will forget. He said "As far as steam ploughing is concerned you must be one in a million, you are a born driver. I have worked with ploughing tackle all my life, having seen drivers come and go, some good, some bad, but I have never before met anyone so young with as much knowledge as you have. There is hardly a thing about the game that you don't know, you can splice a rope, you are an excellent cultivator and plough man, and as far as driving goes you are as good as any on the firm. Mark my words if you stick to it, before many years you will be in charge of someone's ploughing tackle".

I shook hands with poor old George and thanked him once again for what he had done for me and said "If I don't like the Ward set up I shall be back". He had been just like a father to me and as I left him there were tears in his eyes. We had spent some wonderful times together and this was now to come to an end. I looked back and waved my hand to him as I rode out from the wharf, never to see him again. I had parted from a wonderful friend that I will never forget. As I pedalled my bike back to Basildon that early April evening, I kept wondering whether I was doing the right thing. Wilders was a wonderful old firm that had been in the steam engine and engineering business for many years. I was going, much farther away from home, to a firm that we knew very little about, but I had just been told by the right man that I could always go back to Wallingford if I wished and that was a great help.

(I knew that Wilders was a very old firm and had been in the foundry business for many years, but I did not realise that it was as old as 200 years. I have recently managed to purchase a book called 'Men of Iron' which is the history of the Wilder family and Works. The book was published by The Wallingford Historical and Archaeological Society and to me is very interesting. According to this book, their first set of ploughing tackle was purchased second hand at the Oxford Ram Fair in August 1874 for £815-6s-11d, (they had been repairing steam engines as far back as 1861). Now, was this the 'Jingle Bells' that I had worked with, as this had been their oldest set? The book says that the steam ploughing account closed in 1932, although operations continued in a small way until 1935.)

I was now off to pastures new and was going to be a full time plough engine driver. I was just 16½ years old and going to take over an engine of Wards. To me that seemed great. The normal set up was, you spent at least 3 years as a cookboy, another 3 years at least as cultivator man and most plough engine drivers were in their thirties before they took over as a full time driver.

By the time my brother had reached home on Saturday, it was late evening and we went to bed chattering until late in the night. He was putting me right on a few things he thought I might have forgotten, or, perhaps, didn't even know about, but I was pretty confident and sure that I would get by all right. It was just the getting settled in with a new gang that I was not too happy about, but I had done this before and would surely do it again.

I left home early on Monday morning to cycle into Reading to catch the workman's train to Egham. This was my first ever train ride, stopping at every station between Reading and Egham where I walked out from the station with my few belongings in a bag and asked the way to Pooly Green Road. Once on this road, I couldn't go wrong and on reaching Thorpe Lea I could see Ward's yard with a few engines and living vans on the road across the other side of the big pond. As I walked into the yard, I was met by Bill Bantick (he was Ward's foreman) and his first words were "I can see who you are, you are Bert's brother, you are much alike in features but a bit different in build" (Bert was over six feet and weighed around sixteen stone).

We chatted for a short while, then he took me through the workshop and into Sid Ward's office, as he would be taking me out to the engines that I would be working with. Sid Ward eyed me up and down, then said "You look very young" (Bert had put my age on a couple of years), "But if you are half as good as your brother you won't be too bad". He started telling me about the jobs that were coming up and that, as Bert would not be going out with his set for a couple of weeks, he was taking me out to the BB1's as they were short of a driver. I almost fell through the floor, but soon thought this would be great, to go steam ploughing only twelve miles from the heart of London and be in charge of one of their best engines.

He started up his car (an Essex Super Six) and off we went, away up through Staines and along by Stanwell reservoir. As we travelled on, he was telling me about the set of tackle and the gang that I would be working with. It was a make shift gang as Walt Elliott, the chap that had been in charge of the BB1 set from new, was past retirement age and wasn't enjoying the best of health being home sick at that time. Bill Wells was now in charge for a few days until someone else was available. He was a threshing man, but had done a little bit of ploughing. Sid said "You won't like him very much as he is one of those that likes to be heard and will try to push you around a bit but take no notice of him as you probably know far more about it than he does". The other driver was Jim Collins and was in his mid-sixties, as was Fred Bennett, the cultivator man. I began to wonder what I had let myself in for, just a lad going to work with a gang of old timers that should all have been retired and taking it easy.

We made our way across to Colnbrook and onto the A4, or Old Bath Road as it was known then. We turned right towards London for about a mile then left towards West Drayton to a small village called Sipson, where, close to the road, stood the Fowler BB1 that I was to take over. They had set the tackle out the previous week and had a few pulls. The cultivator was close to my engine, just as it had been pulled in on the Saturday. I took a glance at the cultivator and could see that its main frame was down touching the ground, the two wing tines were out, so they were only using eleven tines instead of thirteen. I thought they had extra short tines, but the cultivator was down really deep. I had been warned by my brother what to expect and true enough it was the deepest I had ever seen a cultivator set down. The soil was the heavy grey looking stuff, not a stone to be seen and we were there to break up the hard base that their tractors could not get down to, but, however deep we went down, it would not be enough for these market gardeners. This was far different from the chalky Berkshire and Oxfordshire slopes of my native Thames Valley, which I had been brought up with.

The engines had been fired up, but had not yet got enough steam to make a start, so Fred Bennett put the kettle on to make a cup of tea before the action started. As we sat there drinking our tea, Bill Wells asked me where I had worked and what engines had I worked on. He straight away started pouring it out, "If you have been used to single-cylinder jobs you are in for a big surprise, you will have to keep the steam gauge up close to the red mark all the time as these b——- things are useless below 150 psi". I had a little smile to myself and said "I was driving compound ploughing engines several years before I left school and I do know the difference between a single and a compound, so it won't come strange to me". He got up from his seat and said "Come on then lets see what you are made of".

Now poor old Jim Collins had to walk across to the other side of the

97

field and I could see that he was a bit dodgy on his pins. He suffered badly from gout and I could see that he was wearing a beautiful pair of boots that were cut into ribbons all over the top to relieve the pressure on his feet. By the time he had reached his engine, it was blowing off like mad and so was mine, but I had put the injector on and pulled the pressure back quite a bit as the water was pretty low in the glass. Jim gave a blast on his whistle to show that he was ready to go, Freddie Bennett jumped aboard the cultivator and off they went.

As the cultivator turned and lifted, I could see the depth we were pulling. By the time my drum had stopped and it was my turn to pull, the gauge had crept up to the red mark again. I had fired up and as I dropped in the clutch to start the pull, she began to blow off again and that was the way she stayed for most of the pull across the field. As the cultivator neared my engine, I dropped the damper down to the last notch on the lever, shut down the regulator, so when she started to push it out again, I moved forward and on with the injector. Bill Wells stepped up onto the footplate and said "I can see you know a little bit about it but watch your fire and be careful not to get a hollow place on the bars or you will be in trouble. There is something about the water here that fireboxes don't like and by what I can gather, every time they leave this place, one or sometimes both engines go away with leaking stays or tubes". That's how he went on for about half an hour, do this, do that and don't forget something else. I got a bit fed up with his chatter and said, "Look, you go and do your part of the job and leave me to do mine. Don't keep interfering, I am quite capable of doing the job I came here for".

We plodded on steadily until late afternoon. By then I had found out that, if you let the steam get the least bit low, you would be reaching over to that little lever that is pivoted over the top of the boiler, just inside the left-hand horn plate on a BB1. It was getting on towards packing up time for the day, this was extra early to what I had been used to. The carter and his horses did not work after five o'clock, so no water would be drawn out to us after that time. The cultivator had not gone far from my engine, when it came to a sudden stop and down went several coils of my rope all over the place.

As I looked across to Jim's engine, I could see him getting down from the footplate very slowly, then he went round to the coiling lever to look at his rope. A strand had broken. Unfortunately Jim had not spotted it, so instead of it going through the pulleys on the 'monkey head', it had come outside and had rolled up into a big heap. This meant that about twenty yards of rope was ruined and would have to come out. I lifted the brake pawl on my drum and pulled out several yards of the rope which had dropped when Jim had stopped so suddenly and then waited to see what was going to be done with his rope. I could see the so-called foreman and Jim pulling some rope off the drum, so I thought that they were going to cut the ruined bit out and splice up again, but no one seemed eager to get stuck in. Perhaps they were going to give it a miss until the next morning? I started to clean my engine down and could see that Jim was banking his fire down for the night, so I would do the same.

I was the last one back to the living van and Bill Wells had gone home, which I gathered he did every evening, so the three of us had a good wash, tidied ourselves up and enjoyed a meal in the van. Freddie Bennett said "There won't be much done tomorrow by the time someone has come out to splice the rope". I kept quiet and listened to what they had to say and soon learned that there was no one there who could splice a steam plough rope, or perhaps they just didn't want to. Jim Collins had been a steam plough driver for a good many years and Fred Bennett was far from new with ploughing tackle.

It was getting towards mid-day, when the works foreman rolled up with his T-type Ford van and another oldish chap with him. He was Jack Ward (no relation to the owners). Jack was really a threshing man, but he had done quite a bit of steam ploughing and had often filled in during the last few years when Walt Elliott had fallen sick. He could splice a rope, but was not too keen to do it if someone else was around. They were there talking over what should be done and Bill Bantick looked across to me and said "You have been around with ploughing engines for quite a while can you splice a rope?" I said "I have helped more than once but, as a driver, it's not my responsibility but in this case I will help." He seemed quite relieved and said "You won't lose anything by helping us out".

We decided that there was time for a cup of tea and something to eat before making a start. As we chattered, Jack Ward was asking a lot of questions and seemed a very nice sort of bloke and reminded me very much of George Parkes whom I had just left at Wilders. We set off across the field armed with string and spikes. The ruined length of rope was soon cut out and the ends unpicked ready to be spliced up, but I could see that I was going to be left to do the job. All three of them knew what had to be done but were reluctant to get stuck in. However, as I got on with the job they were all saying that I was doing it differently to how they had ever seen it done (there are two or three ways to set about it, but they all work out the same at the end). It was not too long before we were ready to go again and we now had another foreman for a while at least. I felt sure that he would be far different from Bill Wells and, true enough, Jack and I got on marvellously together, he was one of the nicest chaps you could ever meet.

Our job at Sipson lasted about ten days and we were finished, ready to move, before mid-day on the Thursday of the Easter weekend, but we were both having problems with our engines. Both our fireboxes were leaking and had been gradually getting worse over the last couple of days. Whether it was the water or the way they had been working we didn't know, I think a little of each. No engine could stand up to the way we were working those BB1 jobs without giving trouble sooner or later and we had found out that the market garden's own Foden wagons were always in dock with boiler trouble. They owned five overtype Fodens with trailers to take their produce to Covent Garden market and there was always one of them with the ashpan down.

The next job that we were to set off for was a long trip away, several miles beyond East Grinstead in Sussex, close to Ashdown Forest. Jack was a bit undecided whether to start off with two sick engines or to get Charlie Stewart (the boilersmith) out to sort things out before we left. While eating an early lunch, we had a chat between us and decided that we would take a chance, perhaps, with a change of water and working light (as these engines always did while travelling on the road), our leaks might take up. I had three stays on the left-hand side pushing a spray nearly halfway across the box and Jim had several tubes that were giving trouble.

We were ready for the road by twelve o'clock. I was to take the Thorpe Lea road after crossing Staines' bridge into Surrey, whilst Jim would turn left onto the Chertsey road to find a place wide enough to pull in and wait for us, while we went back to our depot to pick up the mole drainer as our job in Sussex involved several acres of cultivating and a fair amount of draining. Before we set off Jack said "We will push on in front of Jim and perhaps if you hustle it along and try to keep a good bright fire the leaking stays might ease up a bit". My problem was far worse than Jims, so I had to keep some biggish lumps of coal along the leaking side of the box to keep the spray from the rest of the fire. We had filled up with stream water at Stanwell, so by the time we had hooked up the mole drainer, I could see that there was less spray coming from the offending stays and the fire was bright over most of the box.

We made our way back to Staines Bridge, turned towards Chertsey and were soon with our mates again and on our way to Harwoods Farm in the East Grinstead area of Sussex. We had a long trip in front of us and our first night was to be spent at Chertsey, which was Jack Ward's home. Jack suggested that we went to see the police who, he was sure, would let us pull up one of the side streets. As we neared the town we pulled up, Jack hopped on his bike and was away to the police station, returning soon with a smile all over his face. Yes it was OK, but I don't remember the name of the street that was long enough to take a full set of ploughing tackle.

We were to pull up on the side of the street under the lights, which were the old gas lamps and a lamp lighter would be round on his bike with a torch on a pole to light up before darkness fell. Jack had gone home for the night so the other three of us had our meal. Then I walked up to my engine to give her a wipe down before it got dark. Along came the lamp lighter, so I watched him push up the tap with his torch and on came the light. As I talked with him, I gathered he would be round in the morning to put them out, but by the time he reached this street, it would be broad daylight.

I had weighed things up and knew that nature would be calling as usual in the morning, so what were we going to do in a street of houses that would still be lit up with street lamps? About ten yards in front of my engine, I could see a drain and if that could be lifted we would be in business. I hopped up onto the footplate, took out the rope bar which stood up behind the injector's steam pipe and wandered off towards the drain. I gave it a few thumps, then put the rope bar between the bars of the drain top and gave it a heave. It moved and was soon lifted. I thought that's fair enough and if I move my engine forward a few yards so that it is over the drain, we will have a centrally heated loo for the morning.

I took of my damper, moved the engine forward until the rear wheel was close to the drain, the job was done and we were all ready for the morning. By the time that I had the damper back on again, Jim and Fred had come out to see what was going on. I expect they thought I was getting eager and was off on my own, but when I explained what it was about, they saw my point. Next morning would be Good Friday and if we could make East Grinstead that day, which was a bit ambitious, we would work through the Easter as our job there was a bit overdue. It was too far for me to go home anyway, the living van was Freddie Bennett's home and Jim only went home about once a month.

We were up early next morning to get steamed up and so be away as soon as it was daylight. We had a long journey in front of us and the days were still fairly short. As I made my way down the van steps to go out to my engine, I found that the temperature was pretty low and a bitterly cold wind was blowing from the north. I took my damper off, poked up the fire, then went round to the front tool box where there was part of a traction engine sheet folded up. I stretched this sheet out along the footboard and placed a few big spanners on it so that it hung down nearly to the ground. We would be out of sight, over the drain and nice and warm by the firebox.

Before we had finished our breakfast, it had started to rain and the wind seemed to get pretty rough. We were in for an unpleasant journey (or that's how it seemed to me) and true enough that's how it turned out, a journey I shall never forget. We were all ready to go by the time Jack was with us, but it was still hardly daylight. We were both running fairly low on water, but we would be crossing the canal at New Haw which would be the next place we would be passing through, a distance of about two miles. This was soon reached, but by now we were all getting pretty wet and it was almost freezing.

As we pulled away towards Weybridge, the rain started to turn to snow and it seemed to get colder and colder. We were pushing along at a good running pace, about 6 mph (which is no problem to a BB1 when the 'big wheel' is in), through Cobham, Leatherhead and down the side of Box Hill towards Dorking. By now the snow was getting heavier. There was a layer of about 2in. on the road which was now beginning to stick to the wheels and we had gained a set of ice tyres. Our speed was now down to a crawling pace and the road was fairly narrow with no places to pull in with a set of ploughing tackle.

We had to soldier on steadily to Dorking where Jack reckoned we might get a pull in at the brickworks, but we had still a few miles to go before reaching there. Our road was now fairly twisty and mostly down hill, we would have to watch our step as the wheel grip was now almost nil. The snow was building up on the wheels, then suddenly a lump would break off and off we would go, galloping along.

Now, somewhere down the side of Box Hill on that road, was a small village called Mickleham, the road there then was very winding and narrow. In front of us, parked outside a house, was a Rolls Royce Silver Ghost. It was a doctor's car and he had called into home while on his visiting round. We edged out round it very carefully and pulled back into the side, where we would be keeping as close as possible until we could find a place to pull off the road and call it day.

It was now getting difficult to see. It was almost like a blizzard and no place to be with ploughing engines. We were slowly, but surely, making our way towards Dorking, but as we looked back there was no sign of Jim and Fred with the other engine. Had they run into trouble? They had a heavier load than us, we had just the cultivator and mole drainer, but Jim had the living van and water cart (which was full with water) so their load would be almost twice the weight of ours.

We pulled up on the straightest bit of road that we could find and I walked back to see where they had got to, while Jack waited with my engine, as I would get there in about half the time he would. The road was almost like a skating rink and certainly not the place to be with a set of steam ploughing tackle, but luckily for us the traffic was just about at a standstill. I walked for about half a mile and there round the bend I could see Jim's engine. It looked to me to be at an unusual angle.

As I got closer to them, I could see Jim's BB1 was crossways, the front wheels were on the right hand side of the road with the tender hanging over the low bank on the other side. They had pulled out to go round the doctor's Rolls Royce and something had loomed up coming the other way, so Jim had hauled her up a bit quick and she had slid sideways. The rear wheel rim had smashed the picnic box, which was on the carrier of the 'Silver Ghost', pushing the lot down the road several feet and to top it all, they had tried to pull away from it so doing much more damage.

I let the handbrake off the car and let it run a few yards down the hill away from the engine, I could see that the load was pushing the engine sideways each time they tried to move. I got the chain from the engine and chained the wheel of the living van to stop it pushing any further. I decided that if the engine's front wheels were put on an almost full left-hand lock and the ice chipped off her right-hand rear wheel (to give it a bit of grip) and with the van now not pushing, we might get her straightened up. No way could we get the ice from the wheel, so the only answer was something I had seen father do several years before (I knew it was illegal but it was our only hope). A full set of spud pins were put into the holes on the wheel and it worked, so that was where the pins stayed for the rest of that day. I left Jim talking to the doctor (who had now come onto the scene) while I walked back to tell Jack to go back and face the music. It seemed like an hour before they came into sight.

We edged our way down towards Dorking and pulled up outside the brickworks. Jack walked in to explain our position and the management gave us the OK to get off the road until the weather improved, which would not be until the next day at the earliest as it was now late afternoon. As we sat in the van drying out our clothes and eating a well earned meal, Jack was telling us of the places we would be passing through next day, if the weather improved.

We were now all on strange ground, but Jack had the whole route carefully planned for us. This he had collected from the office while I was getting the drainer coupled up. Our route from Dorking was along the A25, Guildford to Reigate road, turn right in Reigate to Horley then on to East Grinstead, which seemed to me a bit complicated, as I had never travelled that way before. There were a few towns to go through and it would be Easter Saturday, so it was bound to be fairly busy, but to me it would be a great experience. As we lay on our beds that night, we could hear the rain lashing down and we hoped it would clear away the snow and let us be away when daylight came.

It was still pouring down when we went out to take off our dampers. The temperature was almost down to freezing point and it was far from pleasant especially for Easter Saturday. To help matters, poor old Jim could hardly walk, the cold and wet from the day before had done his gout no good at all. He was in agony and it looked as if we were going to get another soaking. We filled up our tanks at the brickworks and were on the move before it was hardly daylight. As it was a road that none of us had ever travelled before, we would pick up water at every stream or pond we came to and judging by the amount of rain we were getting it should be no problem.

We set off towards Reigate in the pouring rain and before we had covered the first mile, we were all soaked to the skin, half frozen and no one was smiling much. Luckily the leaks in both fireboxes had dried up and keeping steam up was now the least of our worries, a change of water and lack of hard work had done the trick.

We pushed on towards Reigate, our first pick up of water was at a pond outside the church in the little village of Buckland. As we had only one lift-pipe (which was carried on the front of the living van) we had to wait a few minutes for Jim and Fred to catch up. When they pulled in behind us, I could see that they were both just about fed up (who wouldn't be). I jumped up, unrolled the pipe from its hook on the van, dragged it along to my engine, screwed it onto the lifter and placed the nozzle carefully onto the fire shovel, which I had placed in the water so as not to pick up too much mud. When my tank filled up I unscrewed the pipe and moved up far enough for Jim to pull up by the pipe. By the time that he had reached there, I was back, screwing the pipe up on the lifter, even hardly before he had stopped. I was the only agile one of the bunch and was trying to help them as much as I could. It was still pouring down with rain and as I looked up at Jim he was looking so sorry for himself. He was wearing his usual hat, which he wore rain or shine, a trilby with a rather big brim and the top pushed up to a point. As I looked up the water was pouring down Jim's shoulders almost like water off the roof of a house.

I was stood in the big rear wheel, sheltering from what was now almost a blizzard and as I looked towards the church, I could see the vicar coming storming down the path towards us. I could see by the look on his face that he was going to have a go at us for pinching water from the church pond. He was wearing a long black cloak with a hood over his head and he came straight to me and started tearing me off a strip. I had been told by my father years before that this could happen, but that the best thing to do is keep cool, apologize and keep him chattering as long as possible, for while this is going on your tank is still filling up, after all that is what matters. I was doing just that, but Jim had seen what was going on and, somehow he had scrambled down from the footplate, walked round the front of his engine and back to the rear wheel where I was still talking to the vicar.

Jim came in from behind the vicar, caught hold of him by the shoulders, twisted him round, looked into his face then pushed him back against the van drawbar and said to him "Look here governor you don't fill the b——-pond, that is sent from up above for everybody's use, so p—- off back into church and do your work, and leave us to do ours". While this was going on, I could hardly keep a straight face. I could hear that the tank was nearly full up and would normally have dived under the drawbar, up onto the footplate to shut off the lifter, but Jim was still holding the vicar back against the drawbar and telling him his fortune. So I ran round the front of the engine and reached the steps up to the footplate, just as the tank had filled up. Now anyone who had worked on a BB1 will know that the lifter, when it is working correctly, really pushes it out and it came out of that tank pocket nearly lifting the vicar off his feet. He was drenched to the skin and was soon on his way back to the church with his tail down.

We pulled away from the pond and as we struggled on through the downpour we could see that the rain was turning to snow again. It was now getting difficult to see, our speed was down to a crawling pace again and poor old Jack Ward had pulled his cap down over his eyes, but he was still struggling. I slowed right down and said "Come on over here and let me get on the step for a while", but he would not change saying "If it doesn't soon ease up we will have to stop". Luckily, in a very short time, it was back to rain again and within less than half a mile it had stopped raining. The sun had broken through and it stayed like that for the rest of the day.

As we were getting close to Reigate, Jack said "We had better try and get coal of some sort or another before we leave here as everyone will be closed this afternoon". Our tenders were piled high when we had left Sipson and I had topped up again at our yard when I called in for the mole drainer. Jim had filled up from our reserve in the van bunker before we left Chertsey. We were on the outskirts of Reigate and for once on our trip, luck was with us, for there, in front of us, was a wagon and two horses with a load of coal. They were delivering to some houses and the coalman had seen us coming so he was standing by his horses ready for us to pass.

We pulled up a fair distance behind them and Jack strolled up and asked if he could help us or tell us where we could get a few hundredweight. The coalman was very helpful, letting us have as much as we needed, Jack paid him and we were on our way again. We pushed on towards Horley at a fair pace, as time was not on our side. We were still a long way from our destination, but the weather had changed. The sun was now warming up a bit. We had almost dried out and I was beginning to enjoy our trip.

In those days, if we were passing through a town, smoke was a problem and in some places the police were red hot on this (we were now using ordinary house coal). As we rattled along, our BB1 was pushing a black cloud high into the sky and we would have to make sure to have a bright fire ready to go through Horley and East Grinstead. As we looked across to our right, we could see Gatwick race course, (which I suppose is now the airport), and the sign posts were now bearing the name of the place we were looking for, so East Grinstead was not too far away.

We edged our way through the town, which was quite busy and I remember seeing a clock on a building and the time was half past three. We still had a few miles to do and our main problem now would be finding a shop open so that we could get some food to see us through the weekend. It would almost certainly be my job to get on Jack's bike when we reached Harwoods Farm and dart back, hoping that there would still be a shop open.

We were now a few miles past the town and in front of us we could see Ashdown Forest, so our job could not be too far away and sure enough standing at the entrance to a gravel roadway was the farm bailiff, waiting to show us in. He had seen our smoke signals and had walked down the drive to make sure we did not overshoot our turning. We pulled up into the farm yard, I unloaded Jack's bike from the van and was away back to town to see what was left to eat, but it was now nearly five o'clock, so most of the shops would be closed for Easter.

I passed several shops, all with their blinds pulled down, but as I neared the centre of the town, there was a small general store still open for business. Although they were almost sold out of food, I managed to get three loaves and a couple of tins of corned beef. Also the shop keeper thought I might get some meat at a small butcher's shop just down the road. I dashed off, only to find that he was just closing and had just about sold out, so I cleared him out of all that he had left, which was four pounds of sausages and three pork chops.

By the time I had pedalled Jack's bike back to Harwoods Farm, the kettle had been boiled and a very welcome cup of tea was waiting for me. We could now get down to some cooking. While I had been shopping, Jack had been chatting to the farm bailiff and had managed to twist his arm for some potatoes and he had dished out enough to last us a couple weeks. We were all just about starving, as we had eaten nothing since our early morning breakfast at the Dorking brickworks, so some of the potatoes were peeled and the three pork chops put on to cook. I had told the three old timers to have the chops as I would be happy with sausages (I have never been a big meat lover).

I started to cook some of the sausages, I don't know what they were made of, but as they cooked they got smaller and smaller, whilst the pan became fuller and fuller with fat. By the time they were cooked, there was not one bigger than my little finger, but it would be something to eat and, just then, that was all that mattered. While we were eating our meal, we were going back over our journey and everyone thought the same. It had been a trip that we would remember for the rest of our lives. One thing that was worrying poor old Jack was about Jim Collins and the Buckland vicar. Would the vicar get in touch with Mr. Ward? Jim had been just a bit rude to him and A J Ward & Sons, Egham, Surrey was plastered all over the side of the living van leaving no mistaking as to who owned the tackle.

We turned into bed that night and were soon all fast asleep. We had put a hard day behind us and were just about dog tired. If the weather was all right, the ground not too wet, we would be spending the Sunday yanking our cultivator up and down one of the fields to try and catch up some of the time that we were behind on this job, but it was not to be. We woke up next morning to find that it was pouring again and cultivating would be off for another day at least.

Our dampers were not taken off and we were sitting in the van taking a well earned rest, when the farm bailiff came round to tell us that his wife was cooking us a joint of beef for our mid-day meal. His words were "If you can't work, you have still got to eat", so some more of his potatoes were peeled and cooked ready for when the joint arrived (it turned out to be enough for about three days).

Monday and Tuesday had come and gone, it was still raining and all the fields were under water. It would be at least another week before we would be able to make a start, so Jack decided that we should all go back to Egham, as this was the normal procedure if we had to stand idle for more than a couple of days. We set off together on the Wednesday morning and would go by bus. I think we changed buses four times to get to Staines, then walked to our yard at Thorpe Lea, a distance of at least a mile.

By the time we strolled into the yard, it was almost five o'clock and we had to set up house again. The 14 hp singles *Shamrock* and *Thistle* were still in the yard so we were to use the living van of this set until such times as we could go back to East Grinstead.

We were out of the van ready to start work at seven the next morning and were given our jobs by Bill Bantick (the yard foreman). I was to help Jack take off the rear wheel of his Ransome threshing engine as new keys were to be fitted to the rear axle. We had not been working long, when in came my brother Bert with his steam plough gang, they had been rained off the same as us.

There were now two steam plough gangs working in the yard, but only one ploughing living van, although there were a few roller vans not in use, so we would get by. I had two days with Jack fitting axle keys and getting his

Ransome back into working order. Then Bill Bantick came over to me and said "How would you like to take out the Fowler singles to do some tree pulling, there are ten acres of apple trees to be cleared near Colnbrook". I didn't need asking twice, this was something new and I was eager to have a go on these wonderful old engines (I had heard so much about them). So *Shamrock* was filled up with water, fired up and cleaned up ready for the next morning. I would be on my way along the same route that we had travelled with the compounds the previous week, but this time in the opposite direction.

I was up early next morning to get steam up ready to be away in good time, there was plenty of help to get coupled up to the van and water cart. I was ready to go and looking forward to something that I had never seen being done with ploughing engines before. By what I could gather, no one else on the firm had done either, there being very little of this work, other than the odd hedgerow being removed.

I was all ready to be on my way and had still not been told who would be going with me or who would be in charge of the job. Then, out of the blue, Bill Bantick strolled over and said "Your brother will be going with you and will stay with you for a couple of days while we find a mate for you". Now I knew that I would be quite happy with this old Fowler as she was very similar to the 12 hp Fowlers that I had been working with at R J & H Wilders. However, Bert had never set foot on a single, apart from the Basildon 8 hp traction engine and that had normal geared steering, whereas *Shamrock* and *Thistle* had the old tank-steerage where you turn left to go right, and vice versa. Once on our way, he soon got used to the steering and, to me, it seemed just like going back to my school days again when we had both spent many happy days together on the Basildon K7 engines.

We reached our job by mid-day, but could not make a start until the next morning as there was no one to put the chains on the trees and couple up the rope. The orchard that we were to clear was owned by the Philp brothers and the three of them did most of the work on their market garden, apart from a few women who came in when needed to cut cabbage and any other produce and I would think that they would have been just casual labour.

We were ready to start at seven next morning and sure enough the three brothers were there eager to make a start, the first job being to pull out the rope to the far end of the orchard between the first two rows of trees. Bert and I had weighed things up the day before and reckoned that once the rope was out to the far end, there would be no more pulling out to do for those two rows of trees. If you have never tried pulling a length of steam plough rope across a field, you are in for a big surprise, as 100 yards is more than one man can pull. If a long length has to be pulled out, it is done in stages

108

and takes a long time and is hard work.

Now these old Fowlers were the ideal engines for this job, because the rope drum could be driven to wind out the rope as there was no clutch on the vertical shaft as with most other engines. The bevel wheel on the crankshaft was free to move on four keys and was operated by a huge lever which had to stand the force of the bevel gears pushing themselves apart under load. This lever reached from the crankshaft to the back of the boiler and was supported by a big bracket bolted to the left side hornplate. The lever had to be lifted over a step on the bracket to engage (or disengage) the bevel wheel. If you didn't get it right over the step before the rope tightened up, it would fly out with a bang, lifting you off your feet if you tried to hang on to it. Whereas, with the normal clutch on the vertical shaft, if you don't get it right home, it will pull itself in under the load, providing it hasn't run dry of oil. If this happens, it will work its way out under load and nothing other than use of the oil can will stop this happening. Our rope was pulled out by the three brothers and we were ready to go. The trees were all round about 12in. to 14in. at the base. They were no problem as an apple tree never goes far into the ground, whereas a pear tree has a big tap root and nearly as much under ground as it has at the top.

By five o'clock that day, we had shifted more than a quarter of the ten acres of trees, the Philp brothers had wasted no time and neither had Bert and I. We had broken only a few chains and everything was going well. I was really enjoying myself, I had now got this job off to a fine art and *Shamrock* was performing perfectly. I had found that by working the regulator in time with the crankshaft, I could get a tree up to a sway and the crank turned slightly further as the tree roots snapped, an extra handful would always do the trick. Next morning, the Philp brothers turned up with a Fordson tractor (one of the TVO type) to pull out the rope, we had already done far more than they had expected, but they still wanted more. We had not been told that this was not a piece work job, as all our ploughing and cultivating had been.

When Mr. Ward dropped in on us, his first words to us were "Ease up a bit, this is a new thing to us and there is sure to be a lot more of this work, if it is successful. Some of the work may not be so easy as this and then we shall be in trouble". Our boss had come to see how things were going and also to take Bert back to his K7s as things had dried up, meaning that they could get back to cultivating again. My first thought was, who has he brought to be in charge of the job, as all that I could see with him was a lad younger than myself and he was to be my rope man. He was a real cockney and a right character he turned out to be.

While Bert was collecting his few belongings from the living van, Mr.

Ward told me just what he wanted me to do and that the main thing was to make it seem a bit difficult and to draw the job out a bit more. This way it would be easier, when the time came, to price the next job of tree pulling. He then dropped the bombshell and said "I am leaving you in charge as I am sure you are capable of looking after yourself and the engine. I met Mr. Wilder, your ex-boss, at Reading Cattle Market a few days ago and we had a long chat together. He gave me your whole pedigree and he thinks that as a steam plough man you are great". I was a bit taken back, but agreed to have a go. He gave me a pat on the shoulder, got into his car with Bert and left me to it.

I now had to explain everything to my new rope man and drum it into him that he must keep the rope pulled tight on the drum, otherwise the rope will drop, then it would have to be pulled out and then wound back in properly, taking valuable time. While all this was going on, I could see that the Philp brothers were getting a bit uneasy as nothing had moved for at least a quarter of an hour.

I could see that I was in for a hard time, now that I was in charge, but I had made up my mind that I was not going to be walked all over, although I was not yet seventeen years old. In those days, most of the workers in that area started work, finished work and had their meal times when the siren (at the HMV gramophone works at Hayes) sounded. This could be heard for miles and was always spot on time. That evening, when it sounded at five o'clock, I carried on as if I had not heard it. Sure enough, the Philps were still hooking up the chains, prepared to carry on as long as I was prepared to keep pulling, so at five-fifteen I stopped and put the damper on. They walked up to the engine and one of them said "Didn't you hear the siren at five o'clock"? I said "Yes, but this has made up the time we lost earlier on".

We had by now made a big hole in the ten acres of trees and when we went for our mid-day meal next day, the fire in the van had gone out, the kettle was cold and by the time we had brewed a cup of tea our half hour was up. By the time that we had left the van, walked back to the engine, fired her up and put a drop of oil around, we were about ten minutes late starting. The oldest brother came storming up wanting to know what was wrong and when I explained why we were late he said "I can't help your problems, with me time is time" and went back to the other two to hook up a few more chains.

When the five o'clock siren sounded, I carried on for another ten minutes as we had done the day before and so made up the time we had lost. We would now take care to start spot on time at all cost. We had, by now, found out what sort of people we were working for. Our last day at this job worked out just right. We had started spot on at seven, had just thirty minutes at mid-day, but when the siren sounded at five o'clock, we still had four trees left to pull. I hopped up onto the road wheel, went along the footboard, put the damper on, then one of them came straight up and said "Surely driver you are going to stop and have these few out to save us coming up here in the morning". I was ready for him and said "I can't help your problems, with me time is time" so he went off muttering to himself.

We watched them on their way back to the house, then I took off the damper and between us we soon had the last four trees out. Then I took *Shamrock* back to our living van at the side of the A4 where she would be standing until the trees had been cleared up. *Thistle* and the cultivator would be brought to Colnbrook to mate up with our engine for a cultivating session.

Next morning, Bill Bantick came to pick us up to take us back to Egham. Our job at East Grinstead was much drier than when we had left it, so they were crying out for us to go back and get on with our draining. While we were on our way back to the yard at Thorpe Lea, Bill was asking a few questions about our tree pulling job. I told him about the way we had been working and said "All they need is a load of blacks working for them so that they could stand there with a big whip". I then told him about the last evening there and how I had put the damper on at five o'clock to cramp their style a little bit. Bill was a bit worried about this and said "They will surely tell the boss about this, they are some of our best customers".

By the time we reached Egham, the rest of our gang were waiting ready to go, so we all bundled into the old T-type Ford van and away to East Grinstead. We now had a cookboy which would be a big help. We eventually reached Harwoods Farm and soon had fires going in both engines, getting them ready for the next morning. While our fires were drawing up, we went to have a look at our first job which was the park around the big house. This was a large semi-circular park which reached more than half way round the house, sloping away down to a stream running away towards Ashdown Forest. The soil was thick yellow clay, so we could see that we were in for some hard going, the biggest problem was that it was too far to reach with a doubled rope. Whoever clicked to do the pulling was in for a hard time, as he would almost certainly have to timber his way along, the ground being very soft from all the water finding its way to the stream.

We decided that the best way to tackle this job was to start at the end nearest the farm where the engines were and finish at the far end (you never run over the work you have carried out when mole draining as this can close up the drains that you have made). This worked out so that poor old Jim Collins would be doing all the hard work, but his gout was still giving him a lot of trouble, so I volunteered to do the donkey work. This meant that we

111

would go to the far end of the park and work our way back instead.

Next morning, we hooked the drainer up to Jim's engine and off he went along the top of the park by the house. I followed behind ready to hook onto his rope and make my way down the slope to the stream at the bottom of the park. As I turned along by the stream, I could see that the ground was still pretty soft and wet. We coupled the two ropes together and gave Jim the OK to pull them back to the drainer. Meanwhile, we set about putting the twenty spuds on. (You don't try going backwards on ground like this until you are prepared for it, otherwise you are asking for trouble and I had to reverse about twenty yards to get back into the corner of the park.)

I eventually got back into position ready to start, but could see trouble ahead if we didn't have some timber to run on. A tractor brought in a trailer load of oak cord-wood and dropped it off in heaps alongside the stream so now we could make a start. I had been looking forward to this job as I had never seen a drainer before, only pictures of them. I got both rear wheels up onto pieces of the oak timber and off we went. The mole had been set down nearly to its maximum depth as they wanted it drained as deep as possible. We had also put a sleeve over the mole to bring it up from 3in. diameter to 4$^{1}/_{2}$in. and it took some pulling.

My engine, by the time the drainer arrived, was almost facing the drainer instead of being sideways on. Both front wheels were nearly down to the axle and had she not been standing on timber, this was where the trouble would have started. Jack Ward stepped off the drainer, pushed his hat to the back of his head, walked round the engine and said "Lets put the front wheel angles on before you move, that will help pull you back in line and try to stop her sliding sideways when you are pulling" (it is amazing how these angle irons pull you towards the side that they are bolted onto).

I struggled forward ready for the next pull, Jack jumped aboard the drainer and away to the top of the hill ready for me to have another go. This time she pulled over quite a bit, but not so much as on the first pull. She was blowing off most of the time and was on double high pressure the whole of the time, sounding more like the old singles than a BB1. I wondered how long could any engine stand up to this treatment and expected to be in trouble with leaking stays again.

We soldiered on until mid-day meal time, when I made my way back to the living van for something to eat and a very welcome cup of tea. Over our meal break, we were deciding what could be done to ease the situation. One thing was certain, as we were using more than three quarters of our drum of rope, we could not double the rope (this would have geared the pulling speed down by half and also halved the load on the engine). Also, you cannot make two bites with a drainer (as you can with the cultivator) because, once the mole is in the ground, it must stay there until it reaches the end of the field, otherwise your drain is blocked and therefore useless.

By the time we were ready to go back into battle, Jack had decided that the only thing to do was to take the sleeve off the mole, they would have to be satisfied with a 3in. drain otherwise it would have to be lifted a bit shallower so, after a short chat with the farm bailiff, the sleeve was removed. This made a big difference, but it was still hard going and by nightfall we were ready for a rest. Poor old Freddie Bennett, who had been humping lumps of oak timber all day, was just about shattered as the timbers were very hard to extract after a BB1 has passed over them on a bed of clay.

Next morning, several men from the estate were out in the park with flags on poles, using plans of the park and house. They were marking where the water main and sewer pipes were. They were not certain how deep down they were, but they did not want us to disturb them in any way, so flags were planted along either side of where the pipes were and we were to steer clear of these by a few yards on both sides. By mid-afternoon, we had reached the flags, here Jim had to make his longest move yet, but still only a few yards, whereas I had travelled about 400 yards (our drains were very close together at the top of the hill and about six yards apart at the bottom).

We were making the first pull on the other side of the strip of no man's land (where the pipes were supposed to have been). I was still struggling on with the regulator wide open, occasionally giving a push on the little lever on the left to keep the flywheel turning, although this was not very fast. I had pulled less than half way down the hill, when the front of my engine lifted up from its perch on the front axle, then went back down with a bang. They had slipped up with their measurements and we had sliced through the water main. As I looked up towards the drainer, I could see part of a 4in. water main standing on end with water gushing from the end of it and the best part of it was that no one knew where to shut it off. For at least an hour, water was oozing from this pipe, making its way down the hill to where my engine was standing, so I was soon standing in the middle of a lake and that was the end of operations for that day.

Next morning, before it was hardly daylight, I wandered off down the park to my engine to see if the water had soaked away. To my great surprise, it had almost all found its way into the stream. I removed the damper, poked up the fire then went back to the van for my cup of tea and breakfast. Before seven o'clock, the farm bailiff rolled up to see us, saying that he was sending another load of timber and a couple of farm workers to handle it to make life easier for poor old Fred and our cockney cookboy. They would place the timber down as I moved forward, but would not be pulling it up if it was pushed into the ground too far. These timbers would be removed with the tractor later on when the drains were being dug out at the ends to join the stream.

We had two more full days in the park, then moved over to the other side of the farm to a field of wheat which was now about knee high. This too was to be drained. This time they wanted it drained at about 18in, so the sleeve was put back onto the mole and we were away. No mole draining is easy, but this was a piece of cake compared with the park and by evening we had covered more than half of the field. I was really enjoying every minute of it and if I was able to get home at the weekend, I would have so much to tell my parents and my brother, Bert, as he had never seen mole draining being done. There were no fields in the Thames Valley that would ever need draining, apart from the grey clay around the Wantage area. While I was at Wilders, I neither saw a drainer, nor did I hear anything about one, so I doubt if one was ever used in that area.

By Friday evening the field was finished, so we were ready to hook onto the cultivator and rip up a field of around forty acres that had not been ploughed or cultivated for a good many years. This would not be started until after the weekend, as Jack said that he was going home next morning, but would be back on Sunday evening. I had not made up my mind what I would be doing, but I had not been home for two weeks, so Jack said "You have more than twice as far to go as I have, so get off early in the morning and don't bother about coming back until Monday. You have earned a long weekend and we will manage until you get back". Jack would drive my engine and Freddie Bennett was a good cultivator man. Jim and Fred would be staying put as the van was their home, so Ben Aubrey, our cookboy and I set off early on Saturday for London by bus from East Grinstead. My route would be from Waterloo to Reading, which stopped at every station and took rather a long time as the old steamers were not quite as quick off the mark as the modern trains of today. I had slipped up and should have gone to Paddington, where I could have got a fast train straight to Reading, but I had now got a return ticket and would have to take the slow trip back on Monday.

When I reached home, the family were eager to know what I had been doing over the last two weeks. Bert was really interested in my story but did not seem too happy with his job, things were not going quite as he wanted. A lot of valuable time was being lost through one of his drivers, who in Bert's words was "Too idle to stand up". This was Barry Wickens, son of the old chap that was going round on his bike and getting plenty of work for them, but they were not keeping up with it.

Most of the weekend, we were talking steam ploughing as usual and more than once Bert had said how nice it would be if we could both be together with the K7s close around to home, as he was, on land that we knew so well. There was not much chance of this, as steam plough men were in short supply around the London area. The old ones were past their best and no younger ones were coming along to replace them. Was it the long hard days with the dust and hot oil that gets thrown at you from a compound plougher? There seemed to be no shortage of roller drivers and some of these were, like myself, quite young, but they just didn't want to know steam ploughing.

I arrived back at East Grinstead about three o'clock on the Monday and could see that very little had been done that day. Poor old Jim was in agony with his gout and Jack was complaining that lifting the clutch lever was playing his shoulder up. Putting two and two together, I was the only fit one in the gang, apart from our new cookboy and he had no interest in steam ploughing engines. Ben had said that he had been "Taken on by the firm to help shift rollers about from place to place".

We had finished our field by the Wednesday evening, the forty acres had been double tined both ways and this was the end of our job at Harwoods Farm, so the tackle was parked in a corner of the farm yard until such times as another job came up for us to go to. Bill Bantick was there with his van to pick us up next morning. I was to go and get *Thistle* (the other Fowler single) ready to take her to Colnbrook, as the apple trees had now been cleared. We were to go and cultivate it over, removing all the roots that had broken off in the ground. There were also rows of gooseberry bushes that had been between the rows of apple trees and these all had to be rooted out.

I filled the boiler of the old single, lit up the fire to make sure everything would be OK for the next morning. Meanwhile, Jack was checking round the cultivator, which had not been used for several months and needed a little attention. Bill Bantick came over with a couple of drums of oil, which we would somehow stack on the cultivator. He then said "There will be another driver starting tomorrow. He is a Hampshire man and is on his way here today. He can drive this one when you go tomorrow morning".

Before five o'clock, our new driver was with us, a chap in his late forties who had been working for Watson & Haig of Andover, another steam plough firm with several sets of tackle. His name was Frank Steele and like myself had been brought up with steam engines. He had a good look around the old Fowler and said "Well I have never seen one like this before". He had worked on singles, but only threshing engines, all their ploughers were compounds. I explained a few things to him and told him that they looked a bit fierce, but were not too bad once you get used to them. The steering and the rope clutch were the two main things that he would have to watch out for.

115

As there were five of us to go next morning, it was decided that three would go in the van, while Frank and I would take the engine, so our drums of oil and a couple of sets of cultivator points were loaded into the old Ford van. They set off in the van to get *Shamrock* lit up and steamed up by the time we reached Colnbrook. We oiled all round the engine, also the cultivator wheels and we were then ready to go, but Frank seemed to be in no hurry to get up onto the footplate. I said to him "You are going to drive this old girl when we get there so you may as well take over now and get used to her".

He made a bit of a fist of getting started, but once on the move he was OK. It was the 'monkey tail' regulator that he could not get the hang of. These engines were geared fairly high when the 'big wheel' was on and, as this gear was carried on the footboard when not in use and weighed over one hundredweight, it was never changed for shunting in tight corners. Once it was on the crankshaft for travelling on the road, that's where it stayed.

We were at Colnbrook by mid-day to find *Shamrock* was steamed up and raring to go, so after a bite to eat we set out ready to make a start. It looked a bit of a shambles. There were piles of red hot ashes where the brushwood and tree roots had been burned and rows of holes where the trees had stood, so I could see that poor old Fred was going to be in for a rough ride. It was my lot to go to the far end of the field, so Frank's rope was hooked onto the front of *Shamrock* and off I went backwards.

This was always the best way with any tank steerage engine, as you can see where the holes and humps are so much better, also the rear wheels make a track for the front ones to follow. The best way is to screw up the brake (which is on the steering shaft just under the steering wheel) so that you can just manage to turn the steering wheel, then as you make your way across the field, you can turn it just a little bit to keep a straight course. This way, if either front wheel drops into a hole you are prepared, ready to hang on to the wheel, the rear wheel having pointed out where the low place is before the front wheel reaches it. The brake and your own muscles will generally do the trick.

We found that the best way to fill in the tree holes was to run the cultivator up either side of the holes, keeping as close as possible to them, then run the front wheel straight up the centre of the holes and this way the cultivator keeps an even keel. One problem is, that if you are down deep, the roots are inclined to block up the tines and when you have to stop, to turn round, this unloads the roots. This is where the trouble begins, as you are turning round in holes that were about three feet deep and these cultivators are easily turned over in situations like this. Our biggest problem turned out to be the gooseberry bushes, as these would block the cultivator up solid and

116

were not very pleasant to man-handle. Our new driver reckoned that the engines should have been kitted out with 'Hampshire pokers' as they would be the ideal things to cope with this problem. Our pokers had just a flat chisel end, whereas a Hampshire one had a T-piece about 9in. long blacksmith-welded across the end (we had always used these in Berkshire and Oxfordshire, so I don't know where the Hampshire name came into it).

We had no trouble with time keeping as our boss had put in a price to complete the job and when the job was finished, having been double-tined both ways, the Philp brothers reckoned we had done a grand job. There would almost certainly be a lot more of this work to be done in the area, there being hundreds of acres of fruit trees that were well past their useful life and we had shown the farmers (in that part of the country) what could be done with a pair of ploughing engines.

Our next job was at the same place that I had joined the Ward's set up, so all that we had to do was pull out onto the A4, go towards London for about a mile then turn left into Sipson Lane, then on towards West Drayton for about half a mile. Our job was close to the headquarters of the people that we were working for, Wilde & Robins Ltd the people for whom you could never get down deep enough. The field was nice and clean with not a weed in sight, so it would be a big change from what we had just left.

Three of the Wilde family were there to keep an eye on us, to see that we did not lift the cultivator to ease things a bit. Each one of them (which were father, son and grandson) knew just how the depth of the cultivator was controlled and would jump aboard to take a ride across the field just to make sure that we had not lifted it up a hole. The father even had a steel tipped walking stick that was marked off in inches which he would push it into the ground and hold it up and read off the inches. He was not so fussy when we were using singles, as he could sit back in his office and hear them barking away, so telling that they were working hard. However, the BB jobs foxed him a bit and so he couldn't make up his mind about them.

All the fields at Sipson had a gravel roadway running along either side of them, so there was no problem of having to travel on soft ground, but the disadvantage was that the engines would pull sideways off them. The drill was to drop one front wheel over the outer side of the road (if you were on the right-hand engine the left wheel went over the side and vice versa), the only snag was that you had to reverse back to get onto the road before moving forward.

I had by now spent a good few days on *Shamrock* and had done some real hard pulling, but still had not been able to open the regulator up and let her cough away at a normal speed across the field. On our last job, while picking a way through the tree holes, the regulator was up and down like a yo-yo, but we could now settle down to some continuous hard slogging. The 'monkey tail' regulators on these engines must have been about six feet long, they were pivoted on the cross plate (just behind the crankshaft) and reached back at least a foot behind the boiler backplate where it was just above knee height. Once you had the hang of it, it was very positive and easy to handle. There was a bracket fitted with two bars between which it slid up and down keeping it steady. This bracket was fixed to the gauge glass and pressure gauge manifold on the top of the boiler. These engines worked at 150 psi, had a long stroke, a pretty big piston and pulled a very high gear on the rope drum. It's hard to believe that as they were struggling the cultivator across the field, the regulator went up and down at least $1^{1}/_{2}$in. as the piston went to and fro. This could be nothing other than the cylinder block moving in relation to the back end of the boiler and makes me wonder how much a boiler stretches when under a heavy load. We cultivated three fields at Sipson and packed the engines away in a corner of the field where they were to stand for a while, so that as soon as some more crops were cleared we would be back again.

Photograph: Rural History Centre, University of Reading.

'With the bigger steam plough engines - such as BB1s, you can be up to half a mile apart in a big field and on foggy mornings, when the plough comes out of the mist with its crew and everything o.k., it's a welcome sight to the driver, as when it is out of sight from both engines, anything could happen ...!' **JOE CHALLIS**

Chapter 6

'Further Afield'

T he BB1 set was still at East Grinstead and there was a full gang of us working in the yard, so it was decided that we should fetch them home as there would be a job coming up for them at Enfield, which is in the North London area. As this was a rather long run, it would be better to take the BB1s as they were so much quicker on the road. We went off that day and fired up ready to be away at crack of dawn next morning, as we were going to tackle our journey in the day if possible. This time everything went to plan, the days were much longer than when we had taken them to East Grinstead, the weather just about perfect and Bill Bantick would meet us on our way with a van load of coal. We arrived back at Thorpe Lea about seven o'clock that evening and we had not let the grass grow under our wheels. Frank Steele had taken over the engine that poor old Jim Collins had been driving (he was much happier than he had been on the single-cylinder job), he went in front and set the pace.

There were a few small jobs to do to my engine as she had taken a pasting during the time we had been working at East Grinstead. One of these jobs had been a new set of firebars as the old ones had started to buckle. They had no doubt done their time and were now looking a bit drunk. Another job was to grind in the injector feed-pipe check-valve on the boiler. This had been blowing back into the injector for quite a while and had slowly been getting worse, so it was now time to do something about it. These engines had only one way of feeding the boiler and that was a $3/4$in. White's injector, but these (if kept clean) gave no problems. If you tried to pick up water from a stream that was too far from the road, the lifter would heat up the water and you were then in deep trouble as a White's injector does not like warm water. We steamed up the engines, banked down the fires ready to pull out early next morning as we had a long journey in front of us and a few busy places to go through to reach Enfield. It was early to bed for all of us that evening as we would be up at crack of dawn and away through Staines before most people were on their way to work.

Our route had been planned for us, we would be going through Staines onto the Great West Road, travelling to the far eastern end of this, then left into Gunnersbury Lane across Ealing Common, Hanger Lane and Alperton, onto the North Circular Road past Staples Corner and Hendon, keeping on this road to the Finchley turning. Then left away through North Finchley, on through Enfield onto the Cambridge arterial road, then to make our way

121

north for about five miles and our job would be on our right next to the Sangamo clock factory.

We were away through Staines next morning before six o'clock, then travelled the full length of the Great West Road, Gunnersbury Lane and reached Hanger Hill. Here we both found ourselves running short of water, but managed to find enough to get us down the hill to Alperton where the canal ran under our road. No way could we reach the water with our lift pipe, so out came the buckets and we each found our patch up the bank. We started passing buckets of water to each other, a full one up and an empty one down and, as this was about three gallons each time, it was surprising how quickly we filled the two tanks. This method was known to us as 'chain bucketing' and was carried out many times during my stay at Wards with the BBs.

We knew that from now on we would be lucky if another stream or pond came in sight, but our water cart was full and we also had a Metropolitan Water Board key for the hydrants, but had no permit (as most of the roller drivers in the London area had). So, we would have to take pot luck and hope that no one from the Water Board came along while we were filling up. As we pushed along through Hendon, we could see the 'Welsh Harp', a big lake on our left, but it was too far away for us to reach, so there was no point in stopping. The North Circular Road had not been open long, but was already carrying a lot of traffic. (A couple of years ago I travelled that same route on my way to Basildon in Essex and most of the way it was just solid with traffic and I said to my son, who was driving the car, "Can you imagine a full set of steam ploughing tackle travelling this road today, what a shambles it would be".) As we reached North Finchley, we were both short of water again, so we lifted one of the hydrant lids, put the lift pipe into the hole, turned on the water and sucked it up from the filled up hydrant box. Also, our coal was getting low so a couple of bags of coal each were taken out from the van and we were on our way again.

In those days, the main road through Finchley was cobble stones and it was a rough ride. There were also tram lines to deal with. Our cultivator and harrows would often be coming along behind us sideways. When you pulled out to overtake a parked car (or what have you) you would have to make sure you went wide enough or you could find yourself bringing along a tradesman's van (or something of that sort). There was also the problem of the trams being unable to overtake. So, we would keep going as fast as possible until there were about three trams trying to get by. Then, if there was nothing coming in the opposite direction, we would shoot over to the wrong side of the road and stop to let them go, usually having to listen to a mouthful of slang from the drivers or watch the dirty looks on their faces.

We reached our destination with plenty of daylight to spare and weighing things up, we had not done too badly. We had covered a lot of miles without experiencing any problems and I for one had really enjoyed our trip. I always looked forward to a long journey and with a BB1 you can do seven or eight miles an hour without thrashing them too much. They also steer much easier and don't shake so much as they do when going slowly. We had about two weeks at Enfield, cultivating fields on both sides of the Cambridge road and, before we left, we learnt that in the near future there would be a few orchards (close to where we had been working and some more at Enfield Highway) to be cleared and ploughed up, so some of us would be back again.

With our job finished, we were getting ready to move off early next morning as we were going back to Sipson again (there were more trees to come out and more cultivating to be done). It was decided that *Shamrock* and *Thistle* would tackle the trees and the BBs would be harnessed up to the cultivator. We had finished our job at Enfield before mid-day, but would not be pulling out until next morning as no way could we do this journey before dark. We were near the entrance to the field, having a clean up and doing a few odd jobs to our engines, when on looking towards Enfield, we could see a cloud of smoke coming towards us which surely looked like a steam engine working hard. As it got nearer, we could see that there was more than one engine. Was it another set of ploughers? As they reached us, we could see what it was all about. There were three big Fowler road engines pulling a massive transformer, with another engine behind them pulling a truck load of coal and water. They belonged to Hickies of Richmond and we were told that they were on their way to Ipswich. What a sight it was (wouldn't it be nice to see something like it today).

Our journey to Sipson the next day went without any problems and we were off the road and stood in the corner of the field by seven o'clock. Unfortunately, our job would not be ready for a few days as there was a big patch of cabbages still left in the corner of the field, so we went back to Egham for a few days. We had not been there many hours, when Bill Bantick came over to me and said "I have got a nice little job for you tomorrow. There is an old ten-ton Aveling & Porter roller at Mortlake that needs to come home to be overhauled". This old engine had been stood idle for about three years and had belonged to Percy Trentham, who was then a small construction firm. They had built a block of houses and had used the old Aveling to make the road. There the roller had stood rusting out, but A J Wards had bought it.

We set off next morning to fill the old girl up with water and get her steamed up. On reaching Mortlake, we pulled up alongside the old roller and before I got out of the van, I said to Bill Bantick "She looks as if she should be on the scrapheap" as she looked just a heap of rust. We had taken a hydrant key, standpipe, length of hose, a few bags of coal, a bundle of wood, a couple of cans of oil and a few spanners. Once all was unloaded, Bill left our cookboy and myself to get on with it, while he went on to Kingston to do a job on another roller that was working there. We filled her with water, but I could see water trickling into the ashpan along her left side. I could tell that we had some leaking stays, but I decided to take a chance, so we lit up and hoped that the leak would not be too bad. Frequently, when engines have warmed up, leaks like these seal themselves up. We managed to get a bit of steam and could now see if she would turn over (the two of us could not pull the flywheel round by hand). She seemed to be rusted solid, so we had to let the gauge creep up to 50 psi before she moved, then with a lot of grunting and groaning she started to tick over. After a while, when the oil had worked round, she ticked over pretty well, but the piston and valve glands were blowing badly. The rods were rusty and therefore acted like a file sliding through the packing. By now Bill was back with us, but he could not make up his mind whether we should chance it or not and said to me "What do you think?" We had no idea what the firebox was like, so I said "If we keep her at about 50 p.s.i, it is all level going and as the pump seems to be working OK, we should be able to keep going as long as the box did not get any worse". We had a fire only on one side of the fire bars but, perhaps, a few knobs of coal along by the leaking stays would stop the water reaching too far across.

We pulled out at about two o'clock and would get as far as we could, meanwhile Bill stayed in sight of us all the way. It would be no problem to find a place to park up for the night as we weren't driving anything as big as a set of steam ploughing tackle. We had not gone far, when the gauge started to drop back, but I had got the pump turned on enough to keep the water at the same level. It seemed that she was not working hard enough to keep the fire drawn up, so I stopped. Bill, who was soon with us, said "I think you are going to have problems", as we still had only half a fire. Suddenly, something (that my father had told me several years before) came across my mind. I said to Bill "Have you got a big chain with you?". He just laughed and said "I don't think the old Ford would get far with this lot". I then said "I am serious, have you got a big chain?" and he said "As a matter of fact I have but I don't see what that is going to do to help make some steam". I walked back to the van with him and sure enough there was a big sling chain just about the same as we used on the ploughers, so this was pulled out onto the road and I dragged it up to the front of the old Aveling. I opened the smokebox door and started piling the chain into the smokebox and Bill said "What do you think you are going to get in the way of steam out of that lot?". I said nothing other than "We might out of this" and caught hold of the hook on the end of the chain and hooked it into the hole at the end of the exhaust pipe. While this was going on, she had built up a bit of steam and we could now move on, but the fire still looked pretty black but would, no doubt, brighten up if we would now get a bit more blast from the exhaust pipe. As soon as I started, I could hear a different exhaust note. It was a short cab on the old girl and I could hear that the hook was doing the job. We had not gone far before I could see that the fire was getting brighter and the gauge was beginning to creep up a bit. I could not quite make up my mind whether to drop the damper or take a chance and keep a bright fire, letting the pressure build up a bit more than 50 psi. I decided to drop the damper half way and see how it worked.

We were now making steady progress and would soon have to find somewhere to pull off for the night. Bill went on and found us a park in a brewery, (who this belonged to I don't remember). They seemed very helpful and said "There will be plenty of wood for you to light up in the morning" (they had steam wagons of their own). I had let the fire get fairly low, so there was no need to find something to put over the chimney. We were ready to make our way back to Egham and would have another try next morning. As we were about to leave, I could see water coming from the bottom of the tank, so I got down underneath to investigate and pushed my finger through the bottom of the tank. The base of the tank was about as thick as a piece of newspaper and all that had been holding the water in was a flake of rust and the tank was the same all over. We were now in deep trouble. As we made our way home, Bill was deciding what we should do on the next morning, as the brewery would not want her left there for long. There was no engine in the yard to pull her home, so he was even talking of bringing one of the ploughers back to shift her, but I for one did not fancy coming that distance home backwards, as this is the only way you can tow a roller safely. Bill went home saying that we would decide in the morning what the drill would be. As I sat in the van that evening, I was thinking of some way to put a false bottom in the tank to get us home and then the penny dropped. A layer of concrete would no doubt do the job.

When Bill turned up in the morning, he said that he had decided that we should hang on so that he could have a word with the boss to see what he thought about the problem. I then told him what I had in mind and he agreed to the idea, so a few bags of sand and a bag of cement were loaded up and we were ready to go. This was going to take at least a day to set, so Bill said "Why not take Charlie Stewart with us, then drop the ashpan and firebars to let him have a look at the leaking stays". So Charlie was rounded up, his toolbox put on board and off we went. Between us we soon had the manhole cover off the tank, the ashpan off and the firebars down, so we could now get on with the jobs in hand. Charlie was soon out from under the firebox and said "That will be best left alone. The box is about as thick as a salmon tin and whatever you do don't let that gauge go over 50". Bill straight away said "I think we should get one of the ploughers home and pull it in," but I didn't agree and said "By hook or by crook I will get her home under her own steam" and carried on mixing the concrete. I soon had a layer about two inches thick all over the bottom of the tank and this was left to dry out while we made our way back to Egham. That afternoon, I had a hunt round and found a piece of an old firebox which was about a foot wide with a 3in. flange on one side. This would be about long enough to lay alongside the leaking stays, so keeping the water from spraying the rest of the fire. Next morning, this was loaded into the van with a few more bags of coal and off we went again.

A few of the bars were put back in place and the piece of steel plate placed carefully along by the leaking stays then the rest of the firebars replaced. We soon had a fire going again. Meanwhile, the ashpan was refitted and the tank cover bolted back on so that we could try our luck by filling the tank with water. It worked with hardly a leak from it. We were back in business again. We pulled out from the brewery by about ten o'clock and were soon on our way. I now had a much wider fire than on the first day, my hook in the exhaust pipe was working wonders and I would have to shut the damper down. I kept her down to a steady pace as I did not want to shake the tank or the firebox too much and with a couple of fill ups with water we pulled gently into the yard at about six o'clock that evening. My brain waves had worked and she was home. I was going to say dry, although she was not, the water was pouring from the ashpan and I reckon another couple of miles would have been it. When the time came for Charlie to sort out the firebox, he put his hammer straight through where it had been leaking. As he had said, "It was just about as thick as a salmon tin" and a complete new firebox was fitted.

That old Aveling stood stripped out in the shed for many months having jobs done to almost every part that mattered, a new box and a big patch on the boiler where the barrel joins onto the throat plate. The way that Charlie Stewart had shaped and fitted this patch was little short of a miracle, having to be seen to be believed. There was no welding gear in those days, so he had removed a few rivets, drilled the patch to take longer rivets and round the outside of the patch, which had been beautifully shaped. It reached out far enough to where the boiler was thick enough to be drilled, tapped and screwed into place with $1/2$in. round-head set screws. These screws had a square on top of the head and were screwed in until the square twisted off, they then looked just like a rivet head. A new top and bottom were fitted to the tank. Things like new piston and valve rods and several other bits and pieces were replaced. She was now a fair old tool again, but it took at least eighteen months before she was completed and repainted. It later turned out to be my job to take her out onto her first job for Wards, this was to replace a 10-ton Wallis 'Advance' at Portsmouth which I will tell you about later.

Our job at Sipson was ready, so we were to go and get on with this, but this time Walt Elliott would be in charge. He was now feeling much better and had come back for another spell of cultivating. However, to me, he looked well past this sort of work but, just like myself, he had lived for steam ploughing tackle and I suppose it was hard for him to keep away from it. We finished the cabbage field and now had to move further along the fields towards West Drayton where there were about twenty acres to be ripped up. These fields had been thickly covered with the sludge from the London sewer beds. This was about the only fertilizer they used and being almost half lime, when dried out, it gave off clouds of dust.

As usual, here we were down with the main frame of the cultivator touching the ground and the going was really tough. The hard work and their hard water were beginning to tell the tale on our fireboxes. Both engines had leaking stays and I was now finding it hard to keep the needle up near the red mark. We were struggling along the best we could. Frank Steele on the other engine was now really struggling, his firebox was leaking badly. Walt was steering the cultivator back down the same track that I had just pulled it, so that we could ease the work and so keep going for the rest of the day. Charlie Stewart would be coming out in the morning to stop our leaks. I was now doing all the hard pulling again. The wind was blowing my way and I was smothered with white dust and looking forward to the time when Walt would say "Let's call it a day".

Things were now getting a bit hectic. I was working like a beaver to keep up enough steam, but with everything wide open my BB1 was getting slower and slower. As the cultivator was turning, Walt said "Have one more pull and we will pack up for the day". I had the cultivator within about fifty yards of my engine, still having her wide open when she nearly jumped off the ground. I was almost certain that the rope had broken, but on having a second look, I could see that was still OK. I could see nothing wrong and, as I stepped back up onto the footplate, Walt put his hands up to to his mouth and yelled out "Put some oil on that b——- clutch". The dust that was blowing my way had dried the oil up on the clutch, it had worked its way out. I suppose that I had not found time to get down to give it its normal dose of oil, but that was the one and only time this has ever happened to

127

me. Most of the rest of that summer was spent in this area either pulling trees or cultivating and I managed to get home most weekends. I would either walk to West Drayton station and catch a train to Reading or walk in the opposite direction to the A4 and catch a Thackeray's bus. We always worked until twelve o'clock on Saturdays so, when I reached Reading I still had an eight mile bike ride to my home at Basildon and I reached home late in the evening.

I had saved a few pounds and was thinking of buying myself a motorbike. This would save me a lot of time in getting home and I would not have to leave home until late evening on Sunday instead of around five o'clock. I talked it over with my parents, but they were not too happy about it as they did not like motorbikes. However, I had made up my mind, so that Monday evening, I set off on foot to Ashford, near Staines, where there was a big place that sold secondhand motorbikes and spares, trading as Simpson's of Ashford. Here, I bought a 350cc Rudge Whitworth which I rode back to Sipson and would be making my way home on it at the weekend. I was home that Saturday within a couple of hours, whereas it had taken me the whole of the afternoon and part of the evening when travelling by train, bus and pedal cycle. This was a big difference and I would also be able to have a few extra hours at home on Sunday. Perhaps, now I would be able to put in a few hours on my model Fowler traction engine that had been packed away and I had not set eyes on it for at least two years. I travelled by motorbike for a few weekends and was taking advantage of the time saved by doing a few jobs for my model. Unfortunately, there was a knock in the engine of my bike that I did not like the sound of, so I had to take out the engine and strip it down to find out from where the noise was coming. It was found to be the big end on its way out, so now I would have to go by train again until I could round up the parts needed to put it right.

The days were getting shorter and the weather getting colder. It would, perhaps be as well to use the trains and buses for a while, so I took my time in getting the bike sorted out ready for the spring. So I purchased some books on motorcycle repairs and these would be browsed through during the long winter evenings that would be spent in the living van. I also managed to pick up a shop soiled portable wind-up gramophone and a few records which would also help to pass away the evenings. It is not much fun through the long evenings sitting in a steam plough living van that is only dimly lit by oil lamps, unless there is entertainment of some sort. I was, and still am, a teetotaller and a non-smoker, so I never went to pubs to pass the time away. I still have my gramophone and records in good working order after well over fifty years.

The summer was now well behind us and the 1930/31 winter was almost upon us and we could now look forward to a long spell of tree pulling. We had made our mark on orchard clearing with the market gardeners of Middlesex and Buckinghamshire. There were hundreds of acres of orchards to be cleared and cultivated, therefore the two sets of ploughers, for the first time ever, would be working the full year round. My brother had parked his K7 set away at Great Lea Farm, near Reading and was back with us looking forward very much, to getting stuck into a winter of tree pulling. I had been telling him most weekends of the enjoyable times that I was having clearing the odd little orchards here and there, then cultivating them ready for planting a crop of something that would no doubt pay off far better than the fruit trees that were all past their best.

My first big tree clearing job was on the Wilde and Robins Farm at Sipson, this lies between the A4 and West Drayton. Here, we could get started into about sixty acres of apple, plum and pear trees, some of which were almost two feet in diameter at the butt. They must have been at least sixty years old and would almost certainly take some shifting. We had decided that the singles were far the best for this job, so I took *Shamrock*, the right-hand engine, and my brother, Bert, took *Thistle* to a market gardener near Slough, where there would be several weeks work for him. There were several other small jobs around the Staines and Ashford area, so Frank Steele would take care of these with one of the BB1 engines. These would be much smaller trees and no problem for a compound engine. A BB1 is a wonderful engine for what they were built for, but are not very happy unless the crankshaft is spinning at a fair speed and this is not possible when pulling trees.

We set off for Sipson on a Friday morning and were to be ready to start our job on the Monday morning. Frank Steele was my steersman, our cockney cookboy would be my rope man and there would be a gang of casual labour to pull out the rope and handle the chains. The big depression of the thirties was already beginning to bite and in that area there were hundreds out of work who would be glad of a job, whatever it was, so they flocked around us like flies. It was my job to pick out who I needed and give them a start at 26/- (£1.30) a week, working from eight to four-thirty. Our boss had put in a price to clear the trees and get the ground ready for planting. On having a look at the job in front of us, I had my doubts as to whether we had enough rope to reach the far end of the rows of trees, but after stepping out the distance, we would be left with plenty to spare. It was about eighteen chains (396 yards) and we had twenty-one chains (462 yards) of almost new rope, so we were in business. By mid-day on the Saturday, I had my engine set up in position ready to make a start on Monday. We then made our way home for the weekend, but would be back on Sunday evening so that I would be able to be on the spot early next morning to get steam up for eight o'clock. This would be a slow job as we would be burning only green wood, but I had a bit of coal left in the bunker to make a start and I had also well filled the lockers under the living van, this would be used to keep us warm through the winter evenings.

On the Friday afternoon and Saturday morning, I had sorted out half a dozen good chaps that would do for a start and they were there ready to start on the Monday morning. They were soon shown how the job would be done and in a short while, they had the end of the rope and some chains to the far end of the orchard. The first half of the orchard were apple trees (with a few plum trees scattered amongst them) and although they were big, this gave us no real problems. By nightfall on Monday, we had made a big hole in the first few rows of trees. Our casual workers were really getting stuck in and it looked as if we were going to have a pretty straightforward job, but things did not work out that way. Our boss came to see us on the Wednesday and was surprised to see how well we had done. He seemed really happy about the job and told me to take a couple more workers on to cut the firewood for the engine, so that the other six could keep going with the chains. He also told us that an engine and sawbench would be joining us to saw up the trees into logs. Someone would be coming to look after a gang cutting up the trees, getting them ready for the sawbench and to burn the brushwood and tree roots.

I had found out that plum trees were, by far, the best burning wood for steaming up in the morning and could be split into smaller pieces very easily. All the plum trees were cut into lengths a bit shorter than the firebox, then split up fairly small and each night it would be stacked round the firebox with some in the smokebox. This was used the next morning to light up and it was amazing how easy it was to get going on green wood. Most of the trees were beginning to go rotten in the middle owing to old age, but if you could find a plum tree that was still good in the centre it was a beautiful purple colour.

We pulled out the first half of the orchard with very little problem apart from broken chains, then we came to four rows of big pear trees and guessed we were in for harder times as a pear tree has a lot of roots. Most pear roots go down into the ground a long way and to make matters worse we were now getting some very hard frosts. The apple trees had been bringing up about a ton of earth on each one which is very unusual, but the frost was going deeper and deeper every day. A cold north wind was blowing most of the time, it was bitter and we were in for a long cold winter. While we were on apple trees, our chain men were putting them just as high up the tree as they could reach from the ground and we could cope pretty well. Now, they were climbing the trees with one end of a length of cord tied round their waist, with the other end on the chain and rope, then they would pull it up round the tree, sometimes up to fifteen or twenty feet up. This was taking a long time and was not always successful. It took us almost a week to clear one row and a lot of these had broken off, some close to the ground, others halfway up and most of these were split down to the root. As I stood on the engine and looked up the row of trees, it reminded me of pictures we had seen of World War One in France where the trees had been mangled to pieces by shell fire.

Sidney Ward came to see us and was not too pleased with our progress. He said "All these tree stumps would have to be grubbed out by hand" (there were no such things as JCB's in those days). There was nothing else we could do, but soldier on as we had been doing. We had either pulled out or broken off almost three rows of the pear trees when disaster struck. I had found it impossible to keep the old girl on the hard road that ran alongside the orchard, so we were running on the orchard ground, which was now frozen solid and would carry anything. We played safe and kept *Shamrock* with apple tree timber under her rear wheels and the front wheel up against the tree nearest to us. This way I could keep her pulling from the side and not across the front wheel. We had been back to the living van for our half-hour meal break and as I was putting a spot of oil around, one of the chain men said "We are hooked up to a big one this time, the biggest one yet" and I soon found this out. Neither did it not come out, nor did it break off. There was one almighty crunch and six teeth broke from the drum gear-ring. That was the end of operations for a few days.

Our fitter, Bob Roslin, came out with his kit of tools, ratchet, drills, hammer and chisels and in three days he had done something that I would have thought was impossible. He drilled and chiselled back into the gear-ring. Meanwhile, Charlie Stewart the boilersmith, forged out six teeth in one lump of steel and this was dovetailed into the broken gear-ring. When they had finished, it was hard to see the difference in any of the teeth. They had done a wonderful job and I doubt if we will ever see men like these again. While all this was going on, our chain men had been busy with picks and shovels. Once through the frozen soil, they dug down and cut a few of the roots so the tree came out without much problem. This is how the rest of them were taken out, but not before we had done a lot more damage to poor old *Shamrock*.

We were struggling with another stubborn tree, when I felt the front go over and, as I looked down to see what had moved, I saw that the front wheel was laying at a pretty crazy angle. On further investigation, I could see that the axle had broken off just short of the wheel hub and was now resting on

131

just the flange of the wheel as it laid against the tree. Two more trees were pulled out while she stood perched in this position. Our gang of men were then back to work with picks and shovels again for a couple of days, while Bill Bantick made his way to the Oxford Steam Plough Company to pick up another axle. When he arrived back with it in the old Ford van, it looked quite funny, the passenger seat had been taken out and the axle laid along the left-hand side of the van with a foot or more still hanging out behind. Bill was a big guy and must have weighed at least sixteen stone, but he was perched up high with the other side right down. The T-type Ford had one spring crossways at both front and back so, as one side went down, the other went up. I would think that the axle must have weighed best part of a ton, so as he came up the field track to us, the van looked quite funny and to think he had come all the way from Oxford like this.

Some straight pieces of timber were cut from the nearest trees and the axle was edged out from the van onto these by our gang of workers. Next morning, Bill turned up with jacks, tools, timber and a forty gallon steel barrel. *Shamrock* was jacked up and perched on this one steel barrel while the axle was being changed and I am sure the few hours while this was being done were the most uncomfortable ones of my life. The oil drum was a good strong one, but they were never made to carry that sort of load, so I was glad when two jacks were put under the axle to hold the weight while the wheels were replaced. This was not so easy as one would think, the axle had to be put on almost full lock for the wheel to be clear of the tree that had done the damage. Handling wheels of this size on ground that is far from level is no easy job and I for one was glad when the job was completed.

We soldiered on for a few more days until trouble hit us again, the steel teeth that had been put into the drum gear were still in good shape, but a few more further round had broken out. We were back to square one again, so it was decided that another gear ring would be the only answer. Everything was measured up, then Bill was away to Oxford again to see what he could round up and, to everyone's surprise, it was found that a steel ring from a much later engine was exactly the same. While Bill was on his journey, I removed the ring of bolts that held the gear-ring to the drum and slackened the nuts which hold the drum stud to its fixing plate under the boiler. The worst job was yet to be done. We had to dig some holes under the drum, so that we could get jacks under it to lower it down far enough for the gear rings to be changed. It is surprising how much soil must be shifted to leave enough room to work a bar to turn a big screw jack on each side of the engine. We also had to go deep enough to allow for the jacks to be screwed out to almost full height, so that you could lower the drum enough for the gear rings to be passed under the boiler. Our worst job

Primrose Cottage, Hook End Lane, Lower Basildon, the birthplace on 6th October 1912 of Joe Challis. The cottage was one of many similar properties owned at the time by the Morrison family (who owned the Basildon Estate) and which were leased to estate workers and their families.

Locally obtained flints, complemented with stone dressings, form the attractive buildings of Lower Basildon School. Situated in the middle of the village at the side of the A329 road between Wallingford and Pangbourne, it was in these classrooms that Joe Challis would spend the first four years of his schooling. With about a mile to walk from his home to school, Joe's appetite for steam was whetted on many occasions by the passage of polished and gleaming steam giants going about their business.

With the phrase 'If you have ever travelled the Crowmarsh to Goring road, you will have noticed those big, rolling corn fields stretching from the River Thames far into the Chiltern Hills', Joe Challis creates the typical chalky landscape illustrated here and which he was very familiar with.

Photograph: National Trust Photographic Library/Vera Collingwood.

A close-up of the west facade at Basildon. Untouched since the first Sir Francis Sykes' day, this ranks among the finest late Palladian facades in England. The main block is dominated by a central recessed portico (or portico in antis), a favourite device of architect John Carr. A master of light and shade in architecture, Carr must have been pleased with the way the Ionic columns were thrown into sharp relief against the dark background of the 'loggia'.

In 1895, to enable non-stop runs to be made between London and the West, the GWR laid water troughs at Basildon, between Pangbourne and Goring, the locomotive tenders being fitted with the necessary scoops. For many years, as Joe Challis reports, any tardiness by the fireman in winding up the scoop after the tender had been replenished, provided an exhilarating experience for anyone watching from adjacent fields, or a drenching one for unwary passengers travelling in the first few coaches who may have had their windows down!

In 1869, pressure on space on the existing Wilder foundry in Fish Street, Wallingford, resulted in a new purpose-built foundry of brick being opened in Goldsmith's Lane and it was in this foundry that Joe Challis was to gain experience in the 1930s. Today, the former foundry and machine shop building has been converted to flats.

An early illustration of a steam ploughing gang with their two engines waiting to start work at East Hanney, near Wantage in the Vale of the White Horse, Oxfordshire. Almost certainly a pair of ancient Fowlers then owned by Noah Paxman who owned 2-3 sets and operated from Clifton Hampdon, before selling out to Wilders of Wallingford soon after the turn of the century. One pair of these were later dismantled and some parts used to build the two Wilder engines.

14 hp single Shamrock at Heath Row - note the timber under the rear wheels - normal practice during winter tree pulling jobs when the ground was wet, preventing the low wheels becoming bogged down. Together with the sister engine, Shamrock was rebuilt in 1912 by A. J. Ward & Sons of Egham with John Allen 150 psi boilers, proving to be the most powerful engines Joe Challis ever worked on.

Practically brand new at the time this photograph was taken, the Wilder piston valve engine as it was when Joe Challis commenced his employment with Wilders of Wallingford in late March 1927. At this time, the Wilder was paired up with one of the firm's 12 hp Fowler singles.

Pictured at Sipson, near West Drayton, Joe Challis - then aged 16½ - in charge of the right-hand steam plough engine, the first time he had stepped onto the footplate of a BB1. This was one of a pair of Fowler steam plough engines then being operated by Wards of Egham.

The living van, the ploughing gang's home for much of the Summer, pictured at Stanford Dingley in 1930, with Joe Challis in the doorway.

The horses and water cart that kept the tanks topped up.

Joe Challis (left) with his older brother Bert with the K7s Darby and Joan at Bradfield in 1930. This was a long, dry and very hot Summer and Joe Challis and the gang were stood idle for a few days as the farmer said it was too hot for his horses to work a long day!

Fred Bennett on the cultivator at Ottershaw in 1931.

Taking a brief break from his labours, Joe Challis is pictured with the 15 ton Marshall steam roller, near Aldershot in 1936, after being requested to 'run off' the road to allow around a 100 soldiers and their horses to pass by.

15 ton Marshall No. 83412 being unloaded at the Padeswood Cement Limited works near Mold in 1986, after being moved from the nearby Seffn Mawr Quarry, ready for restoration to begin. During its period out of use, the roller had acquired a thick layer of limestone dust, all of which had to be removed before work could commence.

Re-united with his beloved Wilder piston valve engine - now fully restored - Joe Challis in his el
Saturday 30th August 1997. Note the typical steam ploughman's stance, blurred flywheel spokes and

Photograph: Buxworth Steam Group.

e controls during a demonstration of two-engine ploughing at the Great Dorset Steam Fair on
ble as Joe makes the old engine work hard - and Joe's watchful eye on the approaching implement.

As the restoration progressed on the Marshall, Joe kept an eye on the work being undertaken, travelling to Padeswood on many occasions. During this period, he made several recommendations which were readily taken up and he also provided an exact replica of the Marshall trademark - a brass 'Britannia' - to replace the missing original.

Marshall No. 83412 (Reg. No. JDM 377) Blodwen goes about its paces around the Padeswood Cement works on a bright Autumn day.

Joe Challis pictured in 1989 with his award-winning 2 in.-scale Fowler BB1 and plough and some of the awards he has won. The trophy (far left) is for 'Best' model at the Banbury Rally and the Shield belongs to the Thames Valley Traction Engine Club and is awarded each year to the owner of a Fowler engine.

An onlooker looks on in admiration at the stirring sight of Joe Challis' 2 in.-scale BB1 Princess Mary driving another exhibitor's 2 in.-scale threshing machine and bailer at the 1991 Rudgewick Rally.

Joe Challis pictured with Frank Marchington and the Buxworth Steam Group owned showman's engine The Iron Maiden *at Barren Clough Farm, Buxworth in September 1991. Note the sheeted living vans in the background.*

A very different perspective of The Iron Maiden *as it lights up the night sky. Adding considerably to the scene in a most impressive fashion are the 'Golden Gallopers' which are also owned by the Buxworth Steam Group.*

All action! Taken at Heathfield, Sussex in 1988, Joe Challis is pictured on the footplate of Fowler AA6 No. 13877, as the anti-balance plough is swung into position for the next 'run'.

'A penny for his thoughts?' Joe Challis takes a break, while Fortune *simmers away behind, waiting for the next turn of duty at the 1986 Lyme Park Rally, near Stockport, Cheshire. In years gone by, the refuge provided by the rear wheels of a steam plough engine had frequently been the only shelter to hand for a steam plough gang unfortunate enough to be caught in a heavy downpour!*

Pulling out from Barren Clough Farm on the way to the Lyme Park Rally in July 1985, Joe Challis shows he has lost none of his skills as he negotiates Fortune *through a narrow gateway, watched by driver Frank Marchington.*

With cable taught, Joe Challis concentrates during a ploughing demonstration at Heathfield, Sussex in 1988 while at the controls of Peter Stanier's 18 hp AA6 steam plough engine No. 13877.

Joe Challis on the partly restored Wilder piston valve engine at the Great Dorset Steam Fair at Tarrant Hinton in September 1996, almost 70 years on from when he had first started to work for Wilders of Wallingford.

After a series of storms the previous week, the resulting sea of mud proved a match for both men and machines at the Great Dorset in August 1997. While the Wilder piston valve engine waits for a turn of duty, Fowler BB1 No. 15333 (Reg. No. AL9855) battles with the muddy conditions during a demonstration of steam ploughing.

Photograph: Buxworth Steam Group.

The old master looks on approvingly as the current owners of the Wilder engine, James Hodgson (left) and Neil Mackinlay fit spuds to the driving wheels prior to giving a demonstration of ploughing at the 1997 Great Dorset.

Photograph: Buxworth Steam Group.

The smile says it all! Completely at ease in the world of steam ploughing, Joe Challis poses proudly for the camera as behind him the Wilder goes about its business enthralling the crowds watching a demonstration at the 1997 Great Dorset.

turned out to be lifting the drum back into position and lining up the holes in the drum stud flange with the studs on its fixing plate. The rope drum, almost full with rope, weighs well over a ton and to keep this on an even keel on two screw jacks sunk about two feet into the ground, is no easy job. With our job completed, we could now go into action again with no fears of our drum loosing its teeth, but all the time wondering, what would break next? We were going through about three van loads of chains a week and poor old *Shamrock* had been taking some real stick for a week or two and it was beginning to tell the tale.

While we were doing the repairs, our chain gang had been busy digging around some of the big roots that were left in the ground, but this made very little difference. They would dig under a tree stump, get a chain between the roots then stand back out of the way, often to watch the chain links fly in all directions, without even shaking the stump. We were working hard and getting nowhere. Our boss came out with the wages on the Friday and could see that something else would have to be done. He was even talking ·of getting someone in to blast them out, but that would be pretty expensive and would still leave a lot of roots that our cultivator would not remove. He then said about having two engines pulling on a single stump, but I could not see this working too well, so I suggested a big snatch block and the use of a doubled rope. This sounded a good idea, but there were still a few snags. First of all our rope, when doubled, would not reach much more than half way, so this would mean getting *Shamrock* out into the middle of the orchard which would be fatal if the weather changed and the ground thawed out. Secondly, we would have to use much stronger chains to put round the roots and thirdly, where would we get a big enough wheel for the snatch block.

We walked down through the apple trees that were yet to be removed and I reckoned that, if the tops were cut off of the first row, I could get down between them to the halfway mark and so get into position to reach all that were beyond that point. In doing this, the pulled out trees would disturb the ground, leaving big holes that could not be avoided, but we decided to try this and take a chance on the weather. The next thing was stronger chains, our boss would make a trip to the London Docks to try and purchase some soft wire rope slings, the same as were used for loading heavy machinery.

We still had the problem of from where we would get a snatch block with a big enough pulley to take a steam plough rope. For those who have not used steam plough ropes, you must not pull them round anything much smaller than your rope drum as they are not flexible enough. If a bend is put in the cable then, at the next hard pull, it will break where the bend is, also it will not coil on the drum properly. We were thinking on where to get hold of a big enough wheel, when something flashed across my mind and I said to Sidney "You have got the very thing we need back at the yard, the pulley from a mole drainer". So, off he went and set Charlie Stewart on making up a snatch block that would take the drainer wheel and within three days this was ready to use along with some heavy wire rope slings that had been rounded up.

Our snatch block weighed about three hundredweight, but was plenty big enough, so that three or four men could get round it and so man-handle it from place to place. What a difference this made. We could now move a stump that would bring up a few tons of earth on it, leaving a hole big enough to put our living van into without much problem. The only thing that was holding us back, was digging underneath the stump to get our 1¹/₂in. diameter wire slings through, but we were now moving at least a dozen stumps a day and would soon have the first half of them out.

With the first half removed, I now had to get *Shamrock* out into the middle of the orchard so that we could reach the far end of the rows. The apple tree tops had been cut off and cleared and I decided to go in backwards so that I would not have to shunt too much to get into position. I picked my way down through the rows of apple trees to within a few yards of the nearest stumps to be removed, pushed the tender back towards the first row that had not been cut off and here I could stand to deal with the whole lot of offending tree stumps.

The weather had changed and was now getting quite a bit warmer. The frozen ground was starting to turn into mud, but there was long grass and rows of gooseberry bushes where we were standing, so it was not too bad for walking about. Our chain gang went home each night plastered with mud and were certainly earning their money. We stood in this one position and cleared all the roots, but *Shamrock* had pulled sideways enough to almost bury both right-hand side wheels. Before I could think of making a move, most of the earth that was piled up at the side of both wheels would have to be dug away, also a bit dug away from behind the wheels so that it would not be a sharp lift out. I would have to come out backwards, as straight in front of us was a hole (several feet deep) where a pear tree had stood and no way could we go forward into this lot. I had a full set of spuds on and a piece of an apple tree chained onto the rear wheel. This would give us a lift, so that some more timber could be placed down for the wheels to run onto. As the ground was now getting much softer, this would almost certainly have to be done all the way back onto the hard road.

We were all ready to make a move by about three o'clock, but the sky had gone black. It looked as if the heavens would open and there was *Shamrock* leaning to the right at a crazy angle. By each right-hand wheel, there was a big hole that would hold gallons of water if we did not get her out in time.

I had screwed the brake on the steering shaft hard on, so that the wheels could not go onto a different lock and we were all ready to go. The steam gauge was up on the red mark and something would have to go, either she would lift out or dig herself in deeper and we would then be in bigger trouble. I gave her one big handful and experienced the most frightening half minute or so of my whole life. The second motion shaft of these engines, unlike the compounds, had bearings the same as the crankshaft with a top and bottom bronze bearing held down with two T-headed bolts about 1in. in diameter. The T-heads were slotted back into the bearing bracket with a massive cast iron bearing cap dropped over the bolts and so pulled down into place on the bronze bearing. When going forward, the gears were pulling the shaft down, so there was no load on the bolts but, in reverse, the load was on the bolts and these two broke. The bearing cap (which must weigh at least half a hundredweight) shot high above the engine and landed on top of the boiler, right by the side of the steam gauge. Worst of all, the shaft was being held up by the gears as the crankshaft was mangling round at full chat. This resulted in the 'monkey tail' regulator being held wide open as this was pivoted on the stay plate, between the two hornplates and between the crank and second shafts. Normally, when the regulator was shut off, it almost touched the second shaft, which had now lifted. There was fire flying from the gear wheels, almost like a giant emery wheel at work which really showed up against the dark sky. As the shaft lifted, it had broken the pump rod (which was just over the top of it) and if you have never tried to push the reversing lever of a real big single into the middle notch while it is running on full pressure with the regulator wide open, I can assure you it is not easy. Operations had ceased for another day and we went back to our van, hoping and praying that the rain would hold off.

Next day, while Charlie Stewart was making another set of bearing bolts, I went across to where the log sawing was going on and had a chat with Fred Bailey. He was the chap that had been sent out to take charge of the sawing and clearing up of the trees. We decided that Bill Brown should bring the 7 hp McLaren single down through the trees and pull his rope out to help us out of the holes that *Shamrock* was sitting in. Our new bolts were fitted and we were now ready to have another go. *Old Mac* (as we called the McLaren) was unbelted from the sawbench, the differential gear locked with its second roadwheel pin and away she went, backwards down the same track that I had taken with no problems, keeping one wheel down the thick row of gooseberry bushes that was between each row of apple trees. I had put two and two together and figured out that if we hooked onto the front axle near the right-hand wheel, we could pull her round onto full lock, so lifting the

135

front wheel out of the hole and away from the big hole that was straight in front of us. *Shamrock* could then come out forward with the help of *Old Mac's* rope to pull her partly sideways and it worked.

The rain had kept off, but we now had a thin layer of snow on the ground and were getting sharp frosts at night again. Bert had finished his job at Slough and was on his way back up the A4 to Cranford where there was another big orchard to be cleared. We would be within about 1½ miles of each other and could spend some of the long winter evenings together. We were now making a big show on our remaining apple trees, but they were getting bigger and bigger and some of them were giving us real trouble. The double rope would have eased things a lot, but the ground was now so soft that it would be fatal to get too far from the road, so we would have to make the best of it.

We had pulled two rows of real stubborn ones and were pulling the last two which were real close to the engine. Our whistle was never used on this job, so I had taken the cord from it, because it was always being blown by the twigs from the trees. We were coaxing the last one of these two rows, only a few yards from the engine, when suddenly the chain snapped and about two feet of heavy chain, still on the end of the rope, came hurtling towards me. I ducked down behind the guard over the gear wheels and luckily it went further forward, but hit the whistle, breaking it off at its fitting on the cylinder. I expect that you have seen at fairs, the stalls where you fire air rifles at little ping-pong balls floating on a jet of water. Well, our whistle was doing just that in the jet of steam for at least half a minute before it fell to the ground, never to whistle again. There I was with a firebox full to the top with lengths of apple wood (if you didn't keep it like this you had no fire), so there was no way that I could get this lot out and it would be making steam for another couple of hours at least. The injector would not work under about 80 psi and my pump was now out of order (being just another lump of useless ironmongery), so the only thing that I could do was to fill the boiler as full as possible with the injector and hope that it would outlast the firebox full of wood.

With Christmas only a couple of days away, I was looking forward to a break and a few days at home. There would be some good meals laid on for us and we could sit round a nice fire, chattering about our experiences with these old ploughing engines, which were our pride and joy. A few days previously, we had broken off a length of our rope, it was too long to forget about and throw away as it was around one hundred yards and we may need it to reach the last two rows of trees to be cleared. We would splice it up when the time came, so it was rolled and tied up in a few places, so that it would be easier to carry when the time came to join it on. If you have never seen a steam plough rope that is as good as new, torn to pieces by brute force, it would open your eyes. Some of the strands of wire, before they break, are stretched and pulled out so thin that they are just about as thin and sharp as a sewing needle. As I was tying this odd length of rope in the fading light of that winter afternoon, one of these needle like ends went in one side of the forefinger of my right-hand and out the other side, I had to push hard with my left-hand to release it. I went back to the van and washed it well with hot water (which was about all I could do). All that evening it gave me some stick, but was not too bad next morning. As the day went on, I didn't feel too much of it, but the next day, which was Christmas Eve, my finger started to get bigger and by evening was really giving me some pain, being almost twice its normal size. We packed up at about four o'clock and by now a thick freezing fog had blanked out about everything and I had to make my way to West Drayton Station to catch a train to Reading. Bert would be jumping on Thackeray's bus and going by road and with any luck we might meet up to do the last eight miles from Reading to Basildon together. I reached the station in good time for my train, but the fog had put the trains behind, mine coming in over an hour late. While I was waiting, I paced up and down the platform to keep my feet warm. My finger was now really playing up and I don't believe that I have ever felt so fed up, either before or since in my life. I was glad when I reached home to be in the warm and sit down to a meal. The meals that you cook and dish up for yourself in a steam plough van are mostly from the frying pan and inclined to get a bit boring, but we all seemed to keep amazingly fit on them and were about as tough as nails.

Our parents had yet again moved into another house which was very nice, but was miles from any main road. It was away out in the sticks on the other side of the Estate, in a little hamlet of about six houses called Southridge, one of the last parts of Basildon Estate to be sold. I did not really enjoy the wonderful meal that mother had dished up for us, as I was getting so much pain from my finger. I had just about no sleep that night and I was obviously in for an unpleasant Christmas. The doctors and hospitals were nothing like they are today and no way would our doctor, who lived four miles away at Streatley, see me on Christmas day. I stuck up with the pain until late afternoon, having had enough, I got a razor blade and slit the finger open. What came out of it was nobody's business but, after a few clean ups, it was very much easier. All that night and Boxing day it felt pretty good and I thought it would be OK.

Next morning, I caught the early train from Reading and walked the 1½ miles from West Drayton to Sipson, then steamed *Shamrock* up. By mid-day we had pulled quite a few trees, but my hand seemed to be heavy to lift up to work the reversing lever, which was quite long and almost up to shoulder level for me. As I sat in the van eating my meal, I felt far from right, so I decided to sit there and take it quiet for an hour. While I sat there feeling sorry for myself, my rope man had gone back to put some more wood into the firebox and tell our chain gang to carry on with something else for a while, explaining the position. In a very short space of time, one of them, by the name of Albert Platt, who was well up in first-aid came back to me and said "Let me have a look". He unbuttoned my boiler suit and found that there was a big red mark right up my arm. Straight away he said "I thought as much you have got blood poisoning", so I was carted off to Staines hospital, where I stayed for a few days. I swore that never again would I touch a steam plough rope, neither to splice it nor handle it in a way that was likely to give me problems like this again. (I stuck to my word for well over fifty years until when, a few days before I sat down to write this sentence, I travelled to Buxworth in Derbyshire to show a number of members of the Steam Plough Club how rope splicing was done.)

After my stay at the hospital, I went back to Sipson to finish the tree pulling job there, but I was glad when the time came to pull out and move to our next job. I had done a lot of damage to both my engine and myself, but that was one job that will stick in my memory for a long time. I had done my part of the job, but it was still far from finished. There were hundreds of trees to be cut up, the brushwood and stumps to be burned then someone would have to go back with the ploughers to rip it up and clean it ready for planting. When I left, there were piles of logs all over the place, the costermongers from London were buying these and taking them back to sell. There were horse and carts of all shapes and sizes and even steam wagons with trailers carting them away. There was a fair sum of money being taken every day which would help to offset the cost of the repairs to *Shamrock*, which must have been pretty heavy.

I had a very short trip to our next job. We went back up Sipson Lane to the A4, then turned right and went towards Colnbrook for a short distance to where there was a very old pub called 'The Three Magpies'. Behind this pub was an orchard of about ten acres for us to clear, which belonged to the Philp brothers and was a part of where London Airport stands today. Some of the trees here were big, but they were all apples or plums and so would be no serious problem. However, the job seemed to take a long time, really wet weather had set in, so a lot of time was lost and it was well into March by the time we had finished. My brother had cleared his job up around about the same time, so his engine and van were brought down to stand by *Shamrock*. They would rest here, close to the A4, until the Sipson job was cleared. They would then be taken back there to cultivate the ground and fill

138

in the tree holes. The site looked almost like the Flanders' battlefield of World War One.

While all the tree pulling had been going on, Albert Wickens, the old boy that had been getting work for the K7s around our home part of the country, had been busy and had already got enough work lined up to last Bert a long time. Albert had come to our home one Sunday morning and was telling us about all this, most of the work being within about five miles of where we were living. I thought how nice it would be if we could both be working together over land that we knew so well, but I could not see this working out with Sidney Ward as he needed two full gangs around the London area. The time had come to get the K7s ready for action again. Bert was to get them filled up, steamed and do a few odd jobs to the implements, so that it would all be ready for the big day. The problem was who was to go to make up the gang as Barry Wickens had left in the autumn and Bert had said (and told our boss) that no way would he spend another season with such a time waster as Barry. The set was all ready to go, there was plenty of work for them to do so, all that was needed now, was a good gang that would be prepared to get stuck in and make the best of it. One day Sid Ward called in at Great Lea Farm to see Bert about making the first move out. Bert was ready for him and told him straight out "If I can pick my own gang I am ready to go now otherwise, as far as I am concerned, *Darby* and *Joan* can stay where they are". As he spelt out who he wanted, Sid was a bit taken back and said "But that leaves us with the few old timers and the rest are not really steam plough men". He could see the sense and agreed, so he would now have to advertise for more drivers.

Bert had picked his gang, they were to be Frank Steele and myself as drivers, with Freddie Bennett as our cultivator man. Freddie was an old timer, but was a good cultivator and plough man who, as long as he could get his beer, would work all night if need be. Our cookboy would be Bert Breakspear, he lived at Theale near Reading and had spent the previous summer with my brother Bert. He had been my brother's rope man whilst tree pulling for the winter and had shown himself to be quite a useful lad, not minding a long day's work. We all turned up at Great Lea Farm on the Monday morning then, while the engines were steaming up, Bert got us all in the van to spell out to us what he wanted done and what it could mean to us at the end of the season if we all pulled together. We all promised him our full support and that we would do all we could to make it a bumper year. If Albert Wickens had done what he had told us and the weather was right, we would show Sidney Ward what steam ploughing piece work was all about.

As most of our work was fairly close together, we were not wasting much time travelling from job to job. The weather was holding out well, so the dust was flying from our cultivator and harrows for about sixteen to eighteen hours most days. We washed out the boilers every two weeks without fail, generally on a Sunday. A steam plough engine when on full chat through long days like these, consumes a lot of water and it's amazing how much mud there is to be cleaned out every time those plugs come out. It is bad for everything if mud is allowed to build up, the gauge glasses are inclined to block up, the water will froth up and get into the cylinders (which is known as priming). When this happens, the pistons will grunt and groan, the glands will blow (as all the cylinder oil has been washed away) and the regulator will be hard to work. In other words, everything is suffering, including the driver, so a regular washout is time well spent. As the summer went on, it got hotter every day, the streams and rivers were getting very low, so water was beginning to be a problem. The fields were baked hard, so we were using far more cultivator points than usual. Some days the heat was almost unbearable and we were glad to get down from the tender for a breather between pulls, but we still pushed on, totting up the acres. The farmers were still crying out for us and we were doing our best to keep them all happy.

We were doing a job at Stanford Dingley (a small village away out in the Berkshire hills). It was still scorching hot and our cultivator could hardly be seen for dust as we yanked it backwards and forwards across the field. My engine was standing about right, but the rope was not coiling very well, jumping at both top and bottom which is very unusual. As I looked down at the 'monkey head', it looked to be loose and was jumping up and down. I saw that something was wrong and on making a close check, I saw that the die block (which runs in the cam of the coiling gear and operates the coiling lever) had broken and was missing, so I walked back a little way. There it was in two pieces and that was it for the day, but where would we get hold of another one? Just outside the next village called Bucklebury was a small foundry, so we would try them first to see if they could help in anyway. They were very helpful and would make up a pattern to cast one in bronze, trying to get it ready for us by the next afternoon. By about three o'clock of the next afternoon, I had made my way back to the foundry, the die block had been cast and machined, but the oil engine that powered the works had just packed up, so the oil hole in the new block was being drilled with a small hand drill. I was soon on my way back to my engine and within a very short time the dust was flying again.

We now had to move on a few miles to Bradfield where there were several fields to cultivate. The farmer here was one of the many who at that time was finding it hard going, so Wards had an agreement with all their customers that we should draw our wages from the farmers and this would be deducted from the cost of the work done. We pulled into this farm on the Tuesday and Bert asked if it would be OK for £9 at the weekend (this was the total week's wages for our gang of five)? The answer was "I shall be going to Reading market with some calves tomorrow, if they fetch a good price you can have £9, but if the prices are low you won't get any" and he was quite serious about it.

Three fields had been cultivated both ways and we were half way through the fourth, the temperature was still up in the nineties with no sign of rain. As we made our way back to our van for a well earned wash and meal, the farmer came over to us saying "You will have to pack up for a few days and hope that it cools down a bit. I am not going to kill my horses by drawing water for your engines", so that was it for a few days.

Next morning the weather looked as if it was on the change, the sky was overcast, looking yellow and would almost surely finish up with a thunderstorm. That was how it stayed all day and all through that night the temperature stayed about the same. In our van it was a job to breathe, so there was no way that we could sleep and, as daylight broke, we could see flashes of lightning in the distance, but it was too far away for us to hear the thunder. After breakfast, I said to Bert "I am going to take a walk across the field and sit down by the wood in the shade, there is nothing we can do here". We were all just about shattered with the heat and as we reached the wood, I could see that the River Pang, which ran through the trees at the edge of the wood, was now completely dry. We took a walk along the river bed about half a mile to where there was a sharp bend in the river. Here the water had swirled round the corner over the years and had washed it wider and deeper. There was now a patch of water several yards long and about a foot deep which was almost solid with trout. We stood and watched for a while, wondering how much longer that drop of water was going to last because, if no rain came within the next few days, there would be hundreds of beautiful trout having a sticky ending. So, I said that it would be a good idea to take a few out for a meal, but we would have to be careful as this would be poaching and we would be for the high jump. We wandered back to our van, brewed a pot of tea and sat on the grass in the shade of the van to drink it. No one wanted anything to eat, all that was wanted was cup after cup of drink. As we sat on the scorched up grass, the ground seemed hot, the lightning and thunder were all the way around us and getting closer, but still no sign of rain. We sat there, up to about five o'clock, taking it easy and Freddie Bennett, our cultivator man, said "I am going to have a wash and take a stroll to the pub and get myself a couple of pints". Up till then he had spent very little time at the pub, as our cookboy had been fetching his 'medicine' for him so that he could work into the late evenings.

I armed myself with a bag and wandered off to my engine, where I picked up the clinker shovel then made my way along, under the hedge, to the wood and along the river bed to the bend where the trout were. Each time I put the shovel in, I brought out at least two or three trout. They were so thick in this drop of water I could not miss. I put them in the bag then hung around for a while waiting for it to get dusk so that I could not be seen very easily. As I reached the van, Fred had just returned from the pub and said "I am going to take my bed up under the trees tonight, it's too b——- hot to sleep in the wagon". Bert said to him "It's going to pour with rain presently", but Fred replied "We have been saying this for the last two days" and off he went with his mattress on his back. The lightning was now flashing all the way around us and was almost frightening. As the darkness fell, everything could be seen almost as clear as it had been all day and this was a sight none of us had ever seen anything like before. The hills and trees around us showed out as plain as day, just as if they were being shown on a screen. As we stood watching, poor old Frank Steele kept wondering what his wife would be doing as she was frightened to death of thunder and lightning. She was on her own at South Wonston, near Sutton Scotney, down in the heart of Hampshire some forty miles away.

We were stood there watching this wonderful sight, when a few spots of rain started to fall. They were few and far between, but were big and quite warm. As they hit the top of our van, they rattled like stones. They were so big that Bert said "I reckon this is it", so we made our way up the steps, sat in the van and waited for it. But where was Fred? He was still under the tree not having felt these few heavy spots. We didn't have to wait long, the heavens just opened and it poured in torrents and poor old Fred almost floated down the hill from the clump of trees where he had intended spending the night. He was soaked to the skin, his bed must have weighed about three hundredweight and no way was he going to be able to sleep on it for a few days. It poured all night and was still bucketing down the next morning and that's how it stayed until well into the afternoon. The ground was so dry and hard that very little of it was soaking in.

The field that we were working in was on the side of a hill, my engine was close to the road at the bottom end of the field and as we looked down the hill from our van, we could see the water looking almost like a river as it poured down towards my engine. The Theale to Bradfield road, which my engine was stood alongside, was built up several feet where it passed across the valley at the end of the field. There was just one small brick arch to carry the surface water away down the valley and into the River Pang. There had been so much in the way of twigs and leaves, not forgetting the mud from the field that we had broken up, being washed down that it had blocked the arch. The water had built up and was running across the road, finding its way across the meadows towards Pangbourne. When the rain eased up enough, we could see that my engine was up to the wheel hubs in mud and water. That evening, after the rain had stopped, we walked out into the Southend road and down the hill to where it meets the Theale road (where my engine was standing), the water still running across the road as it made its way down from the hills around us. There was *Darby* stood in about four feet of mud and water which would take days to soak away and the nearest that we could get to her was at least ten feet. The council workers came the next day to clear the drain under the road to let away the water, but after this was all gone, there was mud nearly halfway up the firebox and, if we stayed there until Christmas, this was not going to clear, so something would have to be done.

Bert had been talking to Mr. Wilson, the farmer and had found out that his horses had been working on the other side of the farm through the hot weather. He had just been trying to hold us up for a while to enable him to get some more of his fields cleared before we moved away to the other farmers that were crying out for us. Albert Wickens had called on us to find out when we would be ready to move further afield, but when we explained our position, he said "I will get in touch with the boss and see about pulling out from here as we have too much work in front of us to waste any time here". He was soon back with our orders to pull out and move on, but how was *Darby* going to be removed from the sea of mud she was stood in? It was hopeless to think of steaming her up to help herself out, as the firebox was half full with mud, she would have to be pulled out somehow but it was going to be some job to even get a chain hooked up. *Darby* was about twenty yards from the corner where the Southend road meets the Theale road, but it was a steep pull up either way, so it was decided that our tree pulling snatch block should be brought down from Egham. Hopefully *Joan* could then at least get *Darby* out of the mud, so that I could steam up and help herself up the bank onto the road. There was a gap in the hedge nearly wide enough for her to come through, so next morning *Joan* was steamed up ready for when the snatch block arrived. Our cookboy, Bert Breakspear, had volunteered to take his boots and socks off, then paddle through the mud to hook up the chain. Frank Steele brought *Joan* down the road, while the rest of us man-handled our giant snatch block along the bank to where our two chains, coupled together, could be hooked up. It looked really funny to see our cookboy, with his trousers rolled up above his knees and no boots or socks, making his way up onto the front tool box, over the front wheel, along the footboard onto the footplate and finally onto the step to steer her on a straight course to the gap in the hedge. Frank pulled her, with very little trouble, until the front wheels were almost onto the road (it's amazing what can be done with a double rope and snatch block). Once here, I was able to rake out the mud from the ashpan and firebox, then I soon had a fire going to get steamed up ready to be away next morning. Our cookboy lived only a few miles away, so Bert sent him home for the night with the rest of the trout that I had shovelled from the dried up River Pang. He needed a bath anyway after his paddle through the mud.

My rope was still out across the field and coupled to the cultivator, so in the morning I would pull it in tight with the cultivator still in the ground. It would have to come out into the road through the same gap in the hedge that my engine would be making. Using a few spuds on each wheel, I pulled out into the road with very little trouble. Then I had to go about twenty yards up the road, so that we could pull out some rope to pull the cultivator from behind, thereby lifting it out of the ground by the V-bar. (This is one thing you must always remember that both cultivators and harrows can only be lifted by pulling from behind them.) You can sometimes lift them from the front, by coupling the engine's rope onto the chain that does the lifting by the V-bar. However, this does not always work and certainly not if you are on light soil and not pulling very deep, it just comes closer and closer to you without even looking like lifting.

We were now going to move to Aldermaston, where there were some fields to cultivate close to the A4. As we were coupling our implements up to make our way there, Mr. Wilson came over to us and, when he realised we were pulling out, he went mad, but he had held us up long enough and we were standing for no more. The temperature had dropped quite a bit, but it was still very hot and looking thundery, but this came to nothing. We soon rattled over the fields at Aldermaston and moved on to Shefford Woodlands, which is in the Lambourn area (race horse country at its best). With this job finished our next job was at Midgham, so it was back into Newbury and along the A4 again. This farmer had fields on either side of the Kennet and Avon Canal, but there was no bridge between Reading and Newbury, that would carry us. The nearest one to us was at Newbury, but this was under repair, so we had to make our way back towards Reading, a distance of around sixteen miles. Once at the outskirts of Reading, we turned onto the Burghfield road, then across country back almost to Newbury. This made a journey of well over thirty miles, just to reach the fields that were only about a mile from the ones we had just pulled out from, but this was just one of the ups and downs of the life of a steam plough gang.

On our way back from this, the south side of the canal, we went across to Silchester in Hampshire to do a couple of fields and then on to Wokefield for another few days work (both of these jobs were within a couple of miles of the place where I have lived for the last fifty-five years). From here, our next job was at Hampstead Norris and this would last us several days as the fields were big and had to be double-tined both ways. Our route was onto the A4 via the Burghfield road, then through Theale, right towards Pangbourne, left at Tidmarsh and across country down the dreaded Buckhold hill (this was where a few years previous I had been almost frightened to death with George Parks and Wilders' 6 hp Fowler, *Little Mary*).

When we were on the move, Bert and Frank Steele used to take it in turns to drive the front engine with the cultivator, harrows and water cart, but I always came behind with the van and plough. This day Bert was driving and we were climbing Tidmarsh hill in top gear (we should really have been in low). When these old K7s were being forced up hill like this, they would vibrate, the road gearing guards would rattle and the steam gauge would tremble so much that you could not see if it was registering 80 psi or 180 psi As we neared the top of the hill, I saw a jet of steam go up from Bert's engine. I thought "That's the gauge glass gone", but then I saw it was too far forward for this. When I pulled up close behind them, I could see it was coming from the top of the boiler. It turned out that the brass tap that is screwed into the manifold on top of the boiler to carry the steam gauge, had broken off. I don't think that I have ever seen anyone react so quickly as Bert did that day. The broken steam gauge tap had been blanked off in about thirty seconds flat using a 6in. wire nail that was laying in the tool tray. This tray is fitted to all K7s and BB1s, covering the third motion shaft and is there for your oil feeder, the odd spanner and cleaning rag. That day, amongst the few spanners, was this nail and a pair of pliers and before I could get off my engine Bert had picked up the nail, held it with the pliers and belted it into the broken tap with the coal hammer. We were on our way again in less than two minutes.

About two miles along the road was the dreaded Buckhold hill, down which I had travelled at high speed a few years before with George Parks on *Little Mary*. We would have to go down it to avoid a long journey round to miss it. Bert had tackled it a few years previously with the Gloucester BB1s with no problems, so he was sure we would be OK. On reaching the top of the hill, we stopped to weigh things up and I said to Bert "I have got the heaviest load, so I will wait until you are at the bottom and out of the way. If *Darby* starts to slide I shall just let it go and hope for the best". While they made their way gently down round the corner, I told Fred to keep tight into the side all the way down. When Bert reached the bottom of the hill, he gave

145

a short blast on his whistle, they were now out of our way. We moved slowly to the brow of the hill and carefully round the first corner, once round this the worst was over, but all the way to the bottom the wheels were partly sliding. I was glad when we were round the bottom corner, we could put the 'big wheel' in again and wend our way up through the valley, then to fork off left up the hill through Ashampstead village and across the big flat fields to Haw Farm where we were to spend several days doing some fairly high speed cultivating and harrowing.

These fields were all flat and some of them were well over one hundred acres. (Many years later, they became the home of scores of Lancaster bombers and from here they would took off to blast Hitler's Germany.) We were having a wonderful time here as the fields were very clean, which was unusual in those days as weed killers were not used. The farmer, John Dew, was very old fashioned and would have men walking the cornfields through the spring to destroy any thistles or the like with a paddle and it was paying off. The farm and fields were a credit to him. There was no tractor, but some very fine shire horses which pulled the wooden plough across the fields as straight as any gun barrel. While at this farm, we would talk things over during the evening meal break and it was said many times what a treat it would be if all the other farms were the same as this one. If ever it was our luck to use our five furrow plough here, we would be struggling to match the beautiful work that these ancient single furrow wooden ploughs were turning out. Once a single plough is set right, hundreds of acres can be turned over with very little variation, but its a different story when you have ten or twelve to deal with.

We had a few weeks in this area for different farmers, working our way out as far as Aldworth and Westridge. While working on the last field here, we could look across the Kidlington Valley to the big rolling fields which several years before were just bushes and wild downland. These were the same fields that I had helped to break up with the Basildon K7s, whilst still a schoolboy. Little did I ever think when these engines were sold off and the Estate broken up into many little lots, that I would come back to this beautiful part of the country which skirts the Berkshire Downs with a pair of identical engines, but this time as a full blown driver with my brother in charge. This is wonderful country and is within a couple of miles from where we first saw the light of day. Over the last few years, I have travelled that way many times and gazed across those hills thinking of the happy hours I spent there with steam ploughing engines, something I would not have missed for all the tea in China. We had experienced a wonderful summer and had broken up many hundreds of acres with our cultivator and the odd field or two with the plough. We had worked many late hours and several weekends, the autumn was now on us and the plough would now be earning its keep. We had taken it almost everywhere with us because you could be sure that, if it had been parked up somewhere, a farmer would have a few acres to be ploughed and it's no joke when you have to go back about fifteen or twenty miles with one of the engines to fetch it.

We had gone back to Stanford Dingley to a farm where we had cultivated several fields in the spring and now had a field to plough. It was a very awkward shaped field on the side of a hill, not very steep, but the soil was very light with a lot of flints scattered around. The only way we could tackle this was to plough it up and down the hill. This is always a bit tricky when pulling the end of the plough down at the top of the hill, as it is inclined to be on its way before the shares are in the ground. We had ploughed more than half the field and were pulling it deeper than was really necessary, as it was almost coming down the hill with just the weight of the rope and my engine was working very light for once. Bert and Fred had, several times that day, said that they would be glad when this field was finished as they could see that my rope was doing just about nothing. It was about mid-afternoon, our cookboy had brought out a kettle of tea, the three of us had enjoyed a drink and Bert Breakspear hopped onto the plough to make his way to the top with the tea for Frank. A couple of pulls later, as he rode back down on the plough, Bert said to him "You may as well stay with us for a while, it will help keep the plough down a bit better." Bert could see that the axle on our anti-balance plough was hardly moving from the centre position while coming down the hill and we were now getting to the steepest part. With three of them on board, the plough seemed a bit more stable, but we were now really too deep for this kind of soil and this was the only way to play safe.

We thought we were doing fine, when the worst happened. We were ploughing deeper than anyone had before and hit a big flint (almost as big as a milestone). This lifted the plough out of the ground and she was away. Bert had told both of his passengers that, if something like this happened, to jump for it, so they were all three soon off and clear of the runaway monster. I had dropped my rope clutch out and was in gear ready to move in seconds. Believe me, it's a frightening sight to see something like this coming towards you completely out of control at high speed and could do untold damage to an engine if it came in a straight line. It swerved first one way then the other, so I could not quite make up my mind whether to go forward or backward. It was now coming towards me at a fare rate of knots. When it was within about two hundred yards of me, it swerved broadside and started to slide sideways, but not for long, it just rolled over about three times before coming to a halt on its side.

Although we spent many hours adjusting different parts of the plough, both ends never ploughed the same again as the main beams had been bent out of true and it was now almost a dead loss. We ploughed a few hundred acres with it before it was parked away for the winter, but the quality of our work was no longer as good. We were turning the ground over and that was about all you could say about it. We were not very happy with our work, but the weather had held out very well and we were ploughing right into late October.

We were now going to pack our tackle away in the yard of the 'Perch and Pike' pub at South Stoke, Oxfordshire where Albert Wickens was landlord. We crossed the Thames at Goring and made our way through the R J & H Wilder country to South Stoke, where we had to go under the main Great Western line, but we were sure that the chimneys would have to be lowered to get under any of the three bridges which led into this little Thames side village. Albert Wickens had done his surveying. He had tied some clothes props together and found that the arch nearest Wallingford was the highest by about three inches, so this was the one we would use. On reaching this arch, Bert and Frank lowered their chimney and made their way under with no problems. The chain, that had been hooked into their chimney and back to the cylinder to stop it from dropping right down, was now brought back to us. As we were lowering our chimney down, I said to Bert "Those ventilators on our living van are not going to go under". Sure enough, as we edged our way gently forward, I stood on top of the road wheel and could see that they would not miss by about two inches. What were we going to do? Several ideas were discussed and Albert Wickens, who had made his way up to us, had even suggested pulling the van under the arch, thereby letting the brickwork break off the ventilators, then new lower ones could be fitted the next day. However, this would almost certainly damage the roof of the van, so this was out. I had looked at the springs and could see that they could go down a long way without coming to any harm, so I said to Bert "I reckon that if we put all the spuds from both engines up into the van and all four of you get up in there with them we shall just about make it". The forty spuds along with the two sets of front wheel angle irons were loaded up, then the four blokes piled in with it, I reckoned this was well on the way for a ton and should just about do the trick, which it did.

We spent the rest of the week at the 'Perch and Pike' draining everything out and greasing all the bright work on the engines, plough mould-boards, etc and on the Monday morning we would all make our way to Egham. We would almost certainly be split up into two gangs and away on some more tree pulling expeditions. We knew that there were hundreds of acres of orchards between Colnbrook and Hounslow to be cleared and the owners of all this land had booked up with Wards to deal with this job. Most of these market gardeners had now realised what could be done with a steam ploughing engine and a few men using some good chains.

Mr. Ward had managed to get four more drivers, so both of the Egham based sets had worked most of the summer. However, from what we had gathered, they were not too special even though three of them had come from East Anglia, which was then steam plough country at its best. In those three or four counties, there were more ploughing sets than the rest of the country put together. The fourth driver, Jim Day, had come from the Northampton area and they reckoned he was pretty good. When we arrived at Egham on the Monday morning, Walt Elliott and Jack Ward were there doing a few jobs on the ploughers that they had been running through the summer. These engines' drivers had been sent out on rollers around the country, as both sets had been back at the yard for several weeks. Whilst waiting for our orders as to what we were going to do, we were having a chat with these two old timers and soon found out a thing or two about the new drivers. These drivers were all middle aged, but had still got a lot to learn about steam ploughing. Jim Day was not too bad, but had got a vile temper and no one wanted to work with him.

About nine o'clock, Sidney Ward came out to congratulate us on a wonderful season's work and was soon telling us what he wanted us to do. Bert and Frank were to take one engine and go to Feltham, where there was a big apple orchard to be cleared. Meanwhile, I was to go to Cherry Lane (which is a side road from the Sipson to West Drayton road running back towards Hayes) and Fred Bennett and Bert Breakspear would be going with me. This was a large orchard, although the trees were not very big and took us about six weeks. Bert had finished his job at Feltham around about the same time and now we both had to wait until the new year when there would be more tree humping for us. Our engines were drained out and they would spend a few weeks where we had finished with them and be in sight of the clearing and sawing gangs of both jobs. We were back at the yard doing a few odd jobs and it was looking as if this was where we were going to spend a couple of weeks. This was not very pleasant in the winter, the engine shed was an open fronted job which faced about north-east and you didn't get much warm wind from that direction in the middle of winter. However, I was the lucky one, spending my stay with Charlie Stewart doing a bit of boiler work. A few hours each day were spent at the anvil drawing out scarifier tines and so I was keeping myself warm.

It was Friday afternoon, pay-day and the normal procedure was just before five o'clock everyone working in the yard would make their way up to the office, going in one at a time to collect their wages. Sidney Ward would sit at a long roll-top desk and would count out your wages, place it on a little pull out shelf at the end of the desk for you to count and make sure it was correct. About three o'clock that Friday, Bill Bantick, our works foreman, came out to round Bert and I up saying "The governor wants to see you both together in the office now". We cleaned the grease off our hands the best we could and, as we made our way to the office, we were wondering what on earth had gone wrong or had he got a big job lined up for us. We walked into the office together and Sidney's first words were "Take a seat. I want to talk to you". We still had our greasy overalls on, so we didn't feel too happy about sitting in the leather covered seats of the office chairs, but this did not matter as we were about to get some VIP treatment.

He had the books of the three sets of ploughing tackle on the desk in front of us and started reading out the acres that each set had ploughed or cultivated. He seemed quite happy with the figures of the two sets that had worked near home, then came the figures for our set, the smallest engines of the three. It was almost unbelievable, we had done more work than the other two sets put together. There had been no complaints of poor workmanship, the expenses for our set were far lower than either of the other sets and, to him, how this had been done was little short of a miracle. He went on "It looks as if you just forgot about time and worked all day and half the night. The acres that you have covered are far higher than any of our sets has ever reached in the past. How it has been done is a mystery to me and seems almost impossible". Bert then had his little say, telling Sid "This can only be done with a good gang that are prepared to work together. As you say, we did work long hours but, the main thing being, we worked as a team. To us that is what piece-work steam ploughing is all about. I think the rest of our gang should be here with us, to be congratulated the same as us. We are no doubt the driving force behind this but two can't run a set of steam ploughing tackle on their own".

The other three of our gang were brought in and highly praised by Sid, then he handed out our acreage money which was put up into separate packets with our names and the amount of cash marked on them. When they were all dished out he said that it was "By far the highest amount of money that had ever been paid to any of our ploughing gangs". We had broken all records and also more than surprised ourselves. I don't remember how much the cultivator man and cookboy collected, but Frank Steele and myself walked out of the office with just over £37 each. Bert's money was double mine, so between us we took well over £100 home to Southridge and that in those days was a lot of money. Our efforts had paid off, but the long dry summer had played a big part.

That evening as we sat in our van, Bert and I were deciding what we would do the next day, which of course was Saturday. We would tell Bill Bantick that we were going to leave work a couple of hours early to catch an earlier train, spending the afternoon in Reading doing some Christmas shopping for our parents, brothers and sisters. We had picked up a big sum of money, so it was good presents all round and we pedalled our bikes from Reading to Southridge well loaded. When we reached home and told the family what we had earned that summer, they could hardly believe it. Bert must have had some idea what we should collect, but had kept it to himself as a big surprise for the rest of the gang.

'This picture of a threshing crew at Five Ways, Cholsey near Wallingford, could well illustrate the 6 nhp Fowler **Little Mary** *that I had many happy times with, as Wilders did almost all the threshing in the Cholsey area and as far as I can remember, this was the only Fowler traction engine that they owned - all the others were Marshalls, the famous traction engine builders of Gainsborough in Lincolnshire, or Burrells of Thetford in Norfolk ...!'* **JOE CHALLIS**

Chapter 7

'Gentle Giants'

On Thursday, just over a week before Christmas, I was helping Charlie draw out a few scarifier tines when Bill Bantick walked into the blacksmith's shop. He said to me "I have got a nice little job for you. I want you to steam up the old Aveling roller that you coaxed home from Mortlake and take it to Portsmouth. There is a ten-ton Wallis 'Advance', with a broken crankshaft bracket, which has to come home for an overhaul and have a new bearing bracket fitted. The bracket has been plated and should bring you home with no problems, so long as you keep a close check on the bolts and plates that I have repaired it with". This job was just up my street as I loved long journeys. The old ex-Trentham Aveling had gone through a major overhaul and was nicely repainted, but I knew it would still be painfully slow and noisy on the gears compared with the Wallis that we would be bringing back. I steamed up in the afternoon ready to be away at the crack of dawn next morning. My mate for this trip would be the cockney boy and, as he said, it was the job that he had joined Wards to do. He liked travelling around the country with rollers far better than steam ploughing and this would be a nice long trip for him, but it was really the wrong time of the year.

The coal bunker in the back of the van was filled with coal, then a few bags tied onto the footboard of the water cart and we would surely need it all. Portsmouth was a long way away and we had some long steep hills to negotiate. I figured that if we left as soon as it was daylight, we could, with luck, get at least to Bordon by Saturday mid-day. It was mostly open common ground in that area, so there would be no problem to finding a place to pull off the road for the weekend (we would have our bikes with us to make our way home for a few hours). As we were checking everything that afternoon to make sure we had not forgotten anything, Sid Ward came out. He said "I know you have a long journey in front of you but if you can get the other one back by Christmas there will be a bonus for you. We are short of rollers and would like the Wallis back so that it can be worked on directly after the Christmas holiday".

We pulled out from the yard next morning and were steaming through Egham while everyone else was on their way to work. As we punched up Egham hill, the old girl started to make hard work of it and I could see that the big end was smoking, it had been fitted a bit too tight and had run hot. I thought that's a good start to a long journey, as a bearing that has run hot will not cool off any more while you are still pressing on. I slackened the bearing off, anointed it with cylinder oil and away we went again, but as we made our way towards Virginia Water I could feel the hot splashes of oil on my face. You get these splashes from all four-shaft engines, as the crankshaft is turning back towards you all the time. We pushed on to Sunningdale, but by then everything was well warmed up and there was a strong smell of hot new paint. I was now travelling most of the way with the ashpan damper up, but she was beginning to lag a bit and the fire was not very bright. I thought surely she is not clinkered up already, so I unhooked the poker from its hook on the back of the cab, pushed the clinker off the bars and could immediately see what the problem was. The bars had turned almost onto their sides and were laying there ship-lap or weather-board fashion. They had sagged down in the middle and were almost ready to drop into the ashpan, no way were they going to get us to Portsmouth. During the overhaul, some clown had fitted a new set of bars and as often happens they were a bit too wide to get the last one in, so he had just left that vital one out. The proper thing to do, when this crops up while fitting firebars, is to grind a little off the sides of each one and your troubles are over. A firebar must have room to breathe end ways, but must not be slack sideways, otherwise they will buckle and turn sideways as mine had done.

(Here is a tip for the steam enthusiast who has never fitted bars before. If you get bars that are too long they can be cut to length very easily by heating the end to a cherry red then, holding it over the side of the anvil by the length that you wish to shorten it, using a hammer and sharp chisel it can be sliced off almost as if cutting a piece of cheese.)

We managed to get through Farnham then struggle up the hill at Wrecclesham. There was then a big bus depot here and this is where we managed to get a pull in for the weekend. I pedalled home to Southridge and my mate back to London. He was to make his way back to the yard at Egham on Monday morning to tell Bill to bring another set of firebars and a few more bags of coal (we had been going through our stock at an alarming rate, as most of it had gone straight through into the ashpan). I was away from home very early on the Monday morning and had pedalled my bike back to Wrecclesham by nine o'clock. I had dropped the ashpan, removed what was left of the firebars and was drinking a cup of tea when Bill turned up with my mate and a set of firebars. This time they were a nice fit, so we were back in business again and were steamed up, ready to leave soon after mid-day. Things were going pretty well and we pulled off onto a piece of waste ground near Petersfield for the night. With luck Portsmouth was within reach by a reasonable time the next day, but we would still have to make an early start if we were to be there in time to begin our return journey before darkness fell. I had put a set of lamps in the van before we left Egham just in case they should be needed. We punched up over Butser Hill in top gear, the old girl still seemed to have plenty of guts and steamed better when she was working hard. Then away through Horndean and Waterlooville, it would be all down hill into Portsmouth after we made our way over Portsdown Hill into Portsmouth.

By the time we reached the spot where the other chap's living van was parked, it was getting quite foggy, so we were not going to have a very pleasant trip in the dark. Time was running out for us, but we would take a chance and get as far as we could before pulling in somewhere for a few hours sleep. The Wallis was still out on its job and would not be in before 4.30pm, so the old Aveling was run onto the stand where the 'Advance' had normally stood. We boiled our kettle, made a cup of tea, had a bite to eat and would be ready to start our return journey as soon as the change over could be made. As the Wallis came up the road, we could see how thick the fog was getting, our journey was going to be a bit grim. The next day was Christmas Eve and there was no way that we were going to reach Egham in one day of normal daylight at this time of the year, so we would take a chance and get as far as we could that night. Her driver pushed the Wallis up into a corner of the piece of ground where we were standing and was getting ready to bank her down for the night. I said to him "Hang on. I am going to clinker out and be on my way tonight", to which he replied "What in this lot?". He could see that I meant what I was saying and said "You must be crackers man. It's going to be real thick up over those hills", but I had made up my mind.

We collected the sheets and a few odds and ends belonging to the 'Advance', bundled them into the coal locker which was now more than half empty. Then we filled the two bunkers of the Wallis from the heap by the van, coupled up to the van and fitted the lamps which had been burning for some time. A piece of board was placed on the coal bunker behind the steering wheel for my mate to sit on and keep us on a straight course. Bert had spent quite a bit of time on one of these engines and had told me that they were a bit extravagant on coal and water, but had a lot of guts on hills and could be pushed along at about eight miles an hour with no problem. I had my bicycle lamp so that I could see the gauge glass, which on these engines is away along the side of the boiler. The 'big wheel' was engaged and we were on our way. As we pulled away from Portsmouth and up over Portsdown Hill, we looked back onto the lights of the town, a wonderful sight which I had never seen before. I had been to Southsea in the summer on the Wilder's works outing, but we had left in broad daylight. We had left in thick fog, but it was now clear. We had climbed out of it and could look back over the bank of fog to see most of Portsmouth quite clearly. I was making good use of one of the injectors, while climbing the hill and it was on more than it was off, ensuring that the steam gauge was staying up close to the red mark all the time. As I glanced up at the chimney, I could see it glowing red for more than half its length. It was sure taking a pasting, but was going home for an overhaul and we had somehow got to make it by Christmas.

We pressed on through Waterlooville and Horndean, up and down the hills from here to the top of Butser Hill. We then had a long run down into Petersfield during which time she could cool off a bit. Everything was going fine, the only problem I was finding was knowing whether the injector was spitting out onto the road or feeding the boiler. Both injectors were away up in front of the water tanks and when you are hammering along you can't hear them 'singing' as you can while stood still. However, I had now found the answer to this problem. While the injector was on I would let my fingers just touch the rear wheel occasionally. If the wheel was wet, I knew she was spitting the water onto the road and not into the boiler.

Petersfield was now behind us and we had taken the left fork off the A3, making our way towards Liss. We then had to think of finding a place to pull off for a few hours. Our oil lamps were not very powerful, so we had passed several places before we had even seen them and were now hammering on towards Bordon. As we passed through Whitehill, a small village just before Bordon, there was a fish and chip shop still open and it was well filled with army lads. I pulled up and walked across the road into the chip shop and all the soldiers were gazing at me as if I was a stranger from space. I was as black as a sweep, plastered with spots of oil, but my money was the same value as theirs and we were going to have fish and chips for supper. On returning to the engine, I placed our supper on the top of the boiler to keep warm, until such times as we found our stop for the night.

On our way to Portsmouth, I had noticed that about a couple of miles along the road from here, at the side of a hill, there was a pub with a big gravel yard on the opposite side of the road. We would pull in here for the night if, when we reached the pub, there was anyone about as it was now getting on for midnight. We pushed on for this two miles or so and as we dropped over the top of the hill, I could see the pub. The moon was now fairly high in the sky, there was a white frost but no lights on at the pub, so we pulled across the road into the yard and hoped for the best. The yard had been freshly coated with gravel and was still quite soft. We had left our scotch block on the Aveling, but we would be OK on the soft gravel. The Wallis was left in gear with the lever back and a shovel of fire from the firebox was put into the van stove to make a fire to help keep us warm for the rest of the night. The Wallis 'Advance' rollers have a square firehole with sliding doors, so our kettle was filled and held on the poker in the firebox to boil for a cup of tea. We would eat our fish and chips then think about a wash. As we sat in the van enjoying our chips by the light of a paraffin wall lamp, I said to my mate "You are in a pretty fine mess". He had been sat directly behind one of the big ends which I had been making sure would not run dry to hold us up. His answer was "You have not had a look at yourself yet". We had done really well and with a bit of luck Egham would be in sight in fair time the next day. With a bucket of hot water from the injector, some of the oil and coal dust was removed, so that we could get down to some sleep for a few hours. Our water tanks were almost empty again as we had not picked up any for a long way because, as with the parking places, we had passed them before we could see them. We were not too worried because, at the bottom of the hill where we were standing, there was a stream where we had filled the Aveling up on our way down and could fill our tanks next morning, or that morning as it was then.

We climbed into bed dog tired and were both soon asleep, but not for long. I was a fairly light sleeper, so the least sound would wake me up and something had done just that. We were on the move. I was out of bed in seconds, out of the van door (which lucky for us was at the front), onto the footplate of the engine and span the regulator wheel full open (the Wallis 'Advance' has a wheel regulator which screws the valve open or shut). There was enough steam left to stop us but, as she was still in top gear, there was no way that she going to push our van and water cart back off the road. I could see that the front roller was just about in the centre of the road, a few more yards and she would have been through the hedge and down a ten foot drop into a field. I turned the roller onto almost full lock and pushed the reversing lever forward and let her trickle on down the hill onto the side of the road. By this time my mate was out there with me, so I said "That's it, we may as well move on down to the stream and sit there till we have enough steam to fill up and be on our way again".

We put our clothes on and waited for the steam gauge to creep up, meanwhile we had a cup of tea and a bite to eat. On checking the time, it was now nearly four o'clock, our night had been pretty short. We had been round with the matches and our lights were on again. She was a bit slow steaming because I had banked her down a bit heavy, so the fire had not burned through. By the time we had filled our two coal bunkers, using a bucket to carry the coal from the back of our van, we had enough pressure to work the water lifter for filling our two tanks, then we were ready to go. I had oiled round and was ready to make a start, when something crossed my mind. My bike had been wheeled under the van when we pulled into the pub yard. I had pushed it crossways under the van and leant it against the big wooden cross beam that carried the two brake blocks. As I dashed back up the hill, I was thinking about how much use it would be after the rear wheels of the van and a water cart full of water had passed over it. I have never been more surprised in my life. It was still almost intact and looked as if it had been pushed over by the brake beam which had then dragged it along by the handlebars, twisting it round length ways and the wheels had missed it. As I rode it back down the hill, all that I could find wrong was that the handlebars were slightly twisted. It must have been my lucky day (or was it night?).

We pushed on steadily and were through Farnham before it was really daylight and were much closer to Egham than we had expected to be by this time (our sleeping time having been cut by about three hours), so we could now ease off a bit. We were travelling almost trouble free and our broken crankshaft bracket was holding out wonderfully well. We were now through Aldershot, leaving the main part of the town on our right, making our way through Farnborough with the Royal Air Force Establishment on our left. As we came up the slope towards the 'Clock House', we started to catch up with a rag and bone man with his donkey and cart, which was piled high with pots and pans of all shapes and sizes. It looked as if he had been clearing someone's house out. As we came up behind him, the old boy jumped off the front of the cart and started walking alongside holding the reins, but if anything the donkey went slower. We kept behind him for quite a way as that road in those days was not very wide. Unfortunately, we were by now down to almost a crawling pace, so I said to my mate "Let's pull out round him or we won't get home today at this rate". I gave it a handful and we pulled up alongside the donkey with its well loaded cart and to my surprise the old donkey put on a spurt and was keeping up with us. Then the donkey started to gain on us and was now going at a gallop, I eased off and watched the old boy trying to hang onto the back of the cart. As they turned left at the 'Clock House' and went away down the road towards Cove, we almost stopped, watching them go away down the road with the old boy's feet swinging like the pendulum of a clock as he hung onto the tailboard. The pots and pans were scattering all down the road and that was the only time I have ever seen a runaway donkey.

Somewhere between Sunningdale and Virginia Water, there was a place by the side of the road where we could pull in. We were nearly out of water as we had not, for a long time, seen any that was within the reach of our lift pipe. We uncoupled the roller from our van, reversed back to our water cart and used the water which we had taken to Portsmouth and brought back again. This water should see us home as we were now no more than six miles from Egham, which if need be, could be knocked off in about an hour. We boiled our kettle, made a pot of tea and had a bite to eat and after another oil round we were ready to go. When I had another look at the chimney, which was now more white than black, I said to my mate "We had better do something about that or Sidney will go mad when he sees this lot". So a good coat of cylinder oil was plastered over it, but the copper top had gone blue and we had nothing with us to clean that with. The paint on the saddle was blistered more than halfway along and this we also could do nothing about. I had never seen any engine get as hot in front as this one had, but when you think of the blast that comes from two high pressure cylinders that are being pushed almost to the limit for hours on end, you don't have to think too hard. There is no doubt about it, a Wallis 'Advance' is a wonderful engine to take on a long journey, they are good steamers, nice and quiet and the worm and quadrant steering is very positive. But, as my brother had told me, they are a bit thirsty and like their fair share of coal. They are also good at plastering you with oil from the big ends.

As we passed by the Royal Holloway College at the top of Egham Hill the clock was on 2.30. We were less than two miles from home and were taking it a bit steadier, through the town and fork right into the road that would take us to our yard at Thorpe Lea. As we made our way along Pooley Green Road, we could see Bill Bantick and Charlie Stewart stood at the yard gate, looking across the pond towards us. As we pulled into the yard, Bill said "We did not expect you back this side of Christmas, because of your bad start with the old Aveling". I had never checked the mileage from Egham to Portsmouth but, whatever it was, we had knocked it off in about fifteen hours travelling time, which I thought was pretty good, especially with a sick engine. This is one more steam engine trip that will always stick in my memory.

After the roller and van were parked away, we had a wash and went up to the office to collect our wages and have a little chat with our boss. As he paid us out, I said "Is this all we are getting, don't forget you promised us a bonus if we got the Wallis back by Christmas. That is what we have done and to do this we have worked over twenty hours out of the last twenty four". He refused to cough up, so a few high words started to fly. I told him straight to never ask me to take on another trip like this again, as the answer would be no. Then I said "Don't expect me back for a couple of days after the Christmas holiday". As I was walking away, my mate said "Don't argue with him anymore we will get square with him" and so we did.

I talked it over with Bert during Christmas and said "For two pins I would go back and tell him what to do with his engines". Bert said "I told you when you first started for him what he was like. He can be all mouth and trousers one day and the next day butter wouldn't melt in his mouth. It's just as his mood takes him". I took my two days off, as I had told him I would, and then I went back to be told that there was another tree pulling job ready for me. So it was back to sort out *Shamrock* and get ready for another few weeks tree pulling, but not before I had let him know that I was not very happy and that if another job came my way, I would be on the move. I spent a couple of weeks on this job and thought we were doing pretty well, but when Sidney came out with the wages, he started finding fault and said "I thought you would have got a bit further than this". I jumped down from the footplate and said "Will you ever be satisfied. If you think I am not pulling my weight just bring someone else out here to take over and bring my cards with you. I have had enough". He just walked off, got into his car and was away.

I had my motorbike back on the road so, as I made my way home on it that Saturday, I turned off the A4 at Twyford, across through Hurst to Winnersh and called on Mr. Ford (who owned about thirty rollers and a few traction engines) to see if there was any chance of a job with a roller. I had never seen Mr. Ford before, but had heard what a nice man he was. When I told him what I was there for, he said "But who are you working for now?". When I told him Wards of Egham he straight away said "We don't reckon to poach other firm's drivers". I had a job to convince him that I was finishing with Wards the following Saturday. I was lucky, he wanted a driver for the sawing tackle if I wished to take it. They had a 10 hp Wallis single standing just off the Nine Mile Ride, near Bracknell. Fords had taken her there during World War One to cut out railway sleepers and she had been used on and off ever since. She had to be taken to Cranbourne Forest in Windsor Great Park to cut out gate posts and fencing for the Crown Lands.

I was first home that Saturday, as Bert was making his way by train and bus. When we sat down at the table for our meal, I broke the news to them. "I will be leaving Wards in a week's time". Bert could hardly believe it and wanted to know what had gone wrong. When I started telling of a few rumours that had been pushed around, which he had not heard about, he saw my point, but he was sure (as was my father) that working with an engine, that is, just stood stationary driving a couple of saw benches, was not my scene and they could not see me sticking this for long. As we sat round the fire that evening talking things over, I said to Bert "You may not have heard, but we will not be working together next season as they want one or other of us to be around the London area with the other sets". That would almost certainly be me and I was not really looking forward to this after such a wonderful summer together the previous year. All that weekend, Bert and my father tried to get me to change my mind and stick to steam

160

ploughing, something I had been brought up with and was by now about as good as the best to be found. I was not going to be persuaded at any price and was not going to be pushed around by Sidney Ward. I would be starting for Fords of Wokingham on Monday week.

I did not go back to my tree pulling job until the Monday morning and would start when we had enough steam. I had been too eager in the past and now was in no hurry. I had realised that the more you do, the more you may and I had already put in hundreds of hours that had not been paid for. As the week went by, I kept wondering if I was doing the right thing. Had I been too hasty? Ploughing engines had been just about all I had lived for since before I had even started school. Although I was only just over eighteen years old, I had spent fourteen years around, or on, these gentle giants. In all those years, if there was something I wanted to know about them, or the implements, I only had to ask and the answer was always there as soon as I reached home. I was now going to walk away and let all this knowledge go to the wall. On the Friday afternoon, Sidney Ward came with our wages. He was all smiles and was in a far different mood to what he had been a week before, being prepared to stand and chatter. He seemed to be in no hurry and I began to wonder if he thought that what I had told him the previous Friday was just on the spur of the moment and that I had changed my mind. When I asked if he had brought my cards, the answer was, of course "I haven't. Don't talk foolish". I said "I am finishing tonight and will call at the office for my cards on the way home". I had never seen anyone's face change so quickly before. He almost begged me to stay put and said "If it's money you are leaving for, you have only got to say and it will be put right". I was at the office by about half past five and he was still trying to persuade me to think again. As I left for home, his last words were, "If you don't settle down in your new job there will always be something here for you to do". This was the early thirties when the unemployment numbers were going up at an alarming rate.

I was at Fords yard on the Monday morning by six-thirty as this was their starting time. One of the drivers had steamed up a Marshall traction engine and I was to go with him to Nine Mile Ride, pull out the old Wallis, that had stood in this spot for somewhere around sixteen years, then tow her to Windsor Park (she could not go under her own steam as a gear wheel had been taken off to help someone out during the war and it had never been replaced). With us, we took two trucks to load the saw benches onto and we hoped that there would be plenty of pieces of timber there for use as skids while roping the sections of the long rack bench onto the truck. Our first job when we reached this sawing tackle, was to take out all the bolts which held the rack bench together. This was in three sections, as it was somewhere around forty feet long when bolted up ready for use, but this could all be loaded onto one truck. The push saw bench, which must have weighed well over a ton, could be loaded onto the second truck.

George Noyce, the yard foreman, came out to pick us up in the afternoon and, the next morning he took us back, along with some more help to load the benches. Once loaded, the saws were taken to Windsor and set in position. We then had to pull the old Wallis out onto the road, hook up with a big shunting pole and away to Windsor Park with it. Getting her into position and lined up with the saw benches was not easy, as the ground was very soft, but there were plenty of trees around so, with our rope and snatch block, we got her somewhere near the mark. The positioning was finished off by using a couple of timber jacks. She was a big old engine, almost the size of a ploughing engine and named *The King of the Forest*.

We steamed up the Wallis, fitted the belts, ran the benches for a few hours and so we were all set to make a start on the Monday morning. There was a big stack of oak trees that had been drawn in from the woods by horses and were stacked in line with the rack bench, so they would just have to be rolled across and up onto the bench. We had a couple of days sawing out slabs and skids which would be used to roll the trees up onto the bench. I was there on my own to look after the engine, while four men, from the Crown Lands estate were to do the rest, but they seemed to be in no hurry and could easily have turned out as much in a day as they did in three. They would come onto the job at about eight o'clock, sit down, read their newspapers for about half an hour and then the saws would be sharpened. By the time this was done, it was time for a break, so they sat down for a cup of tea and something to eat, so we would start sawing at about ten o'clock, then there would be about an hour and half break for lunch. By four o'clock, the man that was in charge would walk back to me and say "All right driver, you can let your fire down now it will soon be going home time". I had never had it so easy before, but it was not my way of life, I had always been used to getting stuck in and doing an honest day's work.

The brass on this old Wallis looked as if it had never had a clean since it left the Basingstoke works when new. I had plenty of time on my hands so, within as couple of weeks, using a few tins of Brasso and some Bath Brick powder, everything was gleaming. The bright steel work had received the same treatment, the paintwork (which was very tatty) had been cleaned with an oily rag many times. The old girl now looked pretty good, but how was I going to while away the time now that everything was spick and span.

I spent a few weeks at this job, the engine and saw benches had had a roof built over them, so that everything and everybody would be in the dry on wet days, which, for those times, would be working in luxury. It was not my way of life, I had always been used to the rough and tumble life of a steam plough engine driver, so I just could not settle down. This job went on for around three months and the only thing about it that I was enjoying, was getting home every night. I was now making a big move on my model Fowler, which had been shelved for a couple of years. Bits and pieces were taken to Windsor Park and worked on in the engine shed (a bench and vice had been fitted in one corner behind the old Wallis, so I was making use of it). We had cut out piles of fencing and gate posts, so the saw mill would be closed down for a few weeks while this lot was cleared, then we would come back to have another session. I wondered whether I might now get a chance to go out with a roller somewhere. The warmer weather was on the way, so there was no need to drain the engine out. All the bright work, which was then almost like new, was oiled over, as were the saw benches and saws. I reported to the yard at Winnersh, where I was given a job cleaning down a roller which was in the paint shop for a repaint.

It was getting towards the end of March and this was always the end of the financial year for County Councils and during that week sixteen rollers steamed into the yard for a long stay. Berkshire County Council (like all other Councils at that time) were cutting down on their spending and the rollers were laid off. Things looked a bit black, but this was now going on all over the country. This was the nineteen thirties and the big crunch was on. Mr. Ford was not very happy and would have to stand off some of the drivers. I, being the last to start here, would be one of the first to go. That Friday, he told ten of us that we would be finishing the following week, but he assured us that, as soon as things looked up, he would be getting in touch with every one of us.

We had by now moved house again, as the two farms at Southridge had now been sold and our house went with the farms. This was the end of the Basildon Estate, so Bert and I had decided that father should retire early. We would bring home the bacon, while he settled down to a quiet life. We had found a very nice house at Mortimer, a village about twelve miles from Basildon (I have lived within a few hundred yards of this house ever since). It is a very nice village in beautiful country, but all gravel instead of chalk, and my roots are now firmly into it.

As our last week for Fords went by, there were a lot of long faces, for many there was no hope of another job and the dole money was little short of starvation. There was a long row of very nice rollers, all very nicely painted and just about spotless, but they were to stand idle for several years. One of these was that beautiful compound Marshall that a few years previously had been delivered new to the Newbury District Council. Fords had purchased this roller from the council as they had realised it was too heavy for their by-roads. It still looked and was as good as new and it was a wonderful engine.

I talked things over with Bert and my parents. I could not quite make up my mind about what to do. When I left Wilders, I had been told that there would always be a job there for me and Sidney Ward had told me the same. As things were now getting, it was a very nice position to be in. However, as I had not taken a holiday since I left school, I would take a week off first. I spent most of the week travelling around on my motorbike, seeing many places that I had never seen the sky over before and it was now getting towards the end of the week. I soon would have to make up my mind where I would be steering for. Would it be Wallingford or Egham? Either place, I would be going back to the job that I loved and to me that was all that mattered. I had a long chat with my father on the Thursday evening and between us it was decided that I should go back to Wards. I had enjoyed my time with them so much and would no doubt be happier there, although it was much further from home, but I had a good motorbike, so travelling home at weekends would be no problem.

I made my way to Egham on the Friday afternoon and went straight to the office, where I sat down and had a long chat with Mr. Ward. He was glad that I had come back and I would be starting with them on Monday. From what he was saying, there was not a lot of cultivating lined up, but there was a fair amount of orchard clearing to be done, just as soon as the ground had dried out enough to carry the engines. The old singles were not the best to get around with on soft ground, their low wheels only had to slip for a couple of turns and the tank was on the ground.

I had left home by six on the Monday morning and was at Egham well before seven o'clock. Bert had gone in the opposite direction to get the K7s ready to leave South Stoke for another season around our old home. This time he would have a slightly different gang, as one of the new drivers (that had started for Wards the previous spring) would be going with him. There would also be another cultivator man as Fred Bennett was needed with one of the other sets. I spent a few days doing odd jobs in the yard. Sidney would stop and have a chat most days and he was on about a few jobs that would be coming up in the near future, such as hauling out shingle for the Surrey and Middlesex County Councils. It would soon be tar spraying time and there were several thousand yards of shingle to be drawn out from Thorpe pits to be put into heaps on the sides of many of the roads around Egham and Staines. He said that would be a nice little job for me for a couple of weeks.

Stood in one corner of the yard was a big haulage truck with fairly high sides that could hold about nine yards and somewhere around the countryside was a Foster tractor. Sidney went to check where the engine was, so that I could bring her home and spend a couple of weeks carting shingle. He was soon back from the office, having found that the Foster was stood in the yard at his brother-in-law's farm at Great Lea near Reading. She was there with a set of threshing tackle, but there was still one more rick to be threshed out and the straw baled up with the Ruston baler that was there with it. Great Lea was only four miles from where I was now living at Mortimer. I could go home that evening, then next morning go out to light up the Foster and get the threshing machine and baler set up to the rick ready for the following day. Someone would be sent out to help me bring the tackle back to Egham. With the help of a couple of the farm workers, the tackle was set up and raring to go next morning. It was a big rick and would not be finished in one day, so I could have another night at home.

We were finished, the tackle was packed up and coupled up ready to pull out by about four o'clock. The Foster was banked down for the night and we would be on the road next morning in good time. We had a fair load for a small engine, there were the threshing machine, baler and elevator all hooked up behind this little Foster. She had seen service in France during World War One and still had the broad arrows painted on the motion side plates. Bill Bantick was there by eight o'clock with my mate. He was our cockney cookboy. My motorbike was loaded and tied into the Ford van, then Bill was on his way back to Egham leaving us to follow the same route. I had sandwiches with me so that I could snatch a bite while the tank was filling up. We had a fair journey in front of us with a few hills that would be low gear jobs. This little Foster was fairly quick in top gear, but pretty slow in low, so we would keep moving and not stop for a meal. We made our way across country through Arborfield to Wokingham, onto the main road, away through Bracknell and Ascot, down into the valley then up to Sunninghill. Here there was a fairly steep hill to climb, then down the other side which was quite steep, so we had about half a mile in low gear.

Most of the Foster tractors have an unusual way of holding the pin that goes through the axle and wheel cap on the right-hand side, thus holding the road wheel with the differential bevel up to the differential pinions. Instead of having a pin with a head and split key, as most other engines have, it is just a straight piece of about 1in. diameter steel pushed through the axle and cap. A groove was turned into the cap then a strap, made in two halves (but held together with two nuts and bolts), held the cap in place. Somewhere along the road, these bolts had come loose and we had lost the straps. There was now nothing to stop the pin from falling out except for the load being put on it by the pressure of the bevel wheels under load. As we punched up the hill, the load on the bevel gears kept the pin safely in place but, as we went over the crest of the hill and the load started to push the engine, there was a split second when there was no load on this vital pin. It dropped out and off came the cap, the wheel moved out a couple of inches and the bevels were now out of mesh and we were away. Following us up the hill was an elderly gent with an open top 'Bull-nose' Morris car and he was about to overtake us. He was alongside the engine when the cap came off. It went straight under his rear wheel and nearly lifted the old boy off his seat. He obviously wasn't very pleased about it and pulled round in front of us, no doubt he was coming back to us to complain. We were now gaining speed fast and were close on his tail, so he put his toe down to get away from us, but we were within inches of him for at least a hundred yards before he gradually pulled away. As we rocketed down the hill, I watched the wheel move along the axle and more than once it must have been almost off the axle. Several times it came back against the differential pinions, making the sparks fly in all directions. The road levelled out, then we started to rise up the slope in front of us. I thought that we would be going a long way up that slope only to run back, putting our load all over the place. I could see that there was a shallow ditch, about a couple of feet from the road, this would be soft so, as we came to a halt, I put the wheels along the ditch and it worked, but the other side wheel was now almost off the axle again. I sent my mate back to pick up the pin and wheel cap, whilst I walked on towards Egham for about a quarter of a mile to a blacksmith's shop, to borrow a jack to push the wheel back on. My luck was in, he had a big old fashioned timber jack which must have weighed over a hundredweight. As I was struggling back with it, a chap came along with a van and he gave me a lift back to the engine. We soon had the wheel pushed back on, then put the cap and pin back in place. A length of baling wire from the baler was wound round into the groove to replace the strap that we had lost many miles back, so we were now ready to go again. Our left-hand wheel had sunk into the edge of the ditch, so we would have to put a couple of spuds on to get out of it. The tackle was blocked up and uncoupled, a few spuds were put on this wheel plus a few spud pins in the other wheel, which was still on the road. We were soon out on the hard road again, coupled up and on our way. The blacksmith's jack was laid across the drawbar and my mate sat there holding it until we reached the blacksmith's shop. A check was made on the wire clip and we were again on our way. I think that I must have leant out over that wheel, to make sure the wire was still doing its job, at least a hundred times before we reached Egham. It has crossed my mind many times what might have happened if that pin had dropped out at the top of Egham Hill. Just imagine that lot going down into the town completely out of control, it makes me shudder to think about it.

Our first job next morning, after the tackle had been parked away, was to get Charlie Stewart to make us a new strap for the wheel cap, then we were ready to go shingle hauling and would start by taking her to Old Windsor. At that time, Thorpe pits were very busy and, if you were not there by about four o'clock in the morning, you would be at the tail end of a long queue of steam wagons and lorries. We would need to be up and on our way before most of them if we were to be at the front of the queue. We were to be paid a bonus each week for everything over forty yards and, if we could get in four loads on the Monday, there would be a bonus on every load for the rest of the week. The weather was pretty good, it was really warm and everything drying out. We would soon be out with the ploughers again, but I was enjoying doing a lot of road work. It was a change and I was lapping it up. As they say "Variety is the spice of life".

We had made a very early start and had already taken three loads to Old Windsor and were on our way back with the fourth, when we stopped to pick up water at Runnymede. I thought that it was about time to get some of the clinker off the firebars as she was starting to get a bit sluggish. However, I would have to be careful as everything was bone dry and so a fire could easily be started. I got out the poker and clinker shovel, thinking that if I threw the red hot clinker into the Thames it could cause no trouble. How wrong I was. Some of the clinker dropped into the rushes that were growing at the river's edge and immediately all the dead leaves started burning. The fire travelled at an alarming rate, so there was I, running along the river bank with the clinker shovel, trying to beat out the fire, but it travelled faster than I could run. Had it not been for a break in the rushes, I could still have been running now. The thing that surprised me most was the number of water birds that were flying up in front of the fire as it swept along the river and no doubt a lot of these were nesting. I am sure that there are not many people around that can say they have set fire to the Thames.

In those days there were no hydraulic tippers, so our truck had to be unloaded the hard way, with shovels. This was the hardest part of our job and I thought there must be a way out of this. As we sat in our van one evening thinking of a way to get over this, something crossed my mind. A number of years before (while still a schoolboy) I had seen my father getting his old Fowler and threshing tackle through a gateway at the side of a narrow lane. The only way had been to widen the gap, so the engine's rear wheel was run up close to the post then, with a chain put round the post and onto the wheel, the post was lifted out with no damage to it. Somehow, we must be able to use this idea to lift one side of our truck. In the back of the engine shed there were several pieces of timber and on looking through them I found a piece of 4in. square oak which was about a foot shorter than the distance from the ground to the bed of our truck. I figured that if I pulled the engine alongside the truck and put this piece of timber inside the engine's rear wheel rim (onto the spoke that was about to leave the ground) it would work like a jack, so lifting the side of the truck enough for most of the load to be tipped out.

We went off next morning to give it a try. With our first load, we pulled close to the side of the road, dropped the side of the truck and as usual almost half the load came out. Instead of getting the shovels out, the side of the truck was put back up then we pulled along the road, crossed over to the other side and repeated the operation. We then uncoupled the truck to try our piece of wood and it worked like a charm. The truck was lifted so that the wheels were about a foot off the ground and the bit of our load that was left on board could be easily pushed out with the shovel. We didn't get in many more loads in a week, but we didn't feel so tired at the end of the day as we had been in the past.

This job was to go on for a few weeks, but not for us, the BB1s were to be on the move. Walt Elliott was back for another season and our first job was in Oxfordshire between Reading and Henley, at a place called Shiplake. There were several fields to be cultivated and some to be ploughed, but this would only be about fifteen miles from my home. We had a good run here and our next job was away back in Surrey at Ottershaw, midway between Woking and Chertsey. It was a few hundred acres that had been purchased by a man, from Kenilworth in Warwickshire, who was also the owner of several big hotels in and around London. He intended growing all his own vegetables, so we were to break up a lot of grass-land that had stood uncared for over a long period. There were also a few fields that had grown corn in the past and these were tackled first. We cultivated and harrowed them ready for the tractors to finish off, ready for planting. It was fairly light sandy soil that we pulled up quite deeply, so, as the Fordson TVO tractors made their way, backward and forward across the fields, their sumps were almost on the ground it being so soft. Sand is treacherous stuff to travel over with ploughing engines, so we would have to watch our steps.

We had set out and started on a part of the park that had been grassland for a good many years. It was pretty hard, but being sand, once through the top crust it was no problem, so here again we were pulling it up pretty deeply. However, we would have to be careful where we got to when cultivating the opposite way, as I was at the bottom of the hill, running along the side of a stream, but keeping far enough away from it to be safe. When we reached about the halfway mark, I could see a low place in front of me which, no doubt, had been dug out many years before for cattle to go to the stream for water. I walked along to have a look, but I didn't really like what I saw. It looked a bit suspicious to me so, the next time the cultivator reached me, I gave a blast on the whistle and asked Walt to have a look to see what he thought. He walked through the low place a couple of times then said "I think you will be all right if you don't stop. Have a couple of pulls from where you are stood then go straight through and have two from the opposite side. We will miss the little bit in the middle". I had my two pulls, then into gear and away. While the front wheels went through the low place I kept a close watch, but they hardly made a mark, then, as they went up the other side, the rear wheels dropped into the lowest spot. I had a full set of spuds on the wheels and felt almost certain that I was past the bad spot but, as I opened the regulator just a little bit more to climb the slope, the worst happened, the big slab of top soil that I was stood on just slid back and down, so for a few minutes she kept sinking. The tank was well down into the sand, the holes where the wheels had gone down were filling with water and she looked as if she was stood on end. I stepped off the footplate straight onto the ground, a drop of no more than a foot and to sit on the top of the wheels was just about like sitting down into a chair. I did not attempt to pull the cultivator back, as the coiling gear was buried in the sand and we were already in enough trouble. Plenty of timber and jacks would be the only answer. We were in for some hard work.

A load of sleepers and a few big screw jacks were delivered, so we could get stuck in. What a job we had. We spent a couple of days digging and jacking, but were pushing the sleepers into the ground out of sight without moving the engine an inch. As the sleepers went down, a miniature mountain was coming up about ten feet away. We slogged away until the Saturday and poor old Walt Elliott was there in the thick of it all the time. Day after day, we kept on at him to stand back and tell us what he wanted done, so leaving us to do the donkey work, but he thought it was his pigeon and that he should be in the thick of it. When he left that Saturday afternoon, he looked just about all in. He had left his BB1s for the last time. He had overdone it and never came back.

We went back on the Monday to carry on where we had left off and after another couple of days hard graft we were beginning to get somewhere. We had buried a whole lot of sleepers and there was now a lot of daylight under the tank of my engine. We were without a foreman so, as Bert was standing idle with his set, he was sent out to take charge of operations and was soon thinking the same as I was. We figured that if the big tree-pulling snatch-block was brought out to us, then the other engine was steamed up and brought down from the top of the hill to be in line with the front of my engine. It would be a big help. At least she could be kept from dropping back each time the jacks were screwed down for a fresh bite. This worked out pretty well, so it was time to steam up and hope for the best. We would not take any chances, so the other engine would be doing most of the work until my wheels were well and truly on good firm soil again. That hard crust on the top had been broken and anything could still happen. The OK was given, so we both started pulling together. As she dropped off the timber that had been placed in front of the wheels, the hard crust broke through again. She must have travelled at least thirty yards almost down on the tank before eventually lifting out of the sand and on to the hard top layer of soil. No way were we going to finish cultivating this field, it was far too risky.

We would now start in one of the other fields that were higher up and so much drier. My rope was pulled in, complete with the cultivator and we had soon made a big dent in a field of about forty acres. This time my engine was standing on a hard road which went right up the hill between the fields. It was another couple of weeks before we finished at Ottershaw but, for the last two days, we were working with no one in charge as Bert had gone back to his tackle. The next Monday morning, Mr. Ward would be bringing someone out to take over and tell us where our next job would be. Mr. Ward had visited Walt Elliott every week at his home to take his wages and find out how he was progressing, which was not too well. Walt was a sick man and would almost certainly not be coming back.

On Monday morning we steamed up early, as usual, so that we would be all ready to hit the road as soon as our new foreman arrived, but it was mid-morning before Sid Ward turned up. With him was one of the new drivers that he had started the previous summer. He had been driving a roller somewhere around London. They got out of the car and came straight over to me while I was doing a bit of brass polishing. The gaffer said to me "I want you back at my car, I have the directions for your next job and I want to have a word with you". I walked back to the car where he got out a slip of paper with the name of the farmer, the address of the farm and the best way to get to it. This job was at Hurley, about mid-way between Maidenhead and Henley, he then started telling me which was the best way to go and how much there was to do when we reached there. He started on about several other jobs that were coming up in that area, also that one of these farmers was a Scot and was very particular. We would have to be very careful to do a real good job here as the farmer would be watching us like a hawk, being the sort that would complain about the least little thing. As he went on, I said "Shouldn't you be telling all this to the guy that is going to be in charge, and not me". His answer was "That is what I am doing, I want you to take charge of this set and carry on where poor old Walt has left off". I just could not believe this and I said "I am quite happy as a driver and would like to carry on as I am. Don't forget the rest of the gang, apart from the cookboy, have been at this job far longer than I have. They are also much older than I am, surely one of them should take charge, I am not ready for this job yet". He would not take no for an answer and said "I had a long talk with Walt on Friday. His very words were", "Young Joe Challis should take over. He knows more about this job than the rest of them put together. He is a good ploughman, a wonderful driver and is dead reliable". After a few minutes of hard thinking, I decided to give it a try. But what sort of a time was I going to get being in charge of a gang that were very much older than myself? He said "You know the job inside out and I am sure you are capable of looking after yourself. Just give it a try and I will pay you the same wage as I am paying your brother", this being over the top by a good bit on other firm's wages. There I was, three months short of my nineteenth birthday and in charge of their best set of ploughing tackle. If only I could meet George Parks again as it was only just over two years earlier, when I had left him at Wallingford, that his last words to me were, "Keep going as you are and before many years you will be in charge of someone's tackle". How right he was. I had a fairly hard time for a few weeks, but there was nothing that either of them could show me about steam ploughing, so I had nothing to worry about. I did not try to push either of them around and, if the weather was very hot, I would give both drivers a break for hours at a time, I just loved to be on that footplate.

We had finished our first job near Henley and were on our way to the Scottish farmer. Before we pulled out onto the road, I got the rest of the gang together to tell them that this Jock was red hot so they must watch their step and not give him any rope. The first field here was to be cultivated and double-tined both ways. Although our cultivator man was really good, having been at the job for many years, I would be doing most of it myself, so that, if anything went wrong, I would carry the can. How right our boss was when he was telling me what sort of a man this farmer was. He must have ridden up and down the field fifty times that day. He sat on the seat with me and all the time he was asking questions about this, that and the other. One thing that I could not get into his thick head, was where the front wheel of the cultivator should be running for each tine to be doing its job when double-tining. He was trying to tell me that the wheel should be running in the track of the outside tine on its previous journey, but by doing this, the tines on the half of the cultivator that is running on the soil that has been broken up, will be travelling in the exact same tracks as on the previous run. However, if the wheel is run a few inches outside the track of the outside tine on the previous pull, each tine will be running in between the tracks of the previous pull and so breaking up every inch of soil. That is what double-tining is all about.

If you have a good look at any Fowler cultivator, be it a 9/11 or 11/13 tine job, you will see that they are all evenly spaced with the centre one exactly behind the front wheel. It is plain enough for any one to see that the front wheel must be run to one side of the last track if it is to do its job properly. We had cultivated three fields and, if I thought we could bury the rye grass, there was a big field to be ploughed. The grass was almost knee high, pretty thick and should have either been cut or had sheep turned out to run over it. On having a good look at it, I told him that we could put most of it out of sight, so we would see what we could do with it on the Monday morning.

It was under twenty miles to home and that Saturday I was home before two o'clock. I knew that somewhere in our shed was a set of chains and weights that both father and Bert had used on the Basildon Estate plough. If I could find them, I would take them back to make use of them again. (With a set of chains, fitted in the right place, it is amazing how much grass can be buried.) I went through all the engine bits that had built up over the years and there in a small sack was the set of chains that had been dragged miles and miles over those Basildon hills. They were a bit heavy to carry on my motorbike as one load, so I set off that same afternoon with half of them, spending the rest of the day making a few adjustments to our plough. We had, somehow, got to make a good job of this, but the plough had been neglected and was all out of adjustment. Some were ploughing deeper than the others, some not turning the furrow over the same as the others, but all this is adjustable. I was getting ready to be away again on Sunday morning to finish my tuning but, on checking the rest of the chains before fixing them onto my motorbike, I found that we were one short. Therefore, I had to hunt around to find a piece of chain and something for a weight, but could find nothing in the way of chain to match up with the others, so a length of lighter chain would have to do. I fitted them all onto the plough and was ready for the morning when we could see how they were going to work. We soon found that they worked like a charm, apart from the odd one which was leaving quite a bit of the grass on the top. The farmer twigged this like a shot and kept saying "The little'un is nay touching the grass". We were doing a grand job apart from this one chain and that was spoiling the whole job, but in less than half an hour the farmer was back with a length of chain that was just about the same as our others. A length was chopped off with the chisel, fitted and we were now doing a good job. The Jock was more than happy and when the field was finished he reckoned we had done a grand job. We had been congratulated by someone that was very hard to please.

We were in this area for several weeks and had worked our way through into Oxfordshire and were almost in sight of Reading. Most of our work had been ploughing, so I now had our plough in real good shape, turning out some real fine work and I knew that we could always come back to these farmers again. I had been making my way home at least twice a week, as it was no more than half-an-hour's journey and also, now being in charge, I did not have to be there to get up steam. Being close to home it was nice to get back, have a good meal and take some fresh food back for the rest of the week. I also had another reason for my journey, I had met the girl of my dreams. She was the landlord's daughter from the 'Carpenter's Arms' which was next door to our new home in Windmill Road, Mortimer.

I was now earning good money so I decided to get a better motorbike, this time it was a 500cc Rudge 'Ulster'. It was capable of well over 80 mph, but I was still not satisfied with its performance as the makers reckoned that in the right hands it could be tuned to reach three figures. I decided to have a go at squeezing a bit more out of it, so I purchased some books on tuning for speed. One of these was written by one of Brookland's top tuners and included a lot of information about getting more speed from a Rudge. For a few weekends, the engine was stripped down, things like ports and flywheels were highly polished, different parts lightened and balanced and it now went as fast as I could handle. Most Sundays my girlfriend, Gladys and I would set off early and kept going for most of the day, coming home a bit saddle sore, but with hundreds of miles behind us. We would be up with the Mortimer larks and travel together, far and fast, for the sheer pleasure of motor-cycling, a great change from sitting behind the steering wheel of a steam plough for hours on end.

Our season was finished off around the market gardens of London and it was now time to park our engines away for the winter and get stuck into some more tree pulling.

'This is me with my pride and joy for 12½ years - the big 'S'-type Marshall steam roller No. 83412, which had originally been supplied new to Newbury District Council in 1927. We're pictured at Farnborough in 1935, when we were helping to build 'A'-class roads in North Hampshire. Later - during World War II - we both assisted with the war effort, constructing aerodromes and runways for Wellington and Lancaster bombers to take off and land on. A wonderful engine and surely the best I ever stepped onto ...!' **JOE CHALLIS**

Chapter 8

'A Time of Change'

All the steam plough drivers were sent out on rollers or threshing engines, however, Bert and I went off into Middlesex with *Shamrock* and *Thistle*, to start a long winter removing thousands of fruit trees. What a time we had. At that time, where Heathrow airport stands today, there were then hundreds of acres of orchards and we were there to clear them, not to build an airport, as passenger planes in those days were unheard of. We never dreamed that London would have an airport on the patch of ground that we were working on, although at that time there was a small airstrip where Fairey Aviation would sometimes land with small experimental planes. This was alongside Canes Lane, which then ran through to the Great West Road, between these orchards and the A4. These trees were to be removed as they had served their time and were no longer paying their way, so the land was to grow vegetables, which would be far more profitable. It was our job to clear away the trees, cultivate the land and get it in shape for planting. This was to be done in stages, so that some of the land could be producing a crop while we were struggling with the rest.

We took *Shamrock*, along with our living van and water cart and pulled into this first orchard just off the A4, setting out ready to make a start. We had not been there long, when the unemployed came in by the dozen. They had seen us pull in and were soon on the scene looking for a job, so there was no problem sorting out a couple of gangs. We went back to Egham to get *Thistle* and the cultivator, but on our return went away through the orchard, almost half a mile from the road, to where Bert would make a start, working his way back towards us. This way, a big area could be cleared ready for the cultivator also, this time, there would be two engines with saw benches cutting up the trees for the Londoners to collect with their horse and carts.

I was working my engine alongside the A4, where there was just a low hedge between us and the road so, all day and every day, we had many spectators. There would often be up to a dozen cars pulled up on the side of the road, with their drivers and passengers lined up along by the hedge, some with cameras and some, making their way through the gaps in the hedge, trying to get a bit closer to us. We were constantly telling them to keep far enough away, as there were often a few chain links flying around and I am sure that most of them did not realise how much they were sticking their necks out. It was very risky standing anywhere near the engines when we

175

were pulling the trees close to them, as often the end of the rope (complete with a length of chain) would fly over the top of the engine, finishing up on the opposite side of the 'monkey head'.

Poor old *Shamrock* was by now well and truly battle scarred; there was paint chipped off in many places, there were dents in the cylinder and boiler lagging, but I had been lucky, still being free from dents. As *Shamrock* was the right-hand engine, I could duck down behind the road gearing and its guards when the pressure was really on. With the other engine it was a different story, these old singles were very open on the left-hand side so the drill, with this one, was to point the front of her towards the direction that you were pulling from. As long as the rope was clear of the front wheel, this was the safest way to stand because you were behind the flywheel, which was by now well and truly battered by flying chains.

There were two strong gangs using the two engines, with saw benches going full chat, clearing the trees then burning the tops and roots. Soon, after a few acres had been cleared we set to work with the cultivator. This time, we had put a gang onto grubbing out the gooseberry bushes that were between the rows of trees, so that they would no longer give us any problems. By now the ground was frozen hard, so it was a bit of a job getting the cultivator into the ground, but once through the hard crust we were away, but it was a rough ride for poor old Fred. This crust was a big help for those of us with the engines; it was a big help as those old timers, on their low wheels, were not too happy on soft ground, as they could easily be bogged down, ending up sitting on their tanks. We had cultivated this patch both ways and most of the tree roots had been lifted to the top, picked up and burned.

The ground was ready for the tractors to put in the finishing touch. This was not going to be easy, as there were tons of daffodil bulbs that we had brought to the top. They were to be cleared up and put in heaps to be burned. Think what they would be worth today! Our living van was standing close to the A4 and we were still getting many spectators so, one weekend, I said to Bert "I am going to take a couple of sacks back with me. We can fill them with daffodil bulbs and stand them by the van for people to help themselves for a few coppers." The sacks were filled and stood where everyone could see them, a chisel was put through the top of a gallon oil-can and this was hung on the corner of the van with a card on it marked "Fill your bag for 2d. This is tea money for the workers". The tea, sugar and milk for all the gangs was paid for from this oil-can and at the end of each week, there was almost enough to pay for our journey home. All that we had to do was pick up a few buckets full of bulbs to keep the sacks topped up. My portable gramophone was again going full chat most evenings and each weekend, so as we came through Reading on our way home, we would purchase a couple of new records to help pass the long evenings away and some of these I still have in good shape today.

We spent the whole of the winter on this job and by the spring there were enough trees laid flat to last the clearing and sawing gangs most of the summer. Meanwhile, we would be away ploughing, so the engines were both parked up near the road by the living van. We would be going back to the two compound sets to get them ready for the coming season, but this idea quickly changed. Through the winter, while our tree clearing job was going on at the side of the A4, some of the Middlesex Council officials had been watching us and could see what a couple of ploughing engines were capable of in the right hands. The stretch of the A4, from Colnbrook by-pass to the Great West Road, was to be widened and Wards had been booked to do the clearing on both sides of the Old Bath Road, as it was then known. I went off first with the last cookboy to join us, a lad from Hornchurch in Essex, to get *Shamrock* steamed up and take her down the road to the 'Peggy Bedford', a big hotel at the London end of the Colnbrook by-pass. We would start clearing the right-hand side of the road on the way to the Great West Road and after a few days, Bert would be coming with *Thistle* to make an attack on the other side. After we had cleared a few hundred yards, we would be far enough apart to allow the traffic to keep flowing smoothly.

I pulled out onto the road, facing towards Colnbrook, the start of our job was a mile or so down the road, so the 'big wheel' would be put on as it was too far to go in low gear. These old engines were geared very low in the slow gear and just the reverse in top gear, but it was a job and a half changing the gear wheels. The wheel that was not in use was carried on the footboard and the big one weighed at least a hundredweight. Getting the gear onto the crankshaft was not easy either, as the footboard was not wide enough. You were stood there holding the wheel almost at arms length to reach the end of the shaft. Also, the wheel had to slide over four keys in the shaft, but these were loose and would fall out onto the road, if a piece of string had not been tied tightly around them, holding them in place until the wheel was started over them. I had told my mate to stand by the engine to direct the traffic, while I struggled with the gear wheels, but he was to be sure not to stand underneath the crankshaft. (He was a bit dim and had to be told things over and over again, even then he frequently didn't always do what he was told.) I had the wheel onto the end of the shaft by about an inch, easing it round to line up with the keys, but somehow I lost my grip and knew that the wheel was going to drop. As it went, I yelled out "Look out", but this clown was stood directly underneath me and the wheel dropped edgeways onto the road, landing between his feet without touching him. As we picked it up, I could see that it had gone the full depth of its teeth into the tarmac of the A4 and that was surely the closest he will ever get without losing a few toes. If you have never tried lifting one of those wheels back onto the footboard, don't, unless you are a champion weight-lifter.

We had a whale of a time on this job for a few weeks and removed things of all sorts, shapes and sizes, as everything that came in the way was to be cleared. There were hedges of many kinds, some iron railings, wooden fences and dozens of the big advertising boards, so there was no shortage of firewood. There were also several old houses, some of which were very old, being made of wattle and mud, their ceilings were less than six feet high. They must have been a couple of hundred years old, but had been lived in until a few weeks before we arrived. Some of the hedges were almost new and the shrubs were of various colours, all of these were pulled up by hand very carefully, and tied in bundles as the passers-by were glad to give us a few coppers for them. Once again, our tea, sugar and milk fund was kept topped up. The old houses were no problem, our rope was pulled round behind them and back out to be chained to the nearest tree, a few puffs with *Shamrock* and the rope would slice straight through the house and down it would come in a big cloud of dust. Some of the big trees gave us some serious problems. First they had to be grubbed out by hand, then some of the big roots were chopped off and then finally, using our big snatch block we could finish them off.

We worked our way up the road towards London, Bert was following up on the opposite side a few hundred yards behind us so, for a few weeks, the visibility on that stretch of the A4 was often down to a few yards, as there were huge fires burning on both sides from daylight until dark. There was rubbish of all sorts behind some of these old houses, so we would have a good browse through it before clearing any of it away. One day I had a good find. Stood on an old bench outside the back door of one of these old shacks, was a little single cylinder vertical steam engine. It was a Savage roundabout organ engine and had been stood outside for many years. The steel parts were pitted deep with rust, but the bulk of it was brass and so still in good shape. I pulled it to pieces and took it home, intending to have a go at rebuilding it if ever the chance came that I could find the time. All the bits and pieces were put in a strong wooden box, where they sat waiting for the day when I would make a start on it, but that day never came. Eventually, it was thrown out for scrap and many times since I have thought what a fool I was to get rid of it. Today, there must be many who would give their right arm for one of these precious little engines.

Our job here was almost finished, so we were tying up all the loose ends and doing the final tidying up, but there was one more tricky problem facing us. At Cranford there was a public house called 'The Berkely Arms' and (like several of these old pubs on that stretch of the road) it was hundreds of years old and almost on the road. A new 'Berkely Arms' had been built further back from the road and the old one demolished, but close to where this old pub had stood, there was a massive elm tree which had been sawn down. We had to remove the stump, so a gang was set on grubbing round it and cut the main roots so that we could pull it out. By the time they had got down to the roots, there were piles of earth all around it and there sat this huge tree stump, it must have been at least fifteen feet across. The roots had spread over a big area during the years, but they had not gone down very deep. Our big steel cables were put round it, then the big snatch block was hooked up and it looked as if we would not have too much trouble. I could shake it, but there was still a big root underneath it and this would have to be broken before it would give way. Bert came down to us with *Thistle* and the two engines hanging on to it did the trick. It was rolled over and turned upside down so that as much earth as possible could be removed, ready for us to cart it away, there being no way we could burn something like this.

Between Wards and Pooley Green Road was a big lake, where thousands of yards of gravel had been dredged out and this was now being filled in. The giant stump was to be loaded onto a truck, carted back and dumped in 'Froggy Pond', as it was called. We set off with *Shamrock* to our yard to pick up the hauling truck that we had used with the Foster tractor for shingle carting, the sides and tailboard were taken off and left behind. We made our way back through Staines and Stanwell, arriving back at Cranford that same evening and on weighing up how this huge tree stump was going to be loaded, I knew it was going to be no picnic. Next morning, we pulled the truck alongside the stump, placed the skids (that we had brought with us) into place, the rope was pulled over the truck onto the stump and then the fun started. We were using all the road, so the traffic (although nothing like it is today) soon built up. Some of the drivers were interested in what was going on, but others were getting a bit uptight as they had journeys to do. That day, we set our truck into position and tried to get it loaded at least a dozen times, each time we would get the stump almost onto the truck, then the whole lot would slide across the road into the engine. Each time I then had to shunt *Shamrock* back into the yard of the new 'Berkely Arms' and yank it back into position to have another go. A whole day was spent on this and we had got just about nowhere. The whole problem was that we were geared miles to high for this sort of work. With these old engines, with a drum full of rope, it worked out that one turn of the crankshaft pulled well over a yard of rope. We had found out that when you have a tree stump

179

weighing about three tons, being loaded onto a truck of less than half that weight, using a single cylinder engine, it's no picnic.

I sat in the living van that evening trying to think of some way to tackle this job. I was not going to be beaten by something like this. A big snatch block would have helped, but we just had not got the room to use it, also each time we had tried that day, we had held up everything for about half an hour, so by now the cops were getting a bit niggardly. I sat there that evening, racking my brains on how to solve our problem and then something crossed my mind. As a kid at Basildon, I had seen one horse, loading beech trees as heavy as our tree stump onto a timber wagon for *Big Ben* (that beautiful old Fowler) to take away to High Wycombe. I figured that if we used the same idea we might make it, the only difference being that a tree will roll up the skids, whereas our stump would have to slide, but by this method it would be geared down by half and our truck would be held from sliding into us. We fixed our heavy wire slings onto the springs of the truck, then under the stump and back over the top of it, then to be coupled to *Shamrock's* rope and it worked like a dream. There was this huge tree stump perched on our truck and when we stood back and had a look from behind our load, it looked like a giant mushroom.

Our load was more than twice the width of the truck and this had to go down the Great West Road and through Staines, there were no hopes of bringing it along the narrower roads through Stanwell as nothing would get by us. The police helped us through Staines and we were soon at 'Froggy Pond', the problem now was how to get it unloaded and pushed over the side into the water, which we were told was over thirty feet deep. There was no way that we could pull it off with the rope, as this pond was about 300 yards across, so it would have to be pushed. There was also another snag in that I could see truck and all going over if we were not careful, so the truck was pulled up as close to the edge of the tip as it was safe to go. *Shamrock* was then run close alongside the truck, with a piece of timber put onto one of the spokes (the same as we had used for shingle tipping), but this time a chain was hooked from the truck to the engine wheel so that, if the load took over and was taking the truck with it, we would have it safely on a lead. The stump was lifted so that it was at a steep angle, but the truck was still fairly level and I could see that there was no sign of our load sliding off this way. There was far too much overhang to get onto the truck to tip it, as we had done while shingle carting. There was one way left to try and it worked. The front wheel of the engine was run up close to the truck so that the smokebox was almost touching the tree stump. We could now get our piece of timber under the side of the truck, the chain from the truck was left with enough slack and hooked to the perch bracket. We soon had the whole lot

180

leaning at a pretty crazy angle and, had we not put our safety chain on, we would have lost the lot. The truck was left on its side with the chain stopping it from rolling over into the pond. Our job was completed and I expect that today, amongst the rubbish that filled 'Froggy Pond', are the remains of that giant tree stump.

It was now time to get the cultivator working again, spring was on us and a whole lot of work had been booked for us to get on with. Bert would be working around the Reading area again and I would be staying around London with the BB set. I think that summer was to me, the most enjoyable one of my life with ploughing engines, as we had such a variety of jobs and did a lot of travelling which I always enjoyed. We worked in several parts of Surrey and Sussex, covered most of the small county of Middlesex (where there were still fields and orchards), parts of Buckinghamshire, plus a fair share in Oxfordshire and Berkshire. We had used just about every implement that Wards owned, the mole drainer was used at two farms in Sussex, the cultivator and harrows had covered thousands of acres but, now that autumn was with us again, the plough was earning its money.

A clover field near Bracknell had received our attention and this time the press was used for the first time in several years, but when this field was finished it looked a real picture. I had spent a lot of time round the plough with a few big spanners and had got it just about spot on. The field had not been touched for several years, so it was good and hard, but as we travelled backwards and forwards from one engine to the other, the mould-boards made a whistling noise. Each furrow was polished and dead straight, there was not a bit of green to be seen and when we had finished it looked as if it had been done with a single plough. We moved from this field to the ICI experimental farm at Warfield, where we spent several days and while there had many comments on our last job. Everyone told us that it was a credit to us, several said that it just did not seem possible that a steam plough could turn out such wonderful work. The soil had been just right, as was the plough and I had two good drivers, who kept their engines pulling at a even speed all the time. This makes all the difference between a good job and a bad one.

We finished the season at a big market garden near Slough and from here Frank Steele took his engine, the cultivator, harrows and water cart back to Egham. Meanwhile Jim Day and I made our way up the A4 towards London. Close to Harlington Corner, there were nine big horse-chestnut trees that should have been removed several months earlier when we cleared both sides of the road for widening the A4. However, some of the Middlesex Council boffins reckoned that they would not be in the way, but they had now found out that they would be too close to the side of the wider road, so it was our job to pull them out and clear them away. We had the living van and the plough with us, as we needed the van to sleep in, although the plough would not be needed. We had to take the plough with us, as there are only two places that this can be hooked onto for travelling, these being the coupling on the top of the left-hand side of the engine tender and high up on the left-hand side of the living van. There was another problem, nothing other than the press can be pulled behind the plough. Additionally, you must also remove the last mould-board on the end of the plough nearest the coupling, otherwise, on a short right-hand corner, this will foul either the back of the van or tender of the engine, whichever it is coupled to. The plough is a wonderful implement, but not one of the easiest to travel with.

We pulled off on the right-hand side of the road a couple of hundred yards from where the trees were standing (there was now plenty of room on either side of the road). I figured that we could not pull from too close to the trees because, as our slings had to be fitted high up on the trees, this would be a bit hard on the coiling gear as it would be lifting hard on the 'monkey head'. Also, after you have pulled a few big trees like this and your engine has pulled itself sideways a few yards, it is leaning towards its work, putting even more load on the coiling lever.

Next morning, a ladder and our big snatch block were delivered to us along with all the big steel slings that we had found so useful for tree pulling. All of these slings would be needed to reach from high up in these big horse-chestnut trees down to the ground, so that the snatch block could be coupled to them. Jim Day was a middle-aged man, but although he had spent a lot of time with ploughing engines, he had never had a go at tree pulling, so he was not too keen to have a go at these giant trees. He said to me, "If you don't mind, as you have had experience at this game, I will leave these for you to deal with". There I was, left to drive the engine and how could I expect him to climb the trees with a length of cord, then haul up these big wire slings and fix them round the trees, while I was less than half his age. I did not mind this too much, it was a challenge and that was what I liked. I loved to get stuck into something out of the ordinary and we certainly had that here; a row of big trees and each one of them was well over two feet in diameter at the butt. This was hardly the job for ploughing engines, especially a compound as they are a bit reluctant to run back when the pressure is shut off, whereas the single-cylinder engine will rock backwards and forwards, getting a tree up to a sway and this makes all the difference.

I climbed a long way up the first tree with the cord, hauled up the sling, fastened it round the tree then pulled the remaining slings up one by one and coupled them together as I made my way back down. The snatch block was then coupled to them and we were ready to pull out some rope from the engine, run it around the pulley of our giant snatch block and back to the engine. With *Shamrock* and *Thistle*, we could fix the ropes to some big shackles that fitted onto the end of the rear axle by using a longer pin, after removing the wheel cap but, with the compounds, we had nothing like this. I found that the best way out of this was to put the big sling chain round the wheel rim, then run the engine backwards onto it, so that it was pressed into the ground. With either of the engines, there was always the problem of getting the two lengths of rope crossed when there was enough pressure on the rope to lift the snatch block off the ground. The block would then spin round, twisting up the two ropes and the more rope you had out the more it would twist up.

We were now ready to have a go and by this time my mate was round the other side of the engine out of harm's way. He reckoned he had seen chain links and shackles flying before whilst he had been bogged down and was being helped out by the other engine, so he was not going to be in the line of fire this time. I had used the BB1 before on some pretty tough trees and knew that there was only one way to use them at this job. This was a bit rough on everything, but was the only way you were likely to get any success. I carefully pulled the rope tight, making sure that the rope was safely in the pulley, then pulled the regulator wide open and, as the snatch block went hurtling towards the sky, I leant forward and pushed the 'tickling stick', as we used to call it, holding it there. This way, by the time everything is under full load, you have built up some revs on the crankshaft so, if the tree does not give, your engine will go sideways towards it and so find its footings and next time, something usually goes, either the tree will give or something breaks.

The second time, as the rope went tight and the crankshaft stopped turning, the perch bracket lifted up out of its socket on the front axle and there it stayed. I still had the regulator wide open and, as I looked at the top of the tree, I could see the branches trembling. We could hear the roots cracking then, as the front end of the engine dropped back into its working position and I knew that the tree was on its way down. That is how the big trees were pulled to the ground. With all the trees down, we had to clear all the tops and cut the trunks into manageable lengths, so a few casual workers were given the job. There were still all the stumps to be removed, as we had pulled the trees down, but had not lifted out the stumps. When all the tops had been cleared, I ran the engine onto the A4 to pull the stumps sideways, thereby twisting them and breaking the remaining roots, at the same time this lifted them with no problem.

Our tackle was taken to Egham to be parked away for the winter, but we soon learned that we would be going back to the same area in the new year, as there were some more orchards around Hayes and Uxbridge to be removed. It would be my job when the time came but, until then, I would be taking out a roller as there were several jobs on the go and drivers were in short supply. On the side of the A4 at Taplow in Buckinghamshire (now in Berkshire), there was a big nursery and garden centre, owned by Woods and a ten-ton Aveling & Porter roller of Wards had been working there repairing the roads and car park. The driver had left, so this old Aveling had been stood there for a few weeks and I was to take it to Wickham Street in Welling, Kent. This was a job that was to last to well past Christmas.

Taplow to Welling is a long way and I had to get from one side of London to the other, a journey I would not like to take on in this day and age with a steam roller, what a shambles it would be. My boss had worked out the route that I should take and if we kept strictly to this, they would know where to find us if we ran into any trouble. We were dished out with a Metropolitan Water Board hydrant key, stand pipe and permit, so, for once, we would be in the clear if any Water Board official should roll up while we were filling the tank. Next morning, we left Taplow at the crack of dawn. Our route was through Slough onto the A4 for Colnbrook, across country to Staines, take the Kingston road through Sunbury and Hampton then left just before Kingston, up the hill to Wimbledon Common and Roehampton.

We pushed on all that morning, not stopping for a real meal at mid-day as the days were short and every minute was precious, but as I looked back at my mate sitting in the living van, I could see he was enjoying his sandwiches. I had always made it a rule when a long journey was in front of me, to have a good breakfast then keep moving all day. You don't have to go like a maniac. Just keep moving. This way you get there faster than someone who goes like the hammers of hell for a while, then stops for just a pint or a meal and then tries to make up that time he has been stood still. It just does not work that way.

We had a trouble free journey to Hampton, but this is where time would be lost as, in those days there were tram lines as far as I can remember from Kempton Park to Kingston. The problem with the trams was that they were going in the same direction as us so they could not get by. The drill was to let a couple of trams catch up with us, then look for a break in the oncoming traffic and dive across on to the right-hand side of the road to let them go by. We were climbing the hill that would bring us to Wimbledon Common and I was keeping close to the side of the road but, as the left side rear wheel passed over a drain, we almost came to a halt. I could see that the left side wheel was slipping, but not the right side one. This could only be because the drive pin, in the right-hand wheel, had either broken or had come out and we had lost it (there was no differential gear on these old Avelings). I leant out over the wheel and there it was, the pin was sticking out from the wheel by more than half its length. I reckon the guy that used it at Taplow, had taken the pin out to get round the short corners in the garden centre and had put it back in, but forgot to replace the split cotter.

Most of the old Aveling rollers were fitted with a three-tine Morrison scarifier that was designed to work when going either backwards or forwards, but anyone who has used these engines for scarifying, will tell you that the reverse side of it is just about useless. The engine that I was on my way to Welling with was one of the few that had not been fitted with a Morrison scarifier, instead it had a Bomford & Evershed two-tine job. This type had only one bar from the scarifier to the end of the rear axle and this was just a round bar about $1^{1}/_{2}$in. in diameter, whereas the Morrison had two lengths of heavy angle, one at the bottom and one at the top. The road wheel pin had come out under this bar, which had been snapped off close to the bearing on the axle. This must have been done while we were shaking along over the cobble stones on the Sunbury to Kingston road. The pin had been slightly bent, but there was so much wear in the wheel that the pin still went through without too much trouble and a few clouts with the sledge hammer drove it right home. Our worst job was getting the wheel to slip again to line up the pin holes with the axle.

By the time we had reached Wandsworth, the daylight was beginning to fade, so we had to find somewhere to pull in for the night. This was not very easy as Wandsworth was then a very busy place, but perhaps, if we could find a cop, he might be able to tell us where there was a back street where we could park for the night. As usual when you want the police you can never find them, but just up the road was a road sweeper and I thought that he might know of somewhere. He said, "Almost a quarter of a mile along the road on your left you will find Wondle Wharf and there is William Hampton's yard. They have a fleet of steam wagons, so I am sure that they will let you pull in for the night". They did and proved to be very helpful. As we pulled into their yard, the night shift was coming in (these were the three men that took over the wagons as they came in from their day's trip.) They cleaned out the firebox and smokebox of each one, getting them ready for the next morning, so that the drivers and mates could just jump aboard in the morning and be on their way.

I had not had a meal all day and was now ready for a good feed. Just outside the Wharf, in the main street, was a shop that sold hot faggots and peas so, while my mate was getting the kettle boiled for a cup of tea, I strolled out to get a double helping for myself and a single for him (he had

185

been eating during the day). After tea, I walked out into the wharf to have a chat with the night shift gang and all that evening the Overtype Foden wagons and trailers were rolling in. I don't think that I have ever seen such a line up of Foden wagons, either before or since, as there were at Wondle Wharf that night. There must have been at least a couple of dozen of them and two almost new Undertypes which I suppose were 'Speed 6s'. As I chatted with the chaps that were giving each engine a clean down and clinker out, one of them said "What time do you want to leave in the morning? I will take off your damper and poke up the fire so that you can have an extra hour in bed if you like". I jumped at this, as I was just about dog tired. I had never had it so good.

We were on the road in good time next morning. Our engine was steamed up for us, the tank filled, so all that we had to do was oil round and fill the coal bunker. We were on our way through Clapham in the thick of the morning rush and, as I write this, I wonder what it would be like to do that same journey today with a steam roller. We steamed on through Brixton and Lewisham, picking our way through in the stream of traffic and pushing out as little smoke as possible. In most of the towns in those days, the police were red hot on this but, if you were not held up too much and could push on at a fair speed, the smoke was blasted high into the sky and did not show up so much. It was when you were brought to a halt, just after you had fired up, that trouble began, especially if it was a dull day. We were through Eltham by early afternoon, so Welling was only a short distance away. We had travelled through some very busy parts of London but we would be at our destination in good time and, therefore, able to take it quiet that evening. I stopped to pick up water as we pulled into Welling and, as we were filling up, a postman came along, so I thought he is the chap that will be able to tell us where we find Wickham Street. He pointed down the road to a hut with a few piles of paving slabs stood in the middle of a crossroads surrounded by ropes with lamps hung round it, "That is the end of Wickham Street" he said. We were within a few hundred yards of it and this would be my stand for the duration of this job.

On reaching this crossroads, we were met by the foreman of the job. He was an Irishman and turned out to be one of the best paddies that I have ever worked with as he really looked after me all the time I was on that job. After I had eaten a meal I went out to give the old Aveling a wipe down and soon learned that the whole of this street was to be ripped up and relaid. There would be a few weeks of scarifying to be done but, as I was here with a broken scarifier, I would have to work fast to get something done about it. I pulled the broken bar of the scarifier from the end of the axle and fixed the sling chain onto the bottom of the scarifier then over the axle, where I had taken the broken bar from and back to the top of the scarifier. A bolt was put through the two parts of the chain, just behind the axle, pulling them together and so tightening them up but, with a good supply of oil where the axle was turning inside the chain, it worked quite well.

I had three days ripping up the tarmac, which was thick and hard and had therefore worn out or bent most of the scarifier tines, so I would have to find the nearest blacksmith to get them drawn out and straightened. This was not the only problem, as next morning after about an hour's work, there was a rather expensive noise coming from the gearing. A couple of teeth had broken from the third motion shaft pinion and that was the end of scarifying for that day. I managed to coax the old girl back onto the stand, then I got in touch with the office at Egham. Next morning Bill Bantick would be there with some jacks, so that the wheels could be removed and the broken pinion sorted out. I spent the rest of the day removing the gearcase bolts and getting off as much as possible of the bits that would have to be removed.

The pinion, without doubt, had not been touched from new and was therefore well worn out. As the keys had no heads to them, there was no way that we could get behind them to drive them out, so the gears on the other end of the shaft were taken off. The shaft, complete with broken pinion, was loaded into the old Ford van and we were on our way to Rochester to get things sorted out by having a new pinion fitted. We pulled in through the main gateway of the Aveling works and help was soon with us. As we made our way up and down between the hundreds of gear wheels that laid in rows in that yard, things looked a bit grim as there was nothing exactly the same as we wanted and our luck appeared to be out. We made our way across to one of the big workshops, where there was another heap of gears of all shapes and sizes and, sure enough, there was the pinion that we had been looking for, but it had not been machined. It was now late afternoon and we would not be fixed up that day, so back up the Rochester Way we went to Welling and would go back again the next day. Bill arrived early the next morning and, after a cup of tea, we were soon heading towards Rochester again.

When we left Avelings the previous afternoon, they had assured us that all that was possible would be done and they had stuck to their word. I would think that someone had worked most of the night on it. The pinion had been bored out to fit the shaft, the keyways had been cut and it was pressed onto the shaft, complete with new keys. It was ready for us to push it back through the bearings then fit the other wheels and it was still only about nine o'clock. We were back in Welling before mid-day and the old girl was mobile again before dark, so I could go into action again the next day.

Bill would be returning again, in the near future, with a new scarifier bar and a new split cotter for the roadwheel pin. This was still being held in position by a thin strip of hardwood that I had sorted out from the coal locker of the van a few days before, away back near Wimbledon Common.

The Irish ganger of this job was in digs somewhere close by, so, on his way to work each morning, he would call at a shop to buy some bacon, pork chops or sometimes steak. There was always plenty for the two of us and it was always cooked and eaten in my living van. All the time that I was there, I never missed a day without a good slap-up meal, but he got quite annoyed if I offered to pay my share. I have always said that good 'paddies' are hard to find but, when you do find one, he is really good. I worked on this job until about a week before Christmas, each weekend I travelled home on my motorbike, finding my way across London by several different routes. I was looking forward to the return trip with the old Aveling roller once the job was completed, but it did not work out that way. There was an urgent job with one of the ploughers and it was my luck to have to pass this rolling job onto another driver, who would be taking over on the Monday whilst I was to report to Egham.

I had finished all the scarifying and all the old tarmac had been cleared away and this, of course, left all the drains at least three or four inches above the road surface. Unfortunately, it started to rain, continuing for two days and nights. It poured non-stop and Wickham Street became more like a river than a road, the only answer was to knock a hole in the brickwork of each drain at the foundation level. By Friday evening, after this modification was completed for the whole length of the street, the road could be seen again, but there were a lot of loose granite stones all over the place. The ganger said "I will get you to steam up and run up and down a few times and make it safe for the weekend before you go home tomorrow". I put a fire in the roller that evening ready to be out early in the morning, hopefully getting this job done and make my way home a bit earlier than usual.

The next morning, I was ready to start at seven and as soon as the workers arrived, I was on my way up and down Wickham Street for the last few trips. I went up one side, just missing the drains, then back about half the width of the engine towards the middle of the road. The process was repeated on the other side and I planned to do the same up and down the middle of the road. The ganger reckoned that this would be OK until the Monday morning when the new tarmac would start coming in. I made a trip up the middle to the far end and was on my way back for the last time when, within about a hundred yards of the stand where the old girl would be put to rest for the weekend, I looked back to see that the middle of the road was falling in behind me in many places. The water had soaked into the foundations of the road where, many years before, a sewer had been put right up the middle of the road and had not been properly filled in. The timber shuttering in many places had never been taken out, so that the road had dropped by a depth of four or five feet. Luckily, I was straddling the trench, but Wickham Street was promptly closed for the weekend and I have never set eyes on there since.

I made my way to Egham on the Monday morning and was told to light up one of the ploughers as it was to go to Lobjoit's market garden at Slough. There were several acres of greenhouses whose soil was to be steam sterilized, so *Shamrock* was steamed up and this was to be my job for a few weeks. We hooked up the living van and were off to Slough, where our job was beside the A4, just on the London side of the town. Bill Bantick had drilled and tapped a thread in the filler plug, which was an oval plate held down with two $5/8$in. studs onto the base of the cylinder and had fitted a $3/4$in. stop-cock. The fitter at the market garden would connect the pipes to this, so all that I would be doing was to keep steam up. I placed the engine so that the cylinder was in line with the door of the first greenhouse to get the treatment, then a length of $3/4$in. pipe was fixed to the stop-cock and packed up with pieces of heavy timber to which it was clamped, so that there would be no strain on the brass stop-cock. From here, the lengths of pipe would be screwed up as we worked our way towards the far end of each of the greenhouses. The sterilizing part of the job was a tubular frame, made up similar to the harrows that horses used to pull about the fields, with each spike about a foot long and drilled from top to bottom with $1/8$in. diameter holes. These spikes were pushed full depth into the ground, then the frame was covered up with thick sacks and the steam turned on for half an hour in each place. At the end of that time the soil was well and truly cooked, as were every grub or other pest that was in the soil.

At the entrance to the market garden was a small cafe which was used by a lot of truckers, also the Green Line buses turned and changed shifts here, so it was always full of bus drivers and conductors. It was only about two minutes walk from our job, so we spent a lot of time here. We would shift the tubular steam frame, turn on the steam, then walk down to the cafe for half an hour, playing the bus drivers at darts for cups of tea. I was just about useless at darts, but the fitter, George Cooper, was that year's runner-up in the *News of the World* darts contest and I think that during all the time that I was there, I bought about three cups of tea. We just could not seem to lose.

I travelled home on my motorbike every night, loaded up with something or other from the market garden. This was very useful, as we had always had a good fertile garden at each of the three houses that we had lived in on the Basildon Estate, but we had moved to Mortimer where the garden

189

was small and just a bed of gravel, making it hard to grow anything. After a few days, *Shamrock* began to get a bit slow on steaming so, as there was no blower on these old engines, I had to give her a sharp run about every hour to draw up the fire and this became the first time that I had ever used the tube brush on the old girl. The tube rod and brush had always hung under the footboard but, on normal work, they were never needed as the blast from the exhaust pipe would always take care of the tube sweeping.

This job was completed after a few weeks when I moved back up the A4 and across to Uxbridge, where there was a big cherry orchard to be cleared and this is where I spent almost the rest of the winter. There was one more small tree pulling job for me before going out again with the BB set in the spring and this was off the Great West Road. A short distance from the London end of this road, on the left-hand side as you make your way towards the City, is the Firestone tyre factory and our job was directly behind it. There were about eight acres of mixed fruit trees, which were to come out and, in their place, the McFarlane Lang biscuit factory was to be built. This orchard was cleared fairly quickly and *Shamrock* was taken back to Egham. The next day my brother came home with *Thistle*, he had been working at Feltham and on a big job near Hounslow. The engines were stood side by side in the yard and that is where they remained until the following winter.

Steam cultivating around London was beginning to fade out, as there were bigger and better tractors getting around. These two old singles had taken a pasting which was beginning to show on them, many parts were now badly worn and both engines were almost past doing a good ploughing or cultivating job. The plough had been taken to the K7 set, to replace the one that had turned over and twisted its main frame. The cultivator had taken some stick while ripping out the tree roots that had been broken off, but remained unseen in the ground.

The BB1s were cleaned up and prepared for the spring rush. We were soon on our way back to the Henley area, where we spent several weeks on both sides of the Thames and then made our way back into Surrey to a few jobs. It was getting easy to see that steam ploughing, as I had known it, was on its way out. Nearly all the jobs that we were doing now, were rough ones and were a bit beyond the tractors' ability. We were with the ploughers for a week or two, then away on a steam roller for a while, then back to the ploughers again. It got so that we didn't quite know where we were going to finish up next, so I was beginning to get a bit unsettled. Whenever Bert and I reached home at a weekend, we would sit down for a meal and a chat about the week's happenings. During these times, we had both gradually come to the conclusion that we had seen our best times with ploughing tackle, all that we were doing was travelling a long way to do a small and often rough job.

I had taken over several different rollers and had travelled around London quite a bit. One Monday morning, I went back to Egham and was doing some jobs on *Shamrock*. About ten o'clock that morning, Bill Bantick came to me and said "I want you to go to Slough. There is a roller working for Halbrow & Jones and the driver has not turned up today. You will find the engine at Stamford Hill and, when you get to Slough, any one will tell you where this is". It was November and the fog was thick. It had taken me twice as long to get from home to the yard that morning and, as I made my way to Slough, I could see that it was getting thicker. When I pulled into Slough, I asked several people if they could put me right for Stamford Hill, but not one of them had ever heard of it, so I made my way to Halbrow & Jones yard which was on the Slough Trading Estate.

I walked into the office and asked if they could tell me where I would find the Ward's roller that was working for them at Stamford Hill. The answer was "It is somewhere up in the middle of London" and, sure enough, it was at Hamerst Park Estate, Stamford Hill in North London. I made my way back up the A4 to the little cafe, where I had spent so much time while steaming out the greenhouses, ordered up a cup of tea and something to eat before I started my journey which I knew was not going to be very pleasant.

The farther I went into London, the thicker the fog seemed to get so, by the time I had found the place, the visibility was down to just a few yards. The fog was yellow and, although I was within a few feet of the roller, I still could not see her. Just in front of me was what looked like a lantern of some sort stood by the kerb, but it was the glow from the ashpan of the ten-ton Wallis roller that I was to take over. The driver had turned up and had steamed up, but no tarmac had arrived, so I was soon on my way back towards home, which I reached somewhere around ten o'clock that evening. Although I had done no work that day, my first job was to have a good wash, I was blacker than any chimney sweep could ever be (as were all my clothes) and I reckon this is what they used to call a London 'pea-souper'.

I spent the rest of the week working in the yard at Egham, then on the following Monday, I was told that the driver of the ten-ton Wallis roller at Stamford Hill had packed up and left. I was to go and finish the job, then bring the roller home, so another few weeks were spent in London. By the time that this job was finished, I had found a route through the back streets, so cutting out most of the busy parts. When the time came, the old Wallis was brought across London with very little trouble. By taking the back streets it was further, but usually quicker, as I had found out when travelling home weekends on my motorbike.

191

The yard at Thorpe Lea was getting full of rollers, as most of the Councils were cutting their spending and the big slump was beginning to be felt almost everywhere. There were still a few more rollers to come home and one of these was a big Clayton & Shuttleworth, a fifteen-tonner, that had been standing on the outskirts of Guildford for a few weeks after finishing a job there. It was my job to bring this old single home, so Bert Breakspear and myself went off overnight to get her steamed up. We were to be away early in the morning, thereby getting through Guildford before the early morning rush started. We were given the route that we should take and this brought us down a fairly steep hill into the town (in those days some of the streets in Guildford were cobble stones and this hill was one of them). I knew what a stone surface was like with iron wheels (I had not forgotten our trip down Buckhold Hill with *Little Mary* with a set of threshing tackle behind her).

It was hardly daylight when we reached the top of the hill. I stopped, put the little wheel in and started off very slowly. I thought that, although she was a big heavy engine, with just the living van and water cart behind us we should make it with no problems. However, there was one little snag, it was dustbin day and these were all placed down the gutter at the side of the road. We had to keep out in the road about a yard to miss them, but there was a sharp camber on the road and if the wheels should start to slide we would go into the side. We were about halfway down the hill, picking up a bit too much speed (as I had checked her but very little) and as I eased the lever back I could see that we were going to be in trouble. The lever was pushed forward again, but we were now partly rolling, partly sliding, all the time getting closer and closer to the kerb so, by the time we reached the bottom of the hill, we had the biggest heap of battered dustbins you have ever seen in your life and most of them were now empty.

My brother and I were now spending a lot of time on rollers, but we were looking forward to the time when the ploughers would be going out again, either cultivating or tree pulling. We were halfway through the winter and no tree pulling had come up. We had (over the last few years) really thinned them out around London, so it looked as if there would be but very little of this for us this winter. I went off to Horsham, away down in Sussex, with a ten-ton Wallis 'Advance' roller and was on this job for several weeks. A sewer had been put in around the town and we had to repair all the trenches.

After this job was completed, I was making my way back to Egham, just coming into Guildford after having stopped to fire up, so that I would have a good bright fire to come through the town. Some guy, with a big car, pulled up and came running across saying "Where are you going with this lot?", so I told him that I was on my way to Egham. He said "Stay where you are for a minute while I go across to the phone box" (which was just across the road) but, as he dashed off to phone, I thought who is he to tell me what to do and was just about to pull away when he came out of the box, beckoning me across. He had rung up Sid Ward who now wanted to have a word with me. It turned out that this guy was Mr. Streeter, the boss of a big contracting firm from Godalming. They had a big job at Cranleigh College and wanted an asphalt roller, so I was to turn round and go back over the same ground that I had just travelled. I had come through Cranleigh earlier that morning and was now going back almost to Horsham again, so I was not very happy.

When this job was finished and the Wallis had been taken back to Egham, I was to go out on another job that none of us had ever tackled before. There was a length of 2in. water main to go across some of the fields at Ottershaw Park. This was the same place that a couple of years previously I had been bogged in for over a week with one of the BB engines. Our mole drainer had been quickly converted, so that a coupling could be fixed to the rear end of the mole, with an adaptor to screw onto the 2in. galvanized pipe. Off we went with the right-hand BB, living van and drainer, on our way to something new. All that I was hoping, was that I would not have to get too far off the road on this job, as it was winter time and that sand would be a bit treacherous. There was no way that I would attempt to go into the same field that I had spent over a week slogging away with screw-jacks and timber a few years ago.

We reached Ottershaw and were soon sizing up the job in hand. I was greatly relieved to find that this pipe was to be put in alongside the roadway that ran from the farm to the top of the hill, a distance of about five hundred yards, but it was to be put in as deep as possible. The land was sand and so should give us very little trouble, but this was certainly not the kind of soil that you normally get stuck into with a mole drainer. I made my way to the top of the hill with my engine and backed her into position. She was still on a hard standing, as there was a fair sized patch of hardcore that had been laid at the end of the road for the lorries to turn round on when loading up the market garden produce. One of the farm tractors was brought up to pull the rope down the hill to the drainer. A trench had been dug about the length of two of the pipes, which had been laid in a heap alongside the farm road. The idea of this was so that the pipes could be screwed together and laid into the trench, therefore, stopping the pipes from being bent too much and also reducing the strain on the screwed joints.

The first two pipes were screwed together and coupled to the mole, which had been set at full depth and dropped into the trench. One of the farm workers was to stand by with a big white flag that I could see plainly from the top of the hill and so give me the signal when the pipe had been pulled far enough. Off we went, the first two pipes were pulled in with very little trouble and if the soil was the same all the way to the top of the hill, it would be a piece of cake. We spent the first day with no problems, but I could tell that the farther we went the harder the pulling became. Now, was the soil getting tougher as we worked our way up the hill, or was it the weight of the pipes being dragged through the sand? It was only common sense that a lot of the sand would be falling into the hole that our mole was making and so a couple of hundred yards of 2in. pipe being pulled through a hole that was falling in all the way would take some shifting. How were the threads of the pipe going to stand up to this?

We soldiered on steadily, but by the time our drainer was halfway up the hill we were struggling to get a start each time and it was plain to see that we were not going to get much further. The big wheel from the drainer was back at Egham on the big tree pulling snatch block, so a double rope was out of the question, or should we send back for it. I was not too happy about this, as I was almost certain that the pipes would not stand up to that sort of treatment. The farm manager was talking of doing the rest by hand, but digging a trench about three feet deep in this sort of soil would not be easy and it would take a long time. The burning question was, what was the best way out? We parked up that afternoon at about 4.30pm. It was dark and a thick fog had come down. I was in the van on my own, I had a nice fire going so it was quite warm and I sat there after tea thinking about the best way out of our problem. I just did not like the idea of giving it best, there must be a way out. If I could get the farm manager in the morning and have a chat with him, there was still a way out so that we could still pull in the rest of the pipes. If a hole was dug under the drainer, we could find the mole, uncouple the pipe from it, pull the drainer out of the ground and up to the engine, then start pulling the pipes in from the top to meet up with the pipes that were all ready in. The manager could see my point, but wondered how the pipes would be joined up in the middle. When I explained to him that we could pull the pipes almost together, then connect them up using a short length of pipe with a couple of unions, he agreed.

A tractor and trailer were used to take the remaining pipes to the top of the hill, while I made my way back to the bottom of the hill with the engine. I could stand on the farm road and pull the pipes in down the hill with no problems. We pulled the drainer to within a few feet of the pipes that were already in, the end having been marked with a pole so that the drainer could be steered directly in line to it. There was a big hole here that had been dug to disconnect the drainer from the original pipes, therefore, the mole could be seen and (with a bit of care) we could pull the mole almost to the end of

194

the other pipe. This would leave about three or four feet for the short pipe to be placed in and the unions screwed up. The mole had now to be lifted out of the ground by hand as it normally lifts itself as soon as you start to pull it back in the opposite direction, but there was no way that this could this be done with about 250 yards of 2in. pipe attached to it. The sand around it was dug out, the pipe disconnected and the mole and blade man-handled into its position for travelling on the road. While this was going on, I was having a chat with the manager and I said to him "Why not connect up the pipes with a T-piece and have a standpipe halfway up the fields". He said "What a good idea, this pipe is for irrigation purposes and it would be nice to have a standpipe half way", and this is how it finished up. The BB was taken back to Egham and the mole drainer parked away in the corner of the yard.

My next move was to another big orchard, this time at the side of the Cambridge road about five miles from Enfield. They were not very big trees, but there was a large area that stretched about a third of a mile along the side of this busy road, the trees being removed to make way for several factories and sports grounds. We set off early on this trip, as the days were still short and from Egham to Enfield is a long way over quite busy roads for most of the way. I had travelled this same journey twice before, so I knew that we would not have time to let the grass grow under our wheels and that there would be no time to stop for a meal. We left Egham before it was hardly daylight and were through Staines before many people had surfaced, away up the full length of the Great West Road, across Ealing and Wembley, along the North Circular Road as far as Finchley, where we turned off for Southgate and Enfield. I had kept that crankshaft spinning good and fast for the whole of the day, our only stops being to pick up water (from the hydrants this time) and to get a few bags of coal from the van locker, plus a few top ups with oil around the fast moving parts. We pulled into our job just before dark, but I think that if anyone would care to take on that same journey today with a BB1, van and water cart you would need at least two days and would certainly get your fair share of black looks from the thousands of motorists who use this road, even now the M25 is fully open.

The tree pulling part of this job took us into the spring, several gangs of casual labour were taken on to cut up the trees and do the burning. There were two engines and saw benches going full chat every day. The building contractors were on the scene getting out the footings for the new factories long before the last apple tree was uprooted and things started to move fast. I was told to park the plougher up in the corner of this patch of land, then go back to Egham to get the other engine ready to bring the cultivator and harrows back to this job at Enfield. There was quite a bit of this land to be prepared as sports grounds for the factories, a school children's playing area plus another piece of rough ground at the rear of the orchard that we had cleared, which was as full of rubbish as anything I had ever seen.

We had covered the main part of our journey with no problems and pushed on through Southgate at a good speed, I suppose far too quick for going through a town, but we still had a few miles to go and the daylight was running out. I had a good steersman, whom I could trust, and was putting a few shovels of coal down the hole, but as I turned round to fill the shovel again, I could see that the cultivator and harrows were still coming behind us, but travelling crab fashion. The road had been made up with fresh tarmac over the years but the tram lines had never been lifted, so our narrow iron wheels were following them the same as the trams were doing. We pulled out to pass a parked baker's van, but our implements were still coming in a straight line. I pulled the reversing lever back, even before I had shut off the regulator, so we pulled up in a fairly short distance, but not in time. The rear end of the harrows were still coming sideways and they hooked into the baker's van, bringing it with us. By the time that we had sorted this lot out and were on the move again it was getting dusk, so our journey was finished off in the dark.

The following week, a gang of a sorts was made up as most of the ploughing gangs were spread over the south of England on steam rollers. It looked as if there was going to be very little for any of the ploughing engines to do that coming summer. Even Bert, with his K7s, had very little work lined up as poor Albert Wickens had met with an accident and had not been out from home for a few weeks. Albert had been riding his bike along the bridle path that follows the Thames, from Goring to South Stoke (cutting off about a mile from the road journey). While pedalling hard up a slope, his bicycle chain had broken and he fell onto a short post which was the boundary marker for a big Thames side house. He broke a few ribs and poor old Albert died within a few weeks, a sad end for an old timer who had always been so active.

We had started our cultivating and had cleared what I thought was a reasonable amount for the time that we had been at it, but we were having problems with the gooseberry bushes and couch grass (which was just like a doormat). When Sidney Ward turned up, he was not too pleased as he thought that we should have done a lot more than we had. I had already taken some stick from him over the baker's van job at Southgate and this was brought up again, so I said to him "There is only one thing for you to do. Send someone else out to take over this job, I have had enough". He handed me the envelope containing the wage packets for the gang and went storming off.

That weekend at home, we had long chats between us about what was the best thing to do. Should we look for jobs with some other steam plough firms, or perhaps get a steady job with a steam roller firm? It was now clear to see that there would be no more good money to be earned with Ward's ploughing tackle. We were travelling miles and miles just to do a few acres, often taking longer to get to the job than it actually took us to do the cultivating or ploughing. How much longer could this go on? Most of the steam roller firms were in the same boat, having rows of engines lined up just waiting for the day when things would get back to normal and money would be spent on the roads again (in most counties they were now in a pretty sorry state). The big slump was on and thousands were out of work, so we would soldier on where we were and try to stick it out with the ploughers for another summer.

I went back to Enfield early on the Monday morning to spend another week of what was becoming a pretty miserable job. It is no joke when you only went about a hundred yards before your cultivator was lifted off the ground blocked with rubbish which you then had to turn round, often onto one side to release the rubbish, only to do the same again, time after time. By the end of a day, both drivers and the cultivator man were just about fed up, but it was even worse for the man in charge as he was always left to carry the can. The week went by, but our job was far from finished so, during the week, I told the rest of the gang that I was seriously thinking of packing it in and would try to get a steady job on a steam roller, if one could be found. I did not wish to leave steam engines at any price but, for steam ploughing, the end was in sight (at least around the London area). Most of our jobs were hardly worth the journeys that we were doing to get to them, as most of the orchards had now been cleared.

On the Friday afternoon, we were busy splicing one of the ropes. It had been giving a bit of trouble all the week with odd strands coming out, so I decided the best thing was to cut out this offending piece and splice the rope up again. We were just finishing off when Sidney arrived as usual with the wage packets and I could see he was not in a good mood. I could always tell when he was in one of his moods, he would come across the field kicking clods of earth about and that is just what he was doing this time. The wheels were at a standstill and this did not please him at all. He came up to us and started complaining, we had not done enough for him and a few 'high words' were exchanged. I was just telling him 'his fortune', as I had had enough, when he started to walk away. I said "How about the wages then" to which he answered "I don't think you have earned any" and that just about made up my mind. A few more rather uncalled for words were exchanged, then I told him just what he could do with his BB1s and all the implements. He was to take a week's notice from that day as I was finishing on the following Friday.

I was on my motorbike and away from Enfield before mid-day on the Saturday, being home at Mortimer in good time. Bert was already home as he had been working close to home. As we sat drinking a cup of tea, I told him and my parents that I was finishing the following week, so I would be hunting for another job. They all seemed a bit upset and reckoned that I would be hard pushed to find another steam engine job as there were just no jobs about. Our house was not a very happy one for the rest of the weekend as father was now doing nothing and, at his age, had no hopes of starting another job. Time and time again, they begged me to think again as dole money in those days was just about starvation level, I had got two younger brothers who were still at school and they had to be fed. But I had made up my mind. If the worst came to the worst, I would go back to Wallingford and see what the position was there.

We spent the first half of my last week with the cultivator and had cleared the worst of the rubbish. By the Friday, when Sidney arrived, we were getting on fairly well with the harrows so he came into the field with smiles all over his face and straight away said how well we had done in the week since he was last with us. It looked as if he was prepared to stop and chatter for the rest of the day. He then handed over the wages and was still reeling off how well we had done when I asked if he had brought my cards. His answer was "Don't talk silly, of course I haven't". I looked at him and said "You had better get back to Egham and get them sorted out. I shall be leaving here at five o'clock and will call that way to pick them up". His face then changed. He could see I meant what I was saying. He then went on "You don't say why you are leaving. Is it money or what is wrong?". I had already been getting well over the odds for a steam plough foreman and he was prepared to go a bit higher, but I was going to make a move. I had seen enough of his funny ways and to me he seemed to be getting worse. I suppose the worry of the rollers and ploughers standing idle for so long at a time was getting him down, the future looked bleak. I called at the office that evening, collected my cards and had a long chat with him. He almost begged me to think again, but I had seen enough to know that steam ploughing was on its way out. I was thinking of getting married during the next year and there was no way that I could get married while working with ploughing engines, being away from home for a week at a time. This would never have worked.

I reached home and told the family that I had finished for Wards and would be hunting for another job. No one seemed very happy about this, as I might be out of work for weeks and as I had left my job and not been sacked, I could not draw the few shillings dole money. I sat and ate my meal but no one hardly spoke, mother seemed really upset and I could see that she was taking it hard. We were now paying a fair rent for our house at Mortimer and she was really worried about how we would manage if I did not find another job quickly. We were halfway through the evening when she said "There is a letter here for you that has been waiting for most of the week". I opened it and could hardly believe what I was reading. It was a letter from Mr. Ford (the steam roller owner from Wokingham). He had the contract for the whole of North Hampshire, so fourteen rollers were to go out to different parts of the Basingstoke and Winchester divisions of Hampshire to be ready to start on the first of April (or as soon as possible thereafter). Their roads were getting into very bad shape and thousands of pounds had been allocated for repairs and to build new roads in this area. When Mr. Ford had stood us off a few years previously, he had promised that, if anything changed and work got back to normal again, he would get in touch with all of us and he had kept his word.

Next morning, I made my way to Wokingham and was told that I could start on Monday morning. There were just a few weeks to get all these engines ready and out onto the jobs around Basingstoke and Winchester. It now looked as if I had done my last job with ploughing engines but, how would I settle down to a steady job on a steam roller? I knew it was going to be hard after so many years with the engines that I loved so much, as I had now spent almost twenty years with them, about ten of which were before I had even left school. As I look back over the years, I would think that no one in this world could have had a better chance, than I had, to become a super steam plough man. There was hardly a thing that I did not know about these wonderful engines, their implements and how to use them, long before I was old enough to leave school. All of this knowhow was now to go to the wall, a sad thing really, but as they say, "All good things must come to an end some day".

I was at Ford's yard before 6.30am on the Monday (this was the time all their workers started in the morning) and was taken over to the row of engines that were backed up to a row of poplar trees that were growing along the top of the railway cutting, forming the boundary of the Winnersh works. There were rollers of all makes and sizes. They all looked in pretty good condition, but badly in need of a clean up. Most of them had stood idle for several years and the best of them would be picked to go to Hampshire. This was a new venture, so only the best would do and to my surprise, I was taken to an almost new Marshall 'Universal'. She had been delivered new from Gainsborough to a job at Preston. A few years previously, Fords had done a fair amount of work for the Highways

Construction Company (an asphalt firm that travelled over most of the country), but this job at Preston had come up while most of their rollers were out, so a new one was put on rail direct to Preston and having finished this job she was brought home to stand with the rest.

I was a newcomer to the roller side of this firm, so some of the drivers, who were now back to go to Hampshire, had been on the firm for several years and I don't think I was too popular with a few of them for a while, as I had been dished out with the newest engine of the lot. I got her cleaned up, filled with water and was eager to have a go with this beautiful engine. I had never before stepped onto one of them, although I had seen one at work close to one of our tree pulling jobs, (this had belonged to the Limmer & Trinidad Lake Asphalt Company) and I thought what a wonderful tool she was.

By Wednesday, I was ready to steam up and George Noyce, the works foreman, said "You may as well light up and make sure everything is OK. Give her a run around the yard for half an hour or so to get used to her before you start your journey". I split up some wood, lit up the fire then joined the rest of the drivers on their way to the mess room for a mid-day meal. While we were eating, most of them were asking me questions such as, where I had been and who had I worked for? Most of them seemed to think that I would have a job to settle down with a roller after the roaming life of a steam plough man. Now it was my turn to ask a question, so I asked, "Where is the big compound Marshall that Fords took over from the Newbury District Council?" and George Noyce informed me that she was where she would almost certainly stay for a long time, working for the Reading Corporation. She was their biggest roller and still looked almost like a showman's engine as she had never done any hard work, so she was around the streets of Reading more or less as a showpiece, I suppose she was a good advert for the firm and would be seen by far more people there than if she were out in the country lanes.

The 'Universal' had steamed up while we were eating our meal, so I soon pulled out from the row to have a shunt around the yard. What a wonderful engine she seemed to be and was so quiet. She was the first engine that I had been on that was fitted with the Marshall radial valve gear with its tumbler reverse. This is so easy to operate as its reversing lever is no more than a foot long, so it can be reversed either way with two fingers. I was asking George a few things about these engines as it was something new to me and he walked across to the office and came back with a small book. It was the driver's handbook that had been issued by Marshalls with the engine when it was supplied new. I still have it in good condition today and must surely by now be a collector's item.

I pulled out from the yard on the Monday morning, the first of the fourteen to go to Hampshire on a contract that was to last many years. My job was near the Hampshire/Surrey border on the Farnham to Odiham road which (if my memory serves me right) is the A287 and was a journey of about twenty miles but, whichever way we went, there would be a fair share of hill punching both up and down. I was on the road by 6.20am with George Noyce as my mate. Just the week before, he had been round the area where we were to go to find our best route. He warned me that we had some steep hills to negotiate, the first one was at Eversley and was called Brickhouse Hill. This was a low gear job but, before we had climbed far, I could tell that this roller had very little slogging power and was pretty gutless if you let her revs drop too low. She was even worse for hotting up the front end than a Wallis 'Advance'.

We crossed the A30 onto the Minley road, where I would have kept on this into Fleet, but George reckoned that it was shorter to turn right, down a lane which would bring us onto the Fleet to Hartley Witney road. We had not gone far, when I saw that we had a steep hill to go down, so low gear was engaged and off we went. The farther we went, the faster we were getting and by the time we reached the bottom of this hill, that crankshaft was really hammering round, even though the lever had been right back almost all the way down. I had found out that she was not too good on hills, either up or down, but for level going she was very nice and a treat to drive with no steaming problems.

We eventually reached the Farnham to Odiham road, where I cleaned her down and put some cylinder oil on the chimney which had got very hot. Mr. Ford rolled up to take George home and so, after a chat with the gang that I would be working with, they were on their way back to Wokingham. We would not be working for a couple of days, as the gang were putting in a few drains on the stretch of road that was to be ripped up, reshaped, and later coated with asphalt. I soon found out that I would be doing a lot of scarifying, as this gang was the one that covered most of the 'A' and 'B' roads in the Basingstoke division. Nearly all their work would be reshaping for the Hampshire County Council asphalt gang to follow up with the top coat of their own brand of asphalt from their own plant at Micheldever. They also used their own Robey tandem roller for this job.

The following week, we made a start and within a couple of hours I could see that I was going to be in trouble with this little Marshall, as she was not heavy enough to cope with the ripping up. This road had been made many years before with 3in. granite and had been laid and water bound, with binding gravel. In some places it was about 3in. thick, but in others it was 9in. Anyone who has used a roller and scarifier on this kind of going will know that you cannot split it, so you must get to the bottom of what has been laid and used for years.

We finished this short length of road to the Surrey boundary after a struggle, but we had spent a lot of time trying to keep the many nuts and bolts tight as this beautiful little engine was being quickly shaken to pieces. They were designed as an asphalt roller and were ideal for this task, but not very good for scarifying. The coal bunkers on either side of these rollers were made of fairly light plate and each side had a small single-tine scarifier but, as I was struggling along pulling this single tine, the coal bunker was twisting all shapes. It was plain to see that this could not go on for long without serious trouble.

With about two weeks gone by and this short bit of road reshaped, we moved along this road, towards Odiham for about three miles, to an open bit of country called Rye Common. I was hoping and praying that we would find it a bit softer going than the short length that had taken us to the Surrey border, close to Farnham. This turned out to be harder than the job that we had just finished, so it was clear that I would have to be dished out with a bigger and better engine. When Mr. Ford came out on the Friday with my wage packet, he was not very pleased. That beautiful little Marshall was looking a bit sick, there were a lot of broken and loose bolts, the wooden uprights of the full length cab were split where the coal bunkers had lifted under the strain. Some of the metal stays which brace the uprights were broken and the cab was floating about like a big lump of jelly, all this in less than three weeks.

A different engine would be coming to me early in the next week, but he had no idea what it would be as all the rollers were out. Berkshire County Council were trying to put their badly run down roads in order, so every roller on the firm was out on jobs around the two counties, but one of these would have to come to replace this little 'Universal'. We spent the Monday and Tuesday rolling the 3in. limestone that was being used to shape this length of road and about mid-morning, Mr. Ford pulled up to tell me that another engine was on its way. They had started the day before, but had pulled in for the night as the daylight had run out on them.

I was anxious to know which engine I was going to take over and, was almost certain, that it would be an old Aveling as I knew that they had several of them. They would never be my choice as they were noisy, slow and never the best of steamers, but they did have plenty of guts and this is what was needed on this job. I asked Mr. Ford what was on the way, but he just gave a little smile and said "She won't be long before she's here". He didn't seem to want to let on which engine my new roller was to be but, as we were chatting, from round the bend in the road about three hundred yards away came the roller. As she came closer I saw, from the shape of the saddle, that she was a Marshall then as she got closer, I saw that she was the fourteen-ton piston valved 'S'-type, No.83412. (This was the engine that I had seen, a few years previously, going to her first job near Newbury when she had been supplied new to the Newbury District Council.) I could hardly believe my own eyes, this was the last engine that I thought I would ever get the chance to work on, especially as I was the youngest driver on the firm and the last to start working for them. I had been told, only a couple of weeks before, that this engine would almost certainly be with the Reading Corporation for a long time.

The engines were changed over, my little 'Universal' was to go back to the yard for an overhaul and then into the streets of Reading to replace this big compound that from now on would be my pride and joy. For all the rest of that day, I could not help thinking how lucky I was to be in charge of such a wonderful engine. I was not going home every evening, as I had been told by Harry North, the man in charge of our gang, that the Hampshire Council officials were red hot on time keeping and that, any morning, some of them could be there before seven o'clock to see what time the wheels started turning. I was working about twenty miles from home so, if I should get a puncture, or have any other trouble and was late getting out onto the job, I would soon have someone after me. As a result I was going home only once in the week, at least until I had really settled in and found out a bit more on how the land lay.

I banked down that night, leaving the old girl with the pressure gauge showing 150 psi By ten o'clock (when I turned in) she was still showing the same, then at about 5.30 next morning, when I went to take the damper off, she was well past the 100 mark and this is how it worked out every morning. She turned out to be a most wonderful engine for steaming. You could stand by her with the gauge almost at blowing off point and, apart from the heat and smell, you would never have know that she was a steam engine. There was not a whisper of steam from anywhere and she was as silent as the grave. Scarifying was now no problem, I could do as much in one hour as I had been doing in three and, as I was getting 2d bonus (less than 1p) for every hundred square yards on top of my normal wages, this wasn't going down very well with most of the older drivers. I was using the scarifier for days at a time and had the firm's best engine to do it with. Most of the others were lucky to get a hundred square yards a week and there was I doing many hundreds a day for two or three weeks at a time. Often I would double my wages and all the other drivers knew this.

With the spring and summer behind us, several lengths of 'A' class road had been ripped up, reshaped and in many cases widened. I was still with the same gang, doing the same kind of work whereas most of our rollers that were working in Hampshire, had spent all the warm part of the year chasing the tar sprayers and were now doing odd lengths of patching. This required working on just the sides of the roads, which were getting low and so making the camber too great. On jobs like this a roller driver is for ever hooking up the living van and moving on, whereas I was spending many weeks with, perhaps, one or two moves of about a quarter of a mile or less and would be spending the winter doing the same. At weekends, when my brother and I were together for a few hours, we would chat about what we had been doing throughout the week. Many times through the summer, as Bert told me of his week's work with the ploughers, I would think to myself how nice it would be to get back onto one of those beautiful old engines. The ones with a rope drum under the boiler and watch the crankshaft spinning round as the cultivator came rolling towards me in a small cloud of dust, something that always was and always will be to me a wonderful sight.

As the cold weather began to bite, I could tell that my Marshall was working much harder. I was going through scarifier tines at an alarming rate and many of them were either being broken off or bent so much, that they were a job to get out from their sockets. However, my engine was giving no problems and was taking it all in her stride. I was now working most of the time with the differential gear locked and often would still run out of wheelgrip. It was beginning to show on the wheels. They had never been plated and were beginning to wear thin, so it would soon be time to get something done about it before the wheel rims were ruined. We had finished our job at Fleet and moved to our next length of road which was on the A32 at Heckfield. There was over a mile of road, from the Heckfield crossroads to the Berkshire boundary at Riseley, to be ripped up and reshaped.

We had spent about three days on this job, but we were getting some really hard frosts so the going was a bit tough. From the crossroads, going towards Reading, the road goes down quite a slope and we were on the steepest part of this hill having ripped up all that I could reach working head up hill. I had turned round, now working head down hill and had about three more pulls to go. I was just about in the middle of the road, where the granite (that had been laid many years previous) was about 9in. deep and it was coming up in great big lumps, blocking up the scarifier and lifting the right-hand side wheel off the ground, therefore giving a lot of trouble. We had been smashing up these lumps with a sledge hammer, but this was not easy as you just couldn't get to hit it as it is piled up behind the wheel. I thought that I would try going faster as perhaps this would push the lumps out the side of the scarifier and this seemed to work. I was taking the last pull, half of these frozen slabs of granite were going back under the tank, whilst the other half were going outside the scarifier. I was getting along fine when disaster struck, instead of a slab splitting and going out either side, it just lifted in one big lump. We came to a sudden stop, but although I had been keeping the water low in the glass, as I was working head down hill, the sudden stop caused the water in the boiler to slosh forward and go into the cylinder, bringing our scarifying to an end for that day.

These 'S'-type piston valve Marshalls were fitted with release valves to the cylinder drain cocks, which were set so that they were just lifting when the regulator was wide open, so she was struggling on a steep hill. The drain pipes from these release valves were about ³/₄in. diameter but they were still not big enough to allow this amount of water out when something like this happened. There I was smack in the middle of the road, the crankshaft was solid and there was no way that we could shift it by pulling on the flywheel.

On removing the right-hand side motion cover, I could see that the high pressure piston rod was about as straight as a dog's hind leg and this was what was holding the crankshaft solid. This was about the only fault anyone could find with one of these engines and to my idea was a very bad point. The piston rods were 1¹/₈in. diameter, which is far too small and they were much longer than on most other engines. When the piston was at the end of its forward stroke, the crosshead was at least six inches from what would normally be the packing gland. (Most of the Marshall engines, from 1927 onwards, did not have packing glands.) Instead of having packing that could be pulled out and replaced occasionally, they were fitted with iron rings (known as 'Labyrinth' packing) which had worked perfectly well, giving no trouble, until my problem occurred. Make no mistake, a bent piston rod makes a right mess of these iron rings.

It was mid-afternoon, but the days were short and I was about 200 yards from my stand, somehow I had to get the old girl back there as she could not be left in the middle of the road all night. I sized things up and realised that with luck there was a way out of this problem. These Marshalls are fitted with a nut, on a short length of thread on the piston rod, to enable removal of the piston rod from the taper in the crosshead. So, once the cotter that fixes the piston rod into the taper crosshead was removed and the nut was turned, the bent rod was released. The crankshaft was now free to move but, of course, could not turn full circle as the bent rod was in the way. This rod had to go forward about 2in. to allow the crankshaft to revolve freely. I took off the front cylinder cover then, with careful use of the auxiliary valve and the reversing lever, the high pressure crosshead was used as a sledge hammer to drive the piston and bent rod out of the way.

I soon had the crank turning over then, after just turning the nut back a few turns onto the piston rod, nothing was touching and there was no noise.

The only trouble was that plenty of steam blowing from the port where the cover had been removed. Had this been any other make of engine, there would have been no steam, as when double high is used on Fowlers, Burrells or any make that I have ever used, the steam is taken from a separate supply, but with these Marshalls, the regulator must be opened slightly before any steam can get to the auxiliary valve.

It was a dull foggy afternoon, so any waste steam in this sort of weather always hangs about more, making it difficult to see. I had 200 yards to go and it was just about dark but, luckily, I would be going backwards giving me a clear view. With the help of several of the council gang to take care of the traffic, in a big cloud of steam I managed to get her onto the stand alongside my living van. This is where she stood while the bent rod was removed and until a new one was sent from Gainsborough.

Next morning, I removed the round plate which held in the packing rings and could see that the 'Labyrinth' rings were in a bit of a mess. The first one came out with the help of a hammer and screwdriver in about six pieces, but there were several more still to be removed. I figured that if I drove the piston back with the small sledge hammer and a block of wood it might loosen them up a bit and it worked, as the piston went back into the cylinder, so the packing rings came out at the other end of the cylinder. With a bit more coaxing, the piston was on its way back out of the cylinder. When the piston and rod were finally out, I saw that the back cover was not too badly damaged so, by fitting a new rod and set of 'Labyrinth' rings, with their retaining plate, we would be back in business. Within a few days, I was back in operation again and for the rest of the hard weather everything went to plan. By the time we had reshaped this length of the A32 to the Berkshire boundary, the leaves were beginning to burst out. This is a very pretty stretch of road, so with its silver birch, beech and pine trees plus rhododendrons, this is a picnicker's paradise for most of the spring and summer.

My next job was on the A30. A stretch of $1^{1}/_{2}$ miles of asphalt was to be removed, reshaped and widened to 21 feet which was then a standard width for all Hampshire 'A' roads (either 18 or 21 feet). A heavy wooden template was used to give the exact camber and, if it was half an inch out after we had finished laying the base of a stretch of road, the asphalt gang would refuse to lay the top coat.

(I remember a few years later we were working on a stretch of the A33, the Reading to Basingstoke road and were working in sight of the Duke of Wellington monument. There was a lot of hard frosty weather at the time and we were laying a water bound road with 3in. granite or limestone, but it was not easy in these conditions. You could do a day's work, check it with the template late in the afternoon and it would be perfect, but check it again next morning after a hard night's frost and it would be altogether different. A fresh laid length of wet road will lift at least an inch with a night of hard frost and it does not always go back even when the frost had gone. We had relaid a few hundred yards of the A33 in hard frosty weather, then Mr. Pullen (the district surveyor from Basingstoke) paid us a visit. While he was chatting with Harry North, our foreman, he looked back at this length of road and said to Harry "There is something wrong there". The length had not been checked with the template for a few days, but sure enough, when it was checked in the middle of the road, it was about an inch low. The surveyor was not too pleased and said to Harry "Just look at it, you could throw your b—- hat under it". The length of road had to be ripped up and reshaped again, as there was no way that we could build up a road by one inch whilst using 3in. granite without making a mess of it and for the Hampshire County Council asphalt laying gang it had to be just perfect.)

This big job, on the A30, that I was to go to was a stretch reaching from Hartfordbridge Flats (where several years later Blackbushe Aerodrome was built) to the village of Hartfordbridge and at least half a mile of this is a fairly steep slope, known as Star Hill. My big worry here was working head down hill to get the last eight feet or so width on the right-hand side going down. I had already found out what can happen to a piston-valved engine (working head down hill), when it comes to a sudden stop with the regulator wide open.

This stretch of road had, many years previously, been laid with asphalt on an uneven base so it was now getting like a rough sea, but had not yet started to break up. All the Hampshire roads that are surfaced with asphalt from the Micheldever plant will be found to stand for many years. I am sure that the Hampshire County Council asphalt is about the best in the world and that is one reason why their roads are as good as any in the country today. I am not sure if it is still done today, but in those days from every Sentinel steam waggon load that was delivered to each job, a cubic foot was taken and went back to the laboratories at Winchester to be analysed. A steel box, that could be dismantled, was filled from every load and these went back on the waggon that had delivered the last load for the day.

Everyone knew that this job was not going to be easy but, if it was at all possible, it would save much time and money against using pneumatic drills (which were not too good in those days), so my Marshall would be put to the test. We were all ready to start by seven o'clock that morning and Mr. Pullen (the surveyor) was there to see what luck we were going to have. We soon found that it was going to be no walkover, our progress was very slow and our scarifier tines were being bent or broken at an alarming rate. The big slabs of asphalt were building up between the rear wheel and the scarifier, lifting the engine up and causing us to lose wheel grip. I was dreading the time when I would have to turn round and work head down hill as this would almost certainly spell trouble, probably resulting in another bent piston rod. All the asphalt that we were breaking up had to be carted away so, as the asphalt gang had got no job on the go just then, their fleet of Sentinel waggons were put to use to keep our job going. We were not getting on very fast, but were shifting far more in a day than a couple of drills could ever hope to do in a week and the Sentinel waggons were kept going full chat.

The weather was pretty good, the sun being really warm and, for most of the afternoon, it was high enough to be clear of the trees, thereby warming the road. I figured that this would be the best time to get stuck into the job but, in those days, none of the road was closed and had to be made safe for the traffic to move at night. There were no traffic lights in those days, just a couple of guys with 'stop and go' boards during the day and everything was made safe by five o'clock. With an asphalt road there is far more wheelgrip when it is warm, so it was decided that we would give it a try in the late afternoon and, if it worked out, we could no doubt roll it down again so making it fairly safe for traffic to use over night. I made the first cut between the row of sets, that had been cemented in to form the side of the road and the asphalt. Removing this would allow the slabs of asphalt to go out the side so, by taking a cut at least two feet wide and having a guy walking alongside with a sledgehammer (to give it a bang if it was a bit stubborn) this worked wonderfully well. With enough steam on to keep the old girl just ticking over and the hammer kept in use, we soon had a big area broken up then rolled back down again, perhaps, a bit rough, but safe enough for cars to travel over.

Next morning, within a few minutes, using two tines in the scarifier, we soon had a few tons ready to be carted away, This is how the whole job was done and the council officials were more than pleased with the results. My Marshall had stood up to it well, having certainly earned her keep and I was getting my 2d per hundred square yards bonus twice. My boss was being paid double and the Hampshire Council were happy to do this as we had saved them a lot of money.

'This is my 2 in. scale Fowler BB1 ploughing engine which weighs 2¼ cwt. and which I completed in 1971 after taking 4½ years to build. The sister ploughing engine is now taking shape and hopefully will be on display later in 1998 ...!'

JOE CHALLIS

Chapter 9

'The Steam Bug - Again'

All that summer, whenever my brother and I met at weekends, we would tell each other of the week's happenings, but many times, as Bert was telling of his ploughing or cultivating, I would have a little think of what I was missing. Steam ploughing was still and always would be in my blood. Even today, at over eighty-four years young, I love to go to different steam rallies where I can often get onto the footplate of someone's plougher and have a few pulls, or get behind the steering wheel of the plough or cultivator, or perhaps give a bit of advice to these younger steam plough enthusiasts. They were not fortunate enough to get the training and help that I was lucky enough to get as a youngster. To every owner of a ploughing engine, or perhaps a pair, who takes them to a rally and puts them to the work that they were built for, I take off my hat as they are doing a grand job.

I had settled down to the steady life of a steam roller driver pretty well, I was working much closer to home and could get home every night, if I so wished. Most of all I had a wonderful engine, so what more could I wish for and, as Bert had said many times that summer, steam ploughing had seen its best days and was then a dying thing. He was going from one set to the other, never knowing just where he would be from one day to the next. The singles had stood idle all summer and both sets of compounds had worked very little, so it was clear to see that there was no future for steam plough men or at least nothing like the life we had been brought up with.

At the end of that summer, when Ward's ploughers had been packed away, Bert set off to the Portsmouth area with an Aveling ten-ton single-cylinder roller and this is where he was to spend several years. He, like myself, was to forget about working with those wonderful old Fowlers with a rope drum underneath the boiler. We had both spent many years at the job that we had loved doing and had both done just about everything that it was possible to do with ploughing engines. If I could live my life again I wouldn't want anything to change, I would just love to do it all again.

I was going home every evening, as I was working fairly close to home for quite a long time and would be getting married soon after Christmas. We would be living at the 'Carpenter's Arms', where Gladys had been housekeeper for her father since the day she left school. Her mother had passed away when she was only twelve years old, so she had become an excellent cook and I would be well looked after. We tied the knot on the seventeenth of February 1934 at the little church at Goring-on-Thames and we have now spent 63 wonderful years together. Most weekends, through the spring and summer, we hook up the caravan and are away to a steam rally somewhere or another. She never complains.

By now I had learned a whole lot about motorbikes, resulting in my Rudge 'Ulster' being one of the quickest around, I had breathed on it for many hours, making it very fast and reliable. I figured that anywhere in the district of Hampshire I was covering, would not be too far to travel home every night and getting up early in the morning was no problem as I had always been used to this. Hampshire County Council had a different way of working than most other councils. Our hours through the longer days were 9 hours 10 minutes, but through the winter they were 8 hours 45 minutes. This averaged out to a 48 hour week throughout the year, working until 12 o'clock every Saturday. They were red hot on time and, as I was expected to be on the job ready to start by seven in the morning and often had up to half a mile to run from the roller's stand, this meant that I was on the road soon after 6.30am. Then it would be getting on for 5.30 in the evening by the time I reached the stand and had the fire banked down for the night.

One job I shall always remember was on the A339, the Basingstoke to Newbury road, a stretch of around four miles to be widened and reshaped. This lasted over twelve months and included a very hard winter, but also a wonderful summer to go with it. This stretch of road goes through miles of open fields, some of which is very high and one crossroads (known as 'Piccadilly') is the highest spot for many miles. From this spot on a clear day in summer, many villages and towns can be seen with the naked eye and up to fifteen church spires can be picked out by turning full circle on a foot square patch. It is wonderful country in the good weather, but can be just the reverse in winter, especially when the wind is coming from the north-east. A stretch of this road, at least half a mile from this high spot, going towards Newbury, is cut through the fields resulting in it being about five feet below them. There are no hedges or trees and so, even now, this is always the first stretch of the road to be closed when we get a drifting snow, as it fills level with the fields in a very short time.

We were working in this spot through some very bad weather, but for the gang working in this cutting it was not too bad, as the north-east winds were blowing over the top of their heads. Unfortunately for yours truly on the footplate of the old Marshall, it was a different story meaning that on many evenings during that winter I went home half frozen and often wet through. The road here rises very slightly towards Newbury all the way through this sunken stretch so, you can imagine what it is like when you get pouring rain, it is more like a river than a road.

Towards the end of this winter, after our job had been closed for about a month through snow and frost, we were working at the lower end of the cutting, although the fields around us were still deep with snow. To top it all, the road had been dug out and most of the snow that had been removed was piled high onto the fields on either side. We were laying the usual 3in. limestone and had got a morning's work laid and rolled down ready for the binding gravel to go on after the mid-day meal. The temperature had gone up quite a bit and during the morning the sun had broken through for the first time in several weeks, so things started to thaw very quickly. By three o'clock that afternoon, our length of road was under almost a foot of water, rushing towards us down this long slope. The next morning the fields around the 'Piccadilly' crossroads were littered with many tons of 3in. limestone. All that had been laid that previous day had been washed away and scattered over the surrounding fields.

Several weeks later, after this length through the cutting was finished and ready for the asphalt to be laid, I had to take my living van about half a mile towards Newbury to a fresh stand so that I would be closer to the next length of road to be worked on. This stand was a wide patch of grass at the side of the road that had been very carefully covered with a lorry load of stone and looked very nice, but, little did I know what was underneath. These clowns had spread the load of stone over what must have been a pond.

My living van was pulled into place using the sling chain and set level. All that was left to do was to flatten the load of stone down for the Marshall to stand on, then I would be all set for a few more weeks. The front end of the roller was pushed over it a few times and it looked very nice. She would be going to stand with her front near the road, therefore being slightly head up hill, so I turned the old girl round and started to back onto the layer of stone. I was almost into position when down she went, the right-hand side wheel was down almost to its centre, the scarifier was almost out of sight in a mixture of mud and limestone, so we were in deep trouble.

Some of the gang were sent up to help dig out the mud and see if it was possible to get some timber down so that the jacks could be used to lift her up, enabling us to get something underneath the wheel, which was into the hole by almost three feet. The ashpan and tank were well down into the stone, but my main worry was the oil-bath gearcase. This must almost certainly be damaged because, even on a level road, the oil drain plug was no more than 9in. from the ground and the spur wheel was only about an inch clear of the inside of the case. I figured that, if the case was pushed up onto the spur wheel teeth, they would be torn to pieces as soon as the wheels started to turn, so she would have to be lifted clear of everything before I could attempt to try and drive her out under her own steam.

213

The council lorry was sent to the council yard at Basingstoke to collect a load of timber, along with some big screw jacks, then we were soon pushing some of the timber into the ground, but lifting the engine very little. Several big lumps of the timber had been pushed completely out of sight before she started to lift. Five o'clock was with us, but she was still leaning at a crazy angle, so that was how she spent the night.

Next morning operations started again and by mid-day we had lifted her up enough so that I could see that the oil-bath gearcase was still in perfect shape. The ground under this layer of limestone was so soft that it just pushed out of the way as the case went down into it, so it would be safe to use her own power as soon as we were ready. With a steam roller there is nowhere strong enough on the front end that you can put a chain to take a heavy pull, so she had got to come out under her own power.

Of course, you don't have a set of spuds to put on to increase your grip, as you do with a traction engine or plougher. Using two big screw jacks and the scarifier as the third lifting device, she was up almost on an even keel, but what was going to happen as soon as I started to move. It was obvious that, if we were not careful, she would be back where she had started from. Therefore, I decided to use the same trick as I had done many times with the single-cylinder ploughers, a piece of timber chained to the wheel would give a lift as it was pulled underneath the wheel. A fairly hefty lump of oak timber was pushed across under the ashpan and the big sling chain put round it then through between the wheel spokes.

With the pressure gauge up near the red mark, we were ready to have a go. When doing this we needed all possible power until the wheel was on top of the timber, then we had to come to a full-stop immediately otherwise the timber would be pulled up under the tank and do untold damage. All four road wheel pins were in place, thereby locking the differential gears and I had her almost on to the top of the timber. However, whilst she was being held in this position there was an almighty bang somewhere in the gearcase. She seemed to drop back about a couple of inches and I thought straight away "That's another broken drive pin" (she had broken these several times before on hard scarifying).

When she was eventually on the hard road again, my first job was to check the drive pins. They were all intact so this set me thinking hard. I was certain that something had broken somewhere in the gearing, so there was no way that I was going to risk any hard scarifying until I had found out what this was all about.

Next morning, I got her onto a nice flat piece of road, removed the scarifier bars, took off the rear wheel and there, plain enough to see, was the fault. The differential gear main centre, that carries the four planet wheels in these 'S'-type Marshalls, has four holes to take the road wheel pins, when the differential is locked up. Either opposite pair of these holes can be used, but two of them had burst wide open, although this is a steel casting and the metal around these holes is at least 2in. thick. This gives one some idea of the load that comes onto everything at times like this. I made a thorough check on everything to make sure that nothing else was cracked and some pieces of hard oak wood were shaped and driven into the damaged holes with the sledge hammer, so that they could not be used again and I expect those lumps of oak are still there today.

Another big job with the Marshall that I shall always remember, was a stretch of the A30 from Popham nearly to Stockbridge a distance of around eleven miles, which was to be widened, reshaped and some of the corners straightened out. Altogether, there were about six gangs of men and four steam rollers all working on this length of road. Yours truly clicked for more than half of the ripping up and was kept going full chat for more than eighteen months. This road is now today just about the same shape as it was after we had finished some fifty years ago, a lot of up and down hill, but straight for miles on end. Every time I travel this way, it brings back a lot of memories. I often think of the miles I must have covered on that old Marshall whilst shunting backwards and forwards, getting that road to what it is today, a wonderful stretch of road. It was right by the Hampshire County Council asphalt plant at Micheldever, where some of the best asphalt that has ever been made in this country, is still transported to all corners of Hampshire.

After this job, I travelled all the way back to Fleet. The main street through the town was to be ripped up and reshaped, another job that lasted several months, drawn out a fair bit longer by a railway strike. All our stone in those days came from Somerset by rail and was then carted out to the different jobs by lorries from the nearest railway station. As a rule, it would be ordered in thousands of tons, perhaps six thousand or even ten thousand tons and this would be laid in a stretch of road for as far as it would last. We had started this stretch of road and had used up all the stone that had so far reached Fleet station, so we would be standing idle for a few weeks.

Mr. Ford decided that this was the time to replate the rear wheels of my Marshall as the rims were getting a bit thin. This sort of work usually went to John Allens of Oxford. A pair of wheels would be taken to Oxford by lorry and then collected at a later date, but this would have to be a quick job, so it was decided to try Wallis & Steevens of Basingstoke. I set off from Fleet that morning and was in the works at Basingstoke by mid-day. Mr. Ford came to pick me up in the afternoon and on our way back we were talking about the Marshall wheels. I said "Why not widen the wheels while they were at it?". He too thought it would be a good idea, the wheels were 16in. wide which is a bit narrow for a big engine, so it was decided to add an extra 2in.

She was ready to pick up after about ten days and when I went to bring her out from the Wallis works I was a bit taken aback by the way that they had fitted the new plates. Instead of being riveted on, they were fixed with tapered bolts and I thought straight away "That spells trouble, they will always be working loose". The plates were $2^{1}/_{2}$in. thick by 18in. wide with a 2in. wide ring to fill in the overlapping plates. The people who had fitted them reckoned that she was now well over two tons heavier. Before I left Basingstoke, I was given a long single-ended spanner to keep the 1in. diameter bolts tight for the first week or two. This was easy on the outside of the wheels but, to deal with the inside nuts, I had to get down under the engine and struggle with the spanner, then move her forward for a few feet, only to get down under her again, repeating this process until the wheels had turned full circle. It was only common sense to know that the inside of the wheel would work loose first, as this part of the wheel carries all the weight on a cambered road. I kept a close check on all the bolts for a few weeks and, surprisingly, they moved but very little and that is how those three rows of tapered bolts remained for several years. The wheel grip that I was now getting was amazing, they had done a grand job.

During my years with ploughing engines, traction engines and rollers, I hooked up to and shifted many different things. In the winter of 1936/7, while working at Farnborough, I coupled up to something rather unusual and caused hundreds of pounds worth of damage, almost finishing with a court case. We were widening and relaying a length of the A325 from Farnborough Station to the Surrey boundary at Frimley. The telephone engineers had laid in new pipes for their cables, so that they would be under the footpath, as the old ones would be under the now wider road. The old cables had not been in place more than a couple of years and consisted of one single pipe with a large cable that almost filled it. The new ones being four-way pipes holding several smaller cables, therefore, making them very much easier to handle.

We had watched them remove the giant cables very carefully, then roll them onto drums, ready to be used for some other job. They must have been very expensive, being lead covered and very heavy. Progress on the cable removal was a bit slow, so we were on their heels almost from the start until right up until when we were within about a quarter of a mile from Frimley Green. Here, there was quite a steep mound in the road (almost like an extra-long hump-backed bridge) and this was to be taken down almost fifteen feet. The right-hand side of the road, going towards Frimley, was removed and we were ready to start removing the other side, but there was still an extra long length of this giant cable in the pipes, from the top of this mound going well towards Frimley Green. The telephone engineers had tried with several different winches, but it just did not move. They assured us that they would be bringing something that would sort it out. Until such times, our job was at a standstill. Mr. Pullen, the surveyor, was not very happy and was calling on us most days to see if there was any progress with the cable. The weather was not very good, so the length of road was in a bit of a mess, nothing was moving and there, standing in the middle of the road, was a sewer manhole looking just like a factory chimney. Mr. Pullen had had enough, so he got on the phone to the telephone people at Guildford, who said that they would be there next morning without fail.

Mr. Pullen was a keen steam man and had a small steam railway in his garden at Basingstoke. He would often stand on the footplate of my Marshall roller and chatter for hours about steam engines, as he did that afternoon. It was cold and overcast but, whilst at Farnborough, there was always a lot of air activity, many different planes could be both seen and heard. But, that afternoon something very different was flying around. As we were talking, a plane came very low over us, going at least twice as fast as anything that we had seen before, it was our first Spitfire.

We were ready to go home that evening, but as we left, our foreman, Harry North came over to me and said "If the telephone people are not here by ten o'clock in the morning, we want you to hook onto that cable and yank it out." The next morning we waited until about 10.30, but still no telephone engineers had arrived, so we looked through the shed with all their gear in it and found the long steel mesh stocking that they used for hooking onto the cable (with this the harder you pull the tighter it grips). We had watched them take out the other cables and had seen that they had a gang of men to carry the cable once it came out, so avoiding damage to the thin lead cover on it, but there was no way that we were going to do this. I hooked my big chain onto it and tightened it up steadily, so as to give this steel mesh stocking a chance to get a good grip but, as I put the pressure on, the wheels started to spin, so the other pair of drive pins were fitted. The differential gear was then locked, but it was still a struggle to get it moving but, once started, we were away and down the slope towards Farnborough Station. When the cable was out, it was the biggest and longest telephone cable that I have ever seen. It lay down the side of the road, but was now just about useless as the lead cover was cut through for most of its length. When the engineers at last turned up, some of them went mad as we had ruined hundreds of pounds worth of cable. When the pipes were taken out, we could see why it had been so hard to get the cable started. Both ends of the pipe were higher than the middle and the water had washed the silt into the pipes, filling it up solid.

When you are working on a road with a big steam roller, every one usually tries to steer clear of you. A fifteen-ton roller is not the thing to fall out with if you are driving a car or even a lorry, but you get the odd clown that is ready to have a go and one of these turned up one day when I was working on Farleigh Hill. This is the longest and steepest hill around the Basingstoke area and is on the B3046, Basingstoke to Alresford road. It is almost half a mile long and the last two hundred yards are very steep.

We were working on the steepest part one afternoon, when about twenty three-ton Bedford Army lorries turned up with learner drivers on board. They were, without a doubt, being taken up this hill for gear changing practice so, by the time they reached the spot where we were working, most of them were getting into low gear and some of them were making a bit of a mess of it and doing the cogs no good at all. The last one of the convoy seemed to get quite a bit further up the hill than most before having to change into low gear.

He was well past the Marshall and had pulled back into the side of the road but, when he tried to change down, instead of getting his bottom gear, he finished up with a box full of neutrals and was soon on his way back towards me. He must have panicked, forgetting about his brakes, so I could see what was going to happen. He was coming back straight towards the front roller and just before the crash, I ducked down behind the boiler, waiting for the bang. There were three men laying the stone just behind me, so I could not drop back to soften the blow and my first thought was "That's the end of the forks or saddle" as it does not take much of a bang to break either of these parts, being the weakest points of any steam roller.

I jumped down from the footplate expecting to find some serious damage so, as soon as the driving instructor had taken over control and pulled the lorry away from my engine, I started to make a close inspection. Surprisingly, apart from the front scrapers being slightly bent back, so touching the roll, I could find nothing wrong and the Army were soon on their way. Many months later I was working near Aldershot and, having run onto the stand in the council yard, I ran the engine to pump water into the boiler ready to bank her down for the night.

I gave the old girl a wipe down and as I walked round in front of the roller, wiping the dust off the forks, there was a drop of oil that had run down from the pivot pin. As she rocked, I could see the oil was moving. Sure enough, there was a crack that was opening and shutting, so moving the oil. I reported this to the office at Wokingham and kept a close watch on it every day, but it got no worse and went for many years with no trouble.

I was still trying to get a little bit more speed from my motorbike, which was now one of the quickest around. I had learned a whole lot about motorbikes and had taken up riding in competitions at weekends with a fair amount of success. Most of the local motor-cyclists were bringing their bikes to me to get repairs done and I was earning almost as much in the evenings and weekends, as I was on the Marshall.

As steam was now on its way out, perhaps, one day I would be earning my living repairing and tuning motorbikes, instead of shunting a steam roller up and down the road. I spent several more years around North Hampshire with this Marshall, but every other Saturday through the spring, summer and autumn I would dash home, have a quick meal and was away on my motorbike to the Brookland's race track near Weybridge in Surrey. Here I would watch a bit of high speed motorcycling and have a chat with some of the tuners of these very fast bikes.

By now, I knew just about every inch of main road in North Hampshire and there was very little of it that I had not worked on or travelled over with Marshall No.83412. I had enjoyed every minute of it and, although this wonderful engine had taken a pasting over the years, she was still in real good shape, performing and looking just about as good as the day I took charge of her. To keep her like this, I had spent a lot of hours, during weekends and evenings with the spanners and cleaning rags. I had washed out the boiler every fortnight without fail and it had paid off as, apart from the wheel plating job, a set of firebars and a few drums of oil, she had cost Mr. Ford very little, but had earned him a lot of money. I had, most weeks, taken home a bigger wage packet than any other driver on the firm.

The years rolled by and my brother, Bert, had left Wards and moved back into Berkshire. He was now working for the same firm as myself and my two younger brothers had also joined Fords of Wokingham as roller drivers, so the four Challis brothers were now all on the same payroll, but not for long. Bert and I were working in Hampshire, whilst our two younger brothers, Jack and Cecil, were spending most of their time in Berkshire. Then, in the summer of 1939, Hitler's army started pushing into Poland and other parts of Europe. It was clear to see that we would be dragged into the war before long.

Towards the end of the summer, I was working on the A30 at Hartley Witney. Our job had closed down on Friday and the gang and myself were to start painting white lines in the middle of the roads, on kerb stones and sides of bridges ready for the blackout. We also had to dig up every milestone, then bury them, also pull down all signposts and finger posts. We were to work overtime and all weekends. On the first Sunday morning, we were painting white lines and the river bridge walls at Hartfordbridge, when the landlord from the pub came out and told us that the Prime Minister, Neville Chamberlain, had just announced over the radio that we were at war with Germany.

Anyone old enough to remember, will know that during the winter of 1939/40, apart from food rationing and driving at night with masked headlights, we hardly knew there was a war on, but as the spring came along and the weather improved it was a different story. That spring, as the German Army pushed their way across Holland and Belgium, the younger men of this country were being called up in their thousands and it was obvious that my turn would soon come. My two younger brothers had received their papers with the date and place where they were to report and I thought that it would be my turn before too long, but I certainly did not wish to land up in an infantry regiment.

At that time, we were working on a stretch of the A32 at Heckfield and were being held up for stone so, for several days, my Marshall had not left her stand. I was going every day to do just about nothing. So one day I thought here goes and, getting on my bike, I was away into Reading to volunteer to join the RAF. I thought it would be several weeks before I would be called, but as Hitler was pushing his way into France at such a rate, all volunteers were being taken right away and I was told to report back the next morning. When I told my boss what I had done, he said "What on earth did you do this for? You would almost certainly be exempt from the forces as a lot of rollers will be needed for aerodromes and army camp work".

I was almost certain that I would be going to Uxbridge, as this was where all the RAF volunteers were being sent to, but for me it did not work out that way. That next morning, I reported to St. Giles school again, with fourteen other volunteers, only to be told that we were going to Cardington in Bedfordshire and were dished out with railway warrants. We made our way to the station and were soon on our way to London where we got onto a train for Cardington. Once there, we were joined by a few hundred more guys who had come in from all over the country. Next morning, we were given a few lectures and each of us was dished out with a number (mine was 1162970).

A few of us that wished to join up as flight mechanics, were taken to a workshop where we were asked a few questions about different tools, such as reading a micrometer, filing something to shape and so on. We were at Cardington for four days, then everyone, but the few of us that were to be flight mechanics, were sent out to different stations. However, we were each dished out with a silver RAFVR badge, which we were to wear at all times and were sent home to go back to our jobs, once there to wait to be called.

I went back to the Marshall roller again, which was still standing idle, so I spent a fair amount of time on my motorbike. One evening, while I was doing a bit of high speed motoring, one of the front-fork shackle-pins snapped and this put me in hospital for several weeks with a fractured skull and a badly damaged left hand. When my call up papers arrived, I was far from fit, so for the next six months my doctor was dealing with the RAF, signing the papers which were coming to me almost every week. After a few months, I had to report to a big private house in Reading which had been taken over by the RAF as their medical HQ for our area. Here, I went for another medical exam and was discharged as unfit for service in the Royal Air Force as I was, and still am, stone deaf in my left ear.

By the time that I was fit to start work again, I was eager to get back with the steam engines again so I made my way back to Wokingham, where Mr. Ford was glad to see me back. I could start work the next morning, when luck was with me once again, the big Marshall was standing idle as most of the road jobs were closed down. I was to go to Farnborough to steam her up and bring her close to my home to start on a job at Aldermaston, where Chivers of Devizes where starting to build the aerodrome, which is now the Atomic Warfare Research Establishment. I spent several months here working on runways, roads and footings for the hangers.

My next job was away into the Chiltern Hills at Goring Heath in Oxfordshire. There was a thickly wooded area, where the War Department (now the MOD) were building dozens of big sheds for storing parts for the war machinery and I was to roll the hardcore for the footings of these buildings.

From then on, right through to the end of the war, the life of a roller driver in our part of the world was a little bit hectic, never knowing where you would be from one day to the next. This was especially true for those of us with the heavy rollers, but this suited me fine as I always liked travelling long journeys with either the ploughers or the rollers. My Marshall always made it a pleasure as she was good on hills, both going up and down and was quite fast. I hardly ever changed gears anywhere. I could fill the boiler to the top of the glass with water, half fill the firebox with coal and she would be right for at least five miles without having to put either the injector or pump on or make use of the fire shovel. She was a wonderful tool.

My next move was back to Aldershot in Hampshire (the home of the British Army). Here I was kept busy for a few weeks relaying every major crossroads with asphalt. The Canadians with their American tanks and our boys with their 'Churchills' were making a bit of a mess. All the crossroads around Aldershot, Fleet, Farnborough and Basingstoke were looking more like ploughed fields than roads, the tanks just chewed straight through ordinary tarmac. After we had relayed some of them with asphalt, it was great fun to watch these tanks take the corners. They had been used to grinding their way round in about a foot of loose tarmac but now, until they got the hang of it, they would often find themselves facing back to where they had just come from, as they slewed round on the asphalt as if they were on glass or ice.

From here it was away, deep into Hampshire, to Barton Stacey near Andover where a big Army camp was being built (this is still in full use) and here I would be making the major roads and the entrance from the main A303 road. I had been there only a few days, when another of our rollers turned up, it was a 10-ton Wallis 'Advance' and who should be driving it but Jack Case (another chap from my own village). I had got him the job only a few months before, so now I had some company to help while away the long winter evenings.

We worked a couple of weeks on this job then we were both sent away to Worthy Down Aerodrome for another rush job which lasted only a few days. We both packed our bits and pieces and were ready to move on by ten o'clock that morning. Jack said "I had better go first as the 'Advance' is quicker than the Marshall, so I can be there and find out our standing place by the time you get there". I had different ideas and just gave Jack a little smile and said "OK you do that".

We pulled out together from Barton Stacey and, as Jack had said, the Wallis 'Advance' had a fair turn of speed (which I had found out while working at Wards of Egham), but my big Marshall was just as good and I was on Jack's heels for the first few miles. I could tell that he was trying to get away from me, as he was really pushing the poor old Wallis. I could see the patches of water on the road from where Jock kept putting his injector on, whereas I had not yet used mine, having filled the boiler before we left and then filled the tank. I knew that I could make Worthy Down without picking up any more.

We reached the stream where we had decided to fill up, Jack pulled up for water, so I just pulled out round him and was on my way. I am sure that poor old Jack had a bit of shock when I ambled off into the distance. I pulled into Worthy Down, found the gangs (that we were to work with) and was parked up and unpacked by the time Jack came into sight. The old Marshall was stood there as spick and span as ever, not looking as if she had been pushed along in any way but, when the Wallis arrived, her chimney was almost white and she looked as if she had taken a real pasting.

Next morning, it was a bit foggy with a real white frost and the grass looked as if it had a layer of snow on it. We watched the ground crews load up two Fairey 'Swordfish' planes with torpedoes and, as they took off across the grass, they swept the frost off the grass as clean as any brooms could have done, all done by the exhaust from the engines. A few hours later, one of them came back complete with torpedo, but the other one never came back and this is how it went on day after day. They were wonderful planes for launching a torpedo, but were very slow and so were a sitting target.

We finished our job here and returned to Barton Stacey, but this time I went the day before Jack, so there was no high speed travelling this time. We were here for several weeks sorting out this job (that lasted for the rest of a very hard winter) and almost every night Hitler's bombers were around dropping their loads over the fields of this wild part of Hampshire.

Where the railway goes through a deep chalk cutting at Micheldever, there were and still are, huge supplies of oil in tanks set back under the chalk hills alongside the railway. 'Jerry' knew that they were there and that was what they were seeking, night after night, but they never found it. They had dropped bombs in the fields all around it, but were always several miles away, however it was a bit uncomfortable for all of us around Micheldever.

Jack and I had our living vans parked side by side in this new Army camp and spent the evenings together in one or other of them. As we sat there one evening about 10.30pm (with a couple of cups of coffee on the table), we heard the drone of those German diesel-engined bombers around sky-high for a couple of hours. We watched the searchlight beams all around and heard anti-aircraft batteries open up. Then came a high pitched whistling noise, followed by our van being lifted off the ground by at least a couple of feet. Our cups of coffee and everything else that was movable was on the floor and I am sure that both Jack and I had 'skid marks' in our pants.

Next morning, as soon as it was daylight, everyone was looking around to see where this giant bomb had dropped and, sure enough, in the field on the opposite side of the A303 was a hole in the chalk field big enough to drop about half a dozen houses into. It had not been a bomb, but a mine on a parachute (which had not opened up) and this had caused the whistling noise as it came down.

From here, it was back to the Hampshire Council again, while Jack was left to finish off the camp job. There was a stretch of the A32 at Mattingley which had got very bad, the sides were breaking away, resulting in Army lorries and tanks forever going into the ditches. Thousands of tons of brick rubble, which was the bomb damage from Portsmouth (half of Portsmouth was laid flat) was drawn here to build up the sides and widen the road by a few feet.

Among the brick rubble were hundreds of cast iron window sash-weights of many different sizes. There was several thousand tons of 3in. limestone drawn in by rail to Hook station for this job and a firm from Greywell, with a fleet of Thorneycroft lorries, were drawing this out and tipping it along the sides of the road. One night after we had left for home, they got a lorry bogged in, so they were there for most of the night getting it out and whilst doing this, they had buried some railway sleepers in the ditch, close to the side of the road.

Next morning, I was scarifying the other side of the road just opposite to where these sleepers were buried in the mud and I was almost in the middle of the road, when one of the London Brick Company eight-wheeled AEC wagons came into sight, loaded with bricks on his way to Portsmouth (where there were some new barracks being built). He was in a bit of a hurry and off his proper route, having been to Reading to see a sister whom he had not seen for a long time. He did not wait for me to get out of the road, but instead came pushing through and down went both right-hand front wheels into the ditch where the stone lorry had gone in a few hours before. There he was with both front axles on the ground and no way was he going to back out from this lot under his own power.

We sized things up and I said to him that "It would pay you to chuck off a couple of hundred bricks from the front corner that has gone down", but he would not hear of this. My big sling chain (which I always carried) was hooked onto the back of him, the drive pins for locking the differential gear on the Marshall were put in and we were ready to go, but I for one did not give much hope for success here.

He started his engine and shouted out "Don't stop if she starts to move". The all clear was given, so off we went and to my surprise it moved. We were away but, as we moved, instead of it coming back along the road, the tail end came across the road and completely blocked it. So that was the A32 closed for the rest of the day.

I went back to see what had gone wrong with the wagon and there, out in front of it, were both front axles. They had come back and tangled with the railway sleepers that had been pushed in a few hours before by the stone wagon, resulting in all four of the front springs folding up and tearing the spring hangers from the chassis. The driver was now in deep trouble, as he was off his proper route and had to phone his headquarters to find out the worst. Another of their wagons was sent down to transfer the load and take it to Portsmouth, then their heavy breakdown truck came to take the wreck along the road a few hundred yards to the Hound Green Garage, where it stood for a few days whilst a gang sorted out the problems.

We were working our way along this stretch of the A32 towards Reading and my standing place was by the side of a small stream, close to the corner of Heckfield Park and here one night Hitler's bombers paid us a visit. I had gone home for the night, as it was only about eight miles from home and when I arrived next morning, I had a bit of a shock. Out in the corner of the park were at least a dozen dead cows (some of them blown to pieces), whilst the road was strewn with lumps of clay for about a hundred yards.

I steamed up to make my way up to the job, about a quarter of a mile away and about halfway along this length of road stood a very old timbered cottage. Half of the roof tiles were littered all over the place and the windows were completely covered with mud. A bomb had dropped in a pond on what used to be a brickyard. The pond was now empty, but all the mud and clay was all over the house. Later that morning, the two old boys who were living in this old cottage came out and were talking to us, but they had not know that a bomb had dropped until they surfaced about eight o'clock that morning.

I was having a little chat to these two old timers (who I would think were brothers). They were saying what sort of life they had been through and how they had always been hard up, but happy and still had got nothing. Then one of them said "But we have got two valuable paintings, come and have a look". I went with them around to the back of the house, which was very low, the ceilings being no more than six feet high and there, hung on the wall, were two of the biggest sides of home cured bacon that I have ever seen in my life. They must have been worth a small fortune with food being rationed.

Although this job was far from finished, I had to make a quick move back onto the A30 at Hook, about six miles away, to where the tanks had completely chewed the road away at a crossroads and we had to relay it with asphalt. We had always been told that you must have a fairly light roller with quick reverse (like the Robey tandem, Marshall 'Universal' or Wallis 'Advance') to roll asphalt without leaving dents in it, but with my big Marshall I proved to them that it is a load of rubbish.

We were just putting the finishing touches to this job by about 2.30pm, when our travelling foreman rolled up on his big V-twin BSA motorbike and box sidecar to rush me off to another unexpected job. He was John York and had spent all the early part of his life in the Royal Navy and where he had ever learnt about road making, nobody ever knew (unless he had laid a road across the North Sea during World War One).

He was a tall guy and had a very husky voice owing to him having been injured in the throat at the Battle of Jutland and almost everything he talked about had a bit of naval slang to it. He came up to me and said "We want you to get down to Popham on the A33 where 'Jerry' had dropped a bomb at the side of the road which is now half closed. You won't need to take your living van as there is nowhere to put it, when you get there they will bring coal and water in the morning with the lorry". I let him carry on for a bit, then I said "How about my motorbike, I have to get back home tonight". He stood there muttering away for a while then said "Can't you lash it to the stern" and I had to burst out laughing at him and this didn't please him one little bit. A few sharp words were exchanged, then I told him straight that I would not think of going until the next morning, as it was then 3 o'clock and Popham was 16 miles away and it would be dark by about 5.30pm.

He was still ranting on and said "I told your Mr. Pullen" (he was our divisional surveyor) "That you will be there ready for 7 o'clock next morning", so I said "You had better go and tell him that I won't be there until mid-morning". He then came out with a bit more naval chatter saying "You will not be on my b——- hammock". So I had to have another little laugh to myself, meanwhile he got onto his bike and went.

Putting two and two together, I realised that if I got going immediately, I could knock off the 16 miles in about two and a half hours, but I was going to take the van with me. If there was room for the engine, I would somehow make room for the van. The gang helped to load my Rudge 'Ulster' motorbike into the van and I was away, all on my own, while the gang finished the clearing up. I could hold about 7 mph with this old girl with no problem and I pulled up behind this bomb crater just as it was getting dark, but I now had another problem. How was I going to get my bike unloaded? There was and still is, a transport cafe just up the road, so I wandered off to it and there were about half a dozen truckers in there who were only too willing to help me (back in those days everyone was more helpful than they are today, how times have changed).

With this hole filled in and made safe, it was away back to finish the A32 job at Mattingley and Heckfield, which lasted right through to the end of the summer. Now came something very unusual for the winter. This involved going round to different council dumps to roll out hundreds of tins which had come in on the dustcarts and were then carted off for recycling. Each council dump had a concrete patch laid and there would be a few old timers with stone-forks, each throwing these tins out for me to roll out flat. They would keep throwing them out until the heap was about 3 feet high, by then it was a bit unsafe to get too close to the side of the heap. Wagons would cart them away and I would think that some of these heaps must have weighed at least 100 tons.

My round for this job was Marlow, Wokingham, Ascot West, Slough and Stokenchurch, a nice steady little job, but a bit filthy. As the weather got warmer, the smell was not very pleasant and you were smothered with flies and wasps. Often there would be a tin of fruit or milk that had not been opened and you can imagine what sort of mess this made. Sometimes it would fly up into the engine cab then drip down all over you as you stood on the footplate.

From here I went back to Aldermaston, which was now in full swing with dozens of American Dakotas and Horsa gliders practising for the invasion. This place had been rushed together by Chivers of Devizes. They had laid concrete roads for the living quarters of the camp, but they had not put in any foundations, so the roads were now getting in a bit of a mess, breaking up in a lot of places and we were repairing them with tarmac.

I was stood on one of these roads one morning, while a patch of tarmac was being laid and I honestly thought that the back axle had broken. There was a big crunch and the engine dropped about a foot, leaving it looking as if it was going up a steep hill. The concrete had been laid over what must have been a small pond, but the concrete had broken under the wheels, so the clay and water had splashed up the fir trees on both sides and a bulldozer was brought in to give me a pull out.

I spent several weeks on this job, which was only five miles from home. I got on well with the Yanks, who were well supplied with loads of good tools (which they were quite free and easy with) and I still have some of them today. They also lived far better than we did with plenty of good food while we were struggling. There was one of them (who I think was a Captain or some other high rank) whose parents had some steam rollers in Ohio and he spent a lot of time on the Marshall with me talking about steam engines.

He was there one morning chattering, then had a look at his watch and said "I must make my way to the cookhouse its time to eat". Then he said "How do you go on for meals?". I told him that I brought sandwiches which were not very well filled as the rations did not run to it, so he said "Come with me" and off we went to what I suppose was the Officers' Mess. He introduced me to the guy in charge and said "This chap is working here and will be coming for his meals each day so look after him" and from then until the end of the job, I lived like a lord and their coffee was second to none (but their tea was poor).

From here, it was back to the Hampshire County Council where I spent most of that summer rolling chippings behind the tar-sprayers. I often think of one of these jobs nowadays. This was back near Aldershot and was up quite a slope. In those days, the tar was sprayed by hand from a horse drawn tar pot and the chippings spread with shovels from the back of a lorry.

It was a hot day and a length of tar had been sprayed, but the chippings had run out, as the second lorry had not come back, so there was about 20 yards of wet tar with no chippings to cover it. I was up tight to it with the roller, whilst the flagman, with his red and green flags, was there directing the traffic when, who should come along but a chimney sweep. He was on an old trade bike with his rods and brushes tied along the top bar and a sack of soot in the front carrier.

The flagman held the red flag up to stop him and let the cars through from the opposite way, but the sweep was not going to stop. He pulled out round the roller and on his way, or so he thought. He was struggling up the slope, then suddenly realised that there was not enough room for him, so he pulled over onto the wet tar, which is as slippery as ice. I watched, only to see that as he put pressure on each pedal the back wheel was slipping. I was sure that he would fall off under one of the cars, but instead he fell the opposite way and I have never seen anything so funny in my life. He tried to pick himself up as he laid there on his back, then he rolled over onto his hands and knees, looking just like a duck trying to get across a frozen pond. His bag of soot was strewn all over the place and you can guess what sort of mess he was in. How he cleaned himself up after he got home I will never know, but he went off wheeling his bike and looking very sorry for himself, plastered with tar and soot.

A couple of days later we had to go back to this spot to spray some more tar over it and spread some more chippings. The soot had ruined the tar, making all the chippings come off, leaving a bare patch and this was something that the Hampshire Council were very particular about. Today, anything goes, with long narrow bits missed, some bits sprayed and covered twice. Perhaps that is why the roads are in the state they are today. The old way was slow, but it was done properly and lasted much longer.

We moved back to one of the crossroads at Farnborough to so some patching at the ends of the asphalt that we had laid for the tanks to turn on. This was the crossroads at the Queens Hotel, where on one side of the road were some public toilets and this whole area was now loaded with Canadians. One morning, a couple of them rolled up in a jeep with a big bale of hand knitted socks on board which the Canadian Red Cross had sent over. They unloaded this bale of socks, which must have weighed at least a hundredweight, dragged it into the gents' toilet and cut it open. One of them was sat on the bale, while a couple of them were selling them to anyone who came along and I was one of the customers, as things like this were hard to come by in those dark days. This went on for most of the morning and the bale had become very small, when along came a couple of MPs in a jeep and carted the gang off. I was sweating in case they wanted to have a look around, as I only had the toolbox in which to hide them, but I had it weighed up and the socks were ready to go into the firebox if the MPs had started to come across to me but, luckily, they just cleared off, so I could breath again.

A few weeks later, I was still chasing the tar pot at Maple Durwell, near Basingstoke. It was getting late in the afternoon and we had a short length to finish before moving on to the next road to be sprayed. I was out of water in the tank and it was getting a bit low in the glass, so I said to the foreman "I will have to have some water before we can finish this length" (they had been supplying me with 40 gallon barrels of water carried in the lorry). He said "Finish this bit off then you can shoot down to the canal which is only a couple of hundred yards down the lane".

So I soldiered on, finished the job and was then away down to the Basingstoke canal with water just showing in the bottom of the glass. There was the canal, over sixty feet down in a cutting, as this is close to where it comes out from the Greywell Tunnel, so I had to push the front roller up into a field gateway and walk back to tell them to get some water to me a bit quick. (The foreman lived close to there and must have known that it was out of reach for a thirty foot lift pipe.)

I moved my living van onto my next stand, which was close to the end of the tunnel. There was a brick bridge across the canal, which I would have to cross each night and morning to get into a disused brickyard, where my stand was to be. Here, the canal is a long way down in the cutting and looked a bit frightening, as the bridge was not much wider than my engine, but was very old although still fairly safe. I had been there only a couple of days, when a gang of Ministry men came along and fitted up scaffolding under the bridge to carry measuring instruments for testing to see how much the bridge moved, so that they could see what weight the bridge could safely carry. (This was being done all over the country and each bridge was marked with its safe load.)

With everything fitted up and ready to go, a 'Churchill' tank was driven over steadily, while the instruments showed and recorded the movement. This was OK, but the bridge was just wide enough to take the tank with only an inch or two to spare on each side. They then had to repeat this at speed, so he came hurtling down the lane, but was slightly off course and one track mounted the wall which fell into the canal below for the whole length of the bridge. A big inspection was made, but they decided that it had not damaged the main structure of the bridge, so I had to cross it each night and morning, which was very unpleasant with just a length of chestnut fencing stretched across the opening.

I crossed this bridge several times while it was like this, but never looked over the damaged side. I just kept a close watch on the other side, going as close as possible to the good wall. I would think that this cutting was about eighty feet down and I was glad when I pulled out from there for the last time and I have never been back since.

The Battle of Britain had long since been won and very few German planes were now to be heard overhead, but the V1s and V2s were now coming over. We were working on Fleet railway bridge and I was standing at the bottom of the slope up to the bridge where the Cove road turns off. We were ripping up the old tarmac on the bridge and they had gone a bit too deep, the scarifier tines had tangled with the steel work of the bridge and had bent the tines right back. I was having trouble getting them out to be replaced with straight ones, so I had to run back onto the stand to jack up and take them out of the bottom.

We were all sat in my living van having our mid-day meal (as it was a raw cold day), when an unusual sound could be heard, almost like a two stroke motorbike, but it was coming from up above. We all blundered out of the van just in time to see it go through a break in the cloud. It was a V1 flying bomb or 'doodlebug' as we called them. It was still close enough to be heard, then it went silent, so we just stood and waited for the bang. We knew that we were OK, but it was heading in a straight line for where my home was (and still is) at Mortimer.

All that afternoon, I kept wondering where this thing had dropped and how far away from home. It was about 4.30 when our surveyor turned up and told us it had dropped in a fir plantation at Bramshill and had flattened over an acre of young fir trees.

The winter went by and 'Jerry' had kept most of his bombers grounded, so all that we were being troubled with was the odd 'doodlebug', which came over mostly in daytime and fell chiefly in the London area. With the days getting longer and warmer, I thought I would be back chasing the tar pot again, but it did not work out this way. A length of the A30 from the Surrey boundary at Camberley to the Blackbushe crossroads was to be relayed with tarmac and this would last us well into the summer.

Our tarmac was coming by road from Southampton everyday and the lorry drivers were telling us how the North bound lane of the Winchester by-pass (this was Britain's first dual-carriageway) was closed. Its full length was quickly being filled with tanks, lorries, guns, etc, so we put two and two together and realised that this lot were getting ready for an invasion somewhere or other.

We had resurfaced at least two miles of the A30. I was finding enough petrol to get home most nights and earning myself a few pounds each week repairing motorbikes for my pals in the village, plus a few from further afield. Some of these worked at Woodley, building aircraft and some were timber cutters. I set off from home one morning in brilliant sunshine and it was a real pleasure to be riding a fast motorbike, but there seemed to be a lot of air activity with Spitfires, Hurricanes and many heavy bombers.

When I arrived at the stand where the Marshall had spent the night in steam, there were already two lorry loads of tarmac waiting to unload. The drivers told me that Southampton was very busy and that everything on the Winchester by-pass had gone during the single night. We now were almost certain that the invasion was on, as all the aircraft were painted on the underside with black and white stripes and, as the day went on, we were told that a landing had been made on the beaches of Normandy.

This was the 6th of June, a day that most of us will always remember. One thing that none of us knew was that a pair of Fowler BB1 ploughers had had their drums converted to capstans and would be amongst the first pieces of hardware to arrive on both sides of the channel to pull the PLUTO pipe line across to supply the fuel to feed the war machinery.

Our job on the A30 lasted for several weeks, as we had only three old timers to lay the tarmac (all of whom were past retirement age) and six POWs (who were transported each day from a POW camp at Mortimer, about a mile from my home), who would watch the three old timers slog away while they were just sitting around waiting for five o'clock to come round. There were four Italians and two Germans, six of the most idle guys I have ever seen.

With this job finished, it was back with the tar pot again and most of our jobs now were on the by-roads as some of these were getting in a pretty poor state. A good coat of tar would, without too much expense, make them last a bit longer. We were working on a stretch of road between Greywell and Maple Durwell when one morning Mr. Ford, my boss, came along and said "I am afraid you are going to lose your engine. The Army are after all our best rollers for sending to India". Sure enough, within a couple of hours along came a couple of high ranking army bods to have a good look around the Marshall. Then they perched up on the step and said "Run her up the road a little way". They were soon satisfied so, within a couple of days, my pride and joy was on her way back to Wokingham to have the chimney and cab removed, then to be crated up and labelled for Calcutta but, believe me, this was heart breaking.

I was dished out with another 'S'-type Marshall but this was not a patch on the one I had just lost. The replacement was several years older and quite a bit smaller. Her wheels were the ordinary spoked ones and not the cast type with six wide spokes. It was a compound piston-valve, the same as my other one, but the tumblers for the reversing gear of the radial valve gear were square instead of round. The differential could be locked with a small lever on the right-hand side of the footplate, but this did not last her long. We were doing a job at Chalk Pit Hill on the A32 going out of Odiham towards Alton, a length of this was to be ripped up and relayed.

The first day here, I pushed the differential locking lever over and thought that this is one improvement on the other engine, as previously I had to have someone push against the two drive pins while the wheel was slipping, until the holes in the differential centre lined up with those in the wheel, reversing the process to remove them. We had done only about a couple of hours scarifying, when there was a crunch somewhere in the gearcase and that was the end of the diff locking device. It never worked again and I never bothered to strip it down to see what the problem was. I had lost all interest in this old girl and often thought that she should have stayed in Jersey, where my boss had purchased her from. You just could not compare her with No.83412.

The weeks and months went by. I was managing fairly well with the 'Jersey Cow', as we called her, but I was far from happy with her. I had made up my mind that, as soon as the war was over and labour was decontrolled, I would forget about rollers and start on my own, repairing motorbikes. All the steamers that were left were past their best and if and when a new roller arrived it was diesel powered and they did not interest me one little bit. I had grown up with steam and when the time came to change over to diesel it was the end of the road for me.

We knew that the war with Germany was almost over so, everyone was looking forward to the day when peace would be signed. We were working on one of the by-roads at Bramshill when, one afternoon, some women from the cottages about there came running out to tell us that it was all over. We had had six long years of war and hardship. It was hard to believe that this was finished, but there was still Japan to deal with. I still say that if it had not been for those two atom bombs on Hiroshima and Nagasaki, we would still be fighting them now.

A couple of weeks went by with very little change, apart from most of us feeling much happier, but surely things must soon improve. I thought it was time to have a word with my boss to find out what the position would be about leaving him to start on my own. Mr. Ford came round on the Friday with my wages, so I thought that this was the time to break the ice and he was very nice about it all and could see my point.

He then explained, that he could not release me while labour was still controlled but, as soon as this was lifted, he would have another chat and said "We would hate to lose you but I will not stand in your light". Several more weeks went by with nothing said about me leaving, so I thought that it was time to jog his memory again and he agreed to let me go without saying anything to anyone (we knew that several workers in our area were doing the same thing).

We decided that I would leave the following weekend and that I should

232

go to Wokingham to collect my cards and have a little chat in the office. We were then working on the A30 again, about half a mile from where we were on D-day, but no tarmac would be coming on the Saturday, so I left the 'Jersey Cow' on the Friday evening with the tubes nicely swept, the coal bunker filled and lighting up wood all ready for whoever would be taking over on Monday morning.

The next morning, I made my way back to Wokingham, walked into the office and had a long chat with Mr. Ford (he was one of the nicest men you could ever wish to meet). He explained a few things to me about running your own business, some of them I had not even thought about. He was very helpful and told me that if I was ever in any doubt about anything, he was only a phone call away. We talked for over an hour about different things that had happened during the years that I had worked for him and before I left for home he gave me a 'golden handshake', saying "If ever you are short of work there will always be a job for you here as long as I am around". This meant that I would not have anything to worry about if things did not turn out as I hoped that they would.

I made my way back to Mortimer that Saturday morning to start my own business, full-time. I have thought many times since what a big gamble this was, especially since I had very little money to play with and a wife and family of four to keep (two boys and twin girls), but I never looked back. The jobs began to pile up, the biggest problem finding room for it all and the time to cope with it all. I was back again to steam ploughing hours, about 16 hours a day, but I was enjoying my work repairing motorbikes, something I had always liked since before I had even left school. My biggest problem was getting hold of the spare parts, as all the manufacturers had long since gone into war machinery production. All the bikes that had laid idle for almost six years, needed many parts and the only answer was to get stuck into making them.

I still had the little 3in. Portass lathe that my brother had bought while I was at school and a 1915 6in. Drummond lathe that I picked up a couple of years before the end of the war (and still have in good condition). The next thing to get was acetylene welding gear. I soon got the hang of this and in a very short time, I had taught myself how to use it, being able to weld rusty mudguards and petrol tanks quite successfully, thereby earning myself good money. Things were looking pretty good and work was still piling in and I would soon have to build a bigger workshop to cope with it all. I was getting help from my older brother at weekends. He had taken over the Marshall roller when I left and was still operating in North Hampshire. My two younger brothers were still in the forces waiting to be demobbed.

I had been working on motorbikes for a few weeks and was making a pretty good living, when one morning, right out of the blue, Mr. Ford turned up. He wanted to know how things were going and whether I had any spare time that I could use to help them out (they were by then tied up with John Allen of Oxford, trading as John Allen & Ford). For many years, Allens had been producing their famous Allen Scythes and had sold them in many parts of the world. Almost every County Council in England was using them for cutting the grass on the banks of their roads, (Hampshire and Berkshire were using hundreds of them), but each winter they were sent back to Oxford for overhaul. Those from Hampshire and Berkshire were to go to Wokingham but, as there was no way that they could cope with them, this is where I could help out. I decided that I could, at a pinch, give them two days a week. They built a very nice little workshop for this service and there was also a stores that was stacked with every spare part that would be needed. I would hold the keys for both and was told to run this part of the works as if it was my own.

I would spend a day at Wokingham overhauling the main parts of these machines and then take the engines home to overhaul them in my own workshop. This way, I would not be spending too much time away from home, thereby avoiding upsetting my motorcycle customers and this worked out very well. I spent the whole of that winter this way and just managed to get them all finished, ready for the summer. Unfortunately, I was working under pressure, thereby getting very little time to myself, but I had stood the pace of steam ploughman for a good few years and surely this could be no worse.

I was earning good money (whilst steam ploughing my time was never half paid for) and I now realised that driving a steam roller was a playgame. With this contract finished, I could get down to full time work on the bikes for a few months and catch up on the backlog. There was the odd day when things went a bit wrong and an engine or gearbox would have to be taken apart for a second time to get it perfect. This was when I thought back to the steam engine days, when you could thrash them for weeks on end and they would still come back for more, with just about nothing done to them, year in and year out.

At weekends I was doing a bit of motorbike competition work, either trials, scrambles or even some grass track racing, which I very much enjoyed. I was doing quite a bit of winning, however, I don't think I was that brilliant myself, but my bikes were always dead reliable and just a little bit quicker than most. These were all standard road machines, which I had converted for racing, as genuine competition bikes were few and far between, somewhat different to what it is today.

One Friday afternoon, I was getting one of my bikes ready for a weekend event and who should roll up but Mr. Ford. He had been on his round, paying the roller drivers and called in for a chat to see how things were going and whether I would be prepared to take on the Allen scythe jobs again during the coming winter. He also told me that George Noyce, the yard foreman who had worked for Fords all his life, was past retirement age and so calling it a day in the near future, but they had no one else reliable enough to take on the job. He seemed to be in no hurry to get going and seemed to want to keep chattering, then, right out of the blue, he said "Would you think of coming back to work for us as works' foreman? You know all there is to know about steam engines, you are good with both petrol and diesel engines and, above all, you are dead reliable and a wonderful timekeeper. At the end of the Winnersh yard there are two beautiful bungalows and you can have one of these rent free. You can also fix what your wage packet should be".

This was a big decision to have to make and I would need time to think things over carefully so, before he left, he said "Talk it over with your wife at the weekend and I will call to see you next week". I knew that it would take more than a weekend for both of us to decide what would be best for us on something like this, as we had so much to leave behind at Mortimer. My wife had lived here all her life. I had spent a good few years here and we both had many good friends to leave. I had started to buy the house that we were living in (and are still living in today), a good six roomed house with a big plot of ground. I was well off for work and if things kept going as they were, I had plenty of room to expand, so after much thought we decided to stay put.

On the following Wednesday morning, Mr. Ford came in to see what I had decided upon, but he was disappointed when I told him that I would carry on as I was with my motorbikes and, by then, a fair bit of general engineering. I had, by then, purchased more workshop machinery and could cope with just about anything that came along. Most of the war machinery factories that had sprung up all over the country during the war. were then closing down.

The machines that had been supplied by the War Department to equip the factories were coming to Burghfield, the next village to us, to be sold off and most of them could be purchased at the right price. I managed to get a horizontal milling machine, two drilling machines and two grinding machines so, with my two lathes, I was pretty well set up. Burghfield is now the Royal Ordinance Factory and handles a bit of the hot stuff for the AWRE at Aldermaston. It was built during the war and a railway line had been laid to it from Reading, so this was the ideal spot to hold these machinery sales. Machinery dealers from all over the country turned up in their hundreds, two days a week, to buy these machines, some well worn and some almost new, some big and some small.

I was spending most weekends riding in motorcycle events in the South of England, sometimes going North and into Wales. Mr. Ford knew this, so one Sunday morning, he sent his head man from the office (Mr. Parkin) to call on my wife to try and get her to persuade me to take the job as works' foreman. A few days later, Mr. Ford came and almost begged me to think again, but I was doing well. As much as I loved steam engines, I would give them a miss as it was plain to see that they were doomed.

I applied to our local council for planning permission to build a bigger workshop, so that I could cope with the work that kept piling in.This was passed, but with many strings attached as building materials and labour were still very scarce. I had to use all secondhand materials and do the work myself and because of the way that I was fixed, this was a pretty tall order. But, I always liked a challenge and this would certainly be one.

Around us, there were many war time Army and Air Force camps that were being dismantled, so this would be my only hope for materials. While repairing motorbikes, I had made some friends who were demolishing these sites, so I managed to get a fair supply of windows, concrete blocks and timber together with dozens of sheet steel sections that had been bolted together to make the static water tanks that were set up around the camps, towns and villages during the war.

I was left needing some long heavy timbers for the main structure of my new workshop and these would be my main problem. Much time was spent chasing around to find these, then one day an old pre-war friend turned up to have a chat, he was working for a firm that was clearing up Greenham Common, near Newbury.

This had been a US Air Force base for a few years and was where many of the big Horsa gliders had been taken from their crates and assembled ready for the invasion, but these crates were being broken up and sold off as firewood. The crates were over 40 feet long, but their main frames were built with 8in. by 6in. timbers at the bottom, so that they could be dragged along with no wheels, but they were fitted with thin 3in. square hardened light steel angle. My friend said that I could have what I needed at firewood price, but how was I to get them home as they weighed about four hundredweight each and were over forty feet long.

I tried to get someone with a big wagon to get them home, but without any luck, so I would have to go myself, but my only transport was an old Singer 'Junior' car. This was an 8 hp job and was not very fast on the flat and went dead slow on hills, but it was very reliable. I put two and two together, deciding that I would build myself a trailer and get it home this way. I had to work fast as the timber was being shifted pretty quickly, so I went to the scrapyard and purchased a front axle from an old car, then fitted it up with a drawbar about eight feet long.

An eight foot drawbar is not much use when you have forty foot lengths of timber on it, so a bracket was bolted onto the middle of the axle. This was like two small posts that three of the 8in. pieces of timber could lay between with another clamp, almost the same, bolted to the end of the drawbar and clamped to the pieces of timber. Another clamp, with an eye, was clamped to the end of the timber as a coupling to the back of the old Singer then, with two more lengths of timber, one on each side of the centre (but slightly further back so that when turning corners they did not foul the back of the car), I could bring home five lengths at a time.

The road from Greenham Common to Mortimer is far from straight and with forty feet dragging behind me it was like driving an articulated lorry. I don't think that I would get away with something like this today, but then cops were few and far between and the few that were around then, would shut their eyes to a lot of things that they wouldn't today.

I slogged away every day to get my workshop built, but it was a slow job and work was still piling in, so I had to work most of the day on the building and half the night repairing motorbikes. I was up with the Mortimer larks in the morning (something I had always been used to) and work as a builder up to about four o'clock, have an early tea then get stuck into motorbike repairs, often until well into the morning. Our neighbours often said "You will have a crack up one of these days". However, I had grown up with long hours and had stood the heat and pace of a steam plough engine driver for a good few years, so surely I could cope with this. I did and my workshop is still standing in pretty good shape and is still a hive of industry, being worked by my sons, grandsons and myself.

I had made up my mind when I first started on my own, that I would not get too big and thought of that saying "The higher you go the further it is to fall", so with an occasional bit of help from my brothers, I got by. Not once, right up to the time when I retired, did I pack up for the day and think "I have nothing to do tomorrow". Many jobs came my way, some big, some small. The biggest being a low loader trailer to carry a 10-ton diesel Wallis 'Advance' roller.

A Reading builder had come to Mortimer to build a block of houses and had purchased a new Wallis roller to make the roads, but he would need some transport to shift it from job to job, so someone had put him onto us to see if we could manage such a job. My sons and I talked it over and we decided to have a go, but only if the builder would get all the materials and bring them to us. He said that this would be no problem, so we measured up everything that was needed for the chassis and this was soon with us, so the cutting, drilling and welding was soon on the way. By then, there were plenty of ex-WD wagons being scrapped, so three Bedford axles were delivered to us and within a few weeks a six-wheeled low loader trailer had taken shape.

Our biggest problem was a braking system that would work properly, as the trailer would be towed by a 10-ton ERF wagon that would always have a load on it when transporting the roller. In those days, there were no air brakes on the wagons, so it had to be hydraulics and, of course, the Bedford axles were fitted with this, but they would have to operated by the override on the drawbar. This took a bit of working out, but when finished worked perfectly. For this we used a tandem master cylinder from a scrap wagon. This way, there would be at least one axle with brakes if the others failed.

With this project finished and painted the builder, Mr. Rogers, came to finish paying for it (he had given us some money up front before we started). The Wallis 'Advance' roller was loaded up at the building site (the Avenue, Mortimer) and was on its way to the next job. Mr. Rogers gave us a look-up a few months later to tell us that our trailer was working perfectly and that he was very pleased with it. Before he left, he pushed a bundle of five-pound notes into my hand and said "Before I came to you, I tried several places to get this made and the cheapest one was almost twice your price". When I counted the bundle of fivers it was £150, which was a lot of gold in those days, as this was in the mid-fifties.

A few years before our trailer building job, I took on another contract which took a bit of thinking about. Our Electricity Board, which was then the Wessex Electric, had imported in from Canada hundreds of washing machines, which were the type where the drum just turned backward and forward, being operated by a rack and pinion. But, they had a weak point and were giving a lot of trouble.

There was an aluminium casting, which housed the rack and pinion and this was far too small and nearly all of them had broken where the pinion shaft came through, thereby letting the rack move away from the pinion. When they tried the makers for spares, they found that the firm had gone bust, but the Electricity Board had sold hundreds of these machines all over the South of England. I had never had any training in engineering, but had been around a bit and had always remembered what my father had told me when I left school to join R J & H Wilders. He said "Keep your eyes and ears open, and your mouth shut then you won't go far wrong".

This was a time when doing so had paid off. I had spent some time in the foundry at Wilders, picking up how to make a pattern and a mould, so this casting would be no problem, but it had to be made much stronger than the ones supplied with the machines. I fixed the price, which was accepted, but I would need to have a look at the complete undamaged machine to be sure that there was room for this piece to be 'beefed up'. I still had some small moulding boxes and some sand, which I had been given by the head moulder at Wilders, along with a crucible pot for melting brass or aluminium, so my only need was something to supply the heat. I made my way into Reading, where I purchased a small portable forge. This was a round forge about two feet in diameter with a hand operated fan to blow the fire and this melted aluminium fairly easily.

With a heap of damaged and obsolete motorbike crankcases lying around, I soon got going and could turn out about fifteen castings per day, but these had to be machined. The hole for the pinion bearing was done on the old Drummond lathe, whilst the slot (for the rack to slide in) was done on the shaping machine, as I found this was quicker than milling it out and altogether I produced over 300 of these, all working perfectly with no comebacks.

Over the years, I tackled many tricky jobs and made a lot of parts that had to be made stronger than the originals. Many times, I thought why are these parts skimped when there is plenty of room for them to be made much stronger. This is when one thinks of the steam engine makers and how they got most things right to begin with, as failure of most working parts was unheard of.

I would like to hear from anyone who can point out to me a weakness of any part on the Fowler BB1 ploughing engine as, by the time that these came on the market, they had got everything right. There are still many of them around that have done hundreds of thousands of hours hard slogging and are still in good shape. There are many other makes that are still just as good and this is why I have always maintained that steam is the best power we have ever known.

The years went by with plenty of work coming our way and I was enjoying my weekends, riding motorbikes in scrambles and grass-tracks in summer and trials in winter. I was trying to forget steam engines, as they had become a thing of the past (apart from the odd steam rally now and again, I did not get many chances to look at them).

My older brother, Bert, had left Fords of Wokingham as, like myself, he didn't like diesel powered rollers, but he had managed to get a good job looking after the boilers at the Joint Services Staff College at Latimer in Buckinghamshire. He was living about two miles away at Bedford Close, Chenies, while our younger brothers were still soldiering on with John Allen & Ford at Wokingham.

I would often take a trip into Buckinghamshire to see Bert for a chat, a few cups of tea and spend a few hours in his little workshop in the garden where he was making model steam engines, these were mostly stationary engines. One Sunday, when I was there, I said to him "Why not make a traction engine next?". He thought that this was a good idea, so he soon had a set of drawings and castings for a 1in. scale Fowler 'Tiger' tractor. In just over a year, he and his son between them, had finished this beautiful little engine and it ran like a charm. They were then talking of something a bit bigger.

His son had left the Palladin caravan factory at Hammersham and they were both working together. Between them they had purchased a new Myford 'Super-Seven' lathe and were ready to start something in 2in. scale. I visited them quite often and they had still not made up their minds about what the next project would be, but they were thinking of a 2in. scale Fowler Showman's engine. There were a few things with this that could be hard to come by, one of these would be a suitable dynamo, as the ordinary car or motorbike ones were much too long and so would not look right. One more thing that I pointed out to them, was that they would spend hours making a beautiful crankshaft and link motion only to shut it away, out of sight, with a full length canopy.

They seemed quite keen to have a go at this, but I was trying to persuade them to do something that could be seen more easily if they ever decided to show it at exhibitions or rallies, so I said "Why not a Fowler BB1 ploughing engine? They have a bit more to them than a showman's and everything is there in the open for everyone to see". They saw my point, but a 2in. scale ploughing engine is quite big and a few parts could not be turned on a Myford lathe, so I said "If you get the drawings and castings I will cope with the bigger bits", so a plougher it would be.

The drawings arrived, but they were a bit disappointing to me, as I could see several things that were wrong. The average model maker would know nothing about these points but, when you have stood on the footplate for thousands of hours watching things spin round at high speed, you know what just about everything looks like and if a model does not look right to me, it is never worth the trouble you have put into it.

The drawings for the rope drum coiling gear were altogether wrong and showed the external gear type, which was finished with many years before the BB1 came on the market. This type was used on the old singles for many years, but being out in the open, they collected all the dust and grit. The gears were always well worn so, when the eccentric type came out, with the gears inside and shut away from the dust, it was a big improvement. The external type had one gear wheel on the cam wheel. This had the same number of teeth as there were coils of rope on the drum for two beds, one up and one down, with ten coils up and ten down it had 20 teeth. Keyed to the drum stud was a gear, the same diameter, but with one tooth less than the cam wheel, ie 19 teeth. On one spoke of the rope drum, there was a casting which carried a small pinion which meshed into the two big gears and so pushed the cam wheel round, one tooth for each turn of the drum.

It was my job to sort out the rope drum and coiling gear. This was no problem on the old Drummond lathe but, as there was no place on the casting for the small pinion shaft, we would have to forget about the coiling gear for the time being and hope that some drawings for the proper coiling gear for a BB1 would come about, while we carried on with the other parts.

I made regular visits to Chenies at weekends with bits and pieces that I had machined up through the week and, after about a year, our Fowler BB1 started to take shape. Unfortunately, there were many parts that were correct with the drawings, but looked altogether wrong so, as a result, many parts would not come together. On measuring up the real thing, we found that many parts of the drawings were wrong, so we had wasted a few castings and this is no joke when you have paid a lot of gold for something that is just about useless.

I had packed up riding in motorbike events, as age was beginning to tell for something like this. Instead, I was making regular trips to Chenies to check the progress on our BB1. This was a bit slow as so many parts were being made that did not even look right, although they were true to the drawings. I went there one Sunday to find that Bert and his son, Jim, had spent the evenings of that week making a set of link motion, which turned out a good job, looking very nice, but I could see that the links were far too long, although they were correct to the drawings. When the time came to fit the links, they fouled the top of the boiler, long before they were down to their proper position. This was another week's work down the drain.

A few weeks later, I took a trip to Buckinghamshire and found that Bert was not too good. He had been fitting some new boilers together at work and some of these sections weighed several hundredweight. He had overdone it and was forced to take early retirement, so he would now have more time on his hands for model making, but from then on he did not enjoy very good health and he got very little done in a day. I visited him most weekends, spending the afternoon in the little workshop, then into his house for tea. The rest of the evening was spent sat around the fire chattering the time away, often into the early hours of the morning, even with a 40 mile trip back home in front of me. Our wives would be talking about knitting or sewing or something like that while Bert and I would talk mostly of the days that were gone and those wonderful years that we spent together with the ploughing engines.

Our little BB1 gradually took shape and was then getting a bit heavy to lift about, so there was no way that Bert could do any of this. He was a sick man, so any lifting had to be done at weekends when I was there to help Jim, my nephew, who was a 16-stone giant. (Even so, a 2in. scale ploughing engine weighs over two hundredweight and is not easy to handle.)

The steam bug had started to bite again, so most weekends, through the summer, I was away in the morning to pick up Bert and Jim, then off to a steam rally somewhere or other, leaving the women to do their chattering, while we enjoyed ourselves amongst the things that we had spent the best part of our lives with. If there happened to be steam ploughing or cultivating going on, this was where most of the day would be spent. It really showed up that most of them knew very little about what they were trying to do, but we admired everyone of them for having a go. To us, most of it was pathetic, but we never poked our noses into it, as no one knew who we were or what we knew about the job.

We always remembered that old saying "A still tongue makes a wise head". As the years went by, more and more rallies were coming up and so many different engines were coming out. Most of these were ones that we had never seen or heard of and most of them had been beautifully restored with the odd one turning up as found, mainly looking just a heap of rust but, after a couple of years, they would turn up looking almost as they did the day that they left the works. I take my hat off to everyone who has turned out something like this, as I know how much work must go into a project like this.

Photograph: Buxworth Steam Group.

This photograph shows Tony Marchington on the footplate of his Fowler 7 nhp single **Volunteer** *No. Y9955 at the 27th Anniversary Cromford Steam Rally held on 3rd August 1997. Built in 1913,* **Volunteer** *became part of the Buxworth Steam Group collection in 1996. ...!'* **JOE CHALLIS**

Chapter 10

'Friends - Old and New'

Iwas visiting Bert most weekends, he was far from fit and it seemed to me that he was going down hill fast. He was not the brother that I had known all my life. Before his mishap with the boiler sections at the Latimer College, he was a real tough guy and, like myself, he had never had a day's illness. As ill as he was, he still managed to spend a few hours each day in the workshop, making parts for the Fowler plougher, which was by then almost ready to have pressure in the boiler. We could then see how she was going to perform, but there were still many small parts to be made to complete the job and these are generally the bits that take most time. At last the day came when she was coupled up to the air compressor and, at 40 psi, she worked really well, but we kept her turning over for most of the day to free off all the bearings. We did this several times before all the odds and ends were fitted, then she was ready to be stripped down for painting.

This little Fowler is a replica of *Princess Mary*, works No.15436 Reg.No.NO 1364. She is now in the Avon area and was painted dark green, so it was decided that the model should be painted the same colour and when finished she looked very nice. Each weekend that I visited them at Chenies, I tried to persuade them to put a fire in the box and steam it up. Engines always run better on steam than on compressed air, but they didn't seem to like the idea as they thought that it would discolour the paintwork. I tried to get them to catch on to the idea that a model should look as much like the real thing as possible, as to me all the spit and polish that goes into about 75% of all models around is entirely wrong. None of the real things were like this, apart from the showman's or the odd one that would be going to the Royal Show or some other big event. Engines were just built to tackle the work they were designed for, especially the ploughers which had no fancy work at all on them and most of them that came out during, or just after World War One, didn't even have brass boiler bands. At last they saw my point, so when I pulled up in Bedford Close, Chenies one Sunday afternoon there was little *Princess Mary* in steam, running up and down the path outside the house. That to me was a wonderful sight, looking almost like the real thing had done as we used to make our way across the field towards them in the early morning, to take off the damper and get them steamed up ready for a 5am start.

Both Bert and Jim agreed that it performed much better on steam than on compressed air, but they had one small problem. The pistons were grunting in the cylinders as they had no steam cylinder oil, so I said "Don't try to buy any as I have plenty at home". I had and still do have, more than 15 gallons of Shell B4A the genuine pre-war black treacle-type cylinder oil. The following weekend, with a fill up of this in the little Manzell type pump, she ran just about perfect. The piston rods were black with oil all the time but, as they had warned me, where the oil dropped onto the boiler lagging, it was showing black marks which were hard to remove. She was now running very nicely and was fit to be taken anywhere, so I said "You should take it to some of the steam rallies as it is as good as, if not better than, most that will be there", but they were stumped for transport as Bert had only a 600cc Panther motorbike and sidecar whilst Jim had only a pushbike, so the little plougher just sat in the shed for no one to see.

At that time, I was paying Bert a visit twice a week as his doctor had as good as told us that his days were numbered. However, when the time came, it was a sad day for me. We had worked together for many thousands of hours with the Basildon Estate Fowler K7s and also the K7s, BB1s and 14 hp singles of A J Ward & Sons of Egham. While these wonderful old engines were around, they were about all that we had lived for, our hearts and souls were into steam ploughing and we always prided ourselves that we were a couple of the World's best. I still made my trips to Chenies most weekends, but for several months nothing had been done in the workshop. Jim was a good engineer, but had been used to leaning on his father quite a lot and just couldn't seem to settle down on his own.

Each Sunday that I spent with Jim, I tried hard to get him to have a go at another model of some sort or another, but he did not seem to want to do anything in his workshop. The Myford lathe and all his tools had started to go rusty, so I turned up one Sunday to have a real go at him and said "Look Jim there is hundreds of pounds worth of equipment here going to rack and ruin, while you are getting into a rut. Get your finger out and start doing something or you are going to make yourself ill". I kept away from him for a couple of weeks but, when I did turn up again, I had a bit of a shock. When we had drank our cups of tea, which were always dished up as soon as we arrived, I was taken to the workshop and there, laid out on the bench was a complete set of castings and drawings for a 2in.-scale Fowler showman's engine, a replica of *The Iron Maiden*. We spent the rest of the afternoon and evening weighing up the drawings so that we could make up our minds where to make a start. I left Chenies late that evening, much happier than I had for a good many Sundays, knowing that I had made my nephew at last see sense.

I made my regular trips to see how things were going and it was a pleasure to see Jim busy in his workshop. The little Fowler was taking shape and I soon found myself lumbered with a load of boiler material, this time for a steel one. I had explained to Jim that there was nothing wrong with a steel boiler if it is looked after properly. They come to no harm while they are being used and, if carefully drained out and filled with oil for the winter will last for many years. The only problem with a steel boiler was that they must be tested every year, whilst a copper one is tested every two years.

Jim had a step brother and step sister by his mother's first marriage, but they were both a long way from Chenies, so he saw little of them. The brother was at Blackpool, while the sister was in Australia, so I was his only usual family contact and he always looked forward to the weekends when I turned up for a few hours. The sister in Australia was trying to get her mother to go to spend a few months with her out there and, after a lot of careful thought, she decided to make the trip, although this meant that Jim was now all on his own. As a result, I made my way to Chenies most Friday evenings to pick him up so that he could spend the weekends with us.

We would spend most of the time in my workshop where Jim would be working one of the lathes or milling machines turning out parts for the 2in. Fowler showman's engine and, as he said "Anything that you can do on a small lathe you can do better on a big one". My big lathe is a World War Two 16in. Southbend and is just about as good today as it was when it left the States, it still even has the lease lend tag on it. The engineering works at Little Chalfont, where Jim was now working, was closing down for two weeks holidays, so I asked him if he was going to Blackpool as he had done the previous year or spend the time with us. It didn't take him long to make up his mind, he would be coming to Mortimer. I picked him up on the Friday evening as usual and, at the end of the fortnight with us, he reckoned that it was the best holiday that he had ever had and he looked really sad when we left him at his home on the Sunday evening.

Jim cycled home from work on the Monday evening, lifted the up and over door to his garage, to put his bike away and dropped dead from a heart attack. When his step brother phoned us from Blackpool next morning, we just could not believe it, Jim was 6ft and 15 stone, the sort you would bank your life on. There was a lot of sorting out to be done and Jim's brother, Frank, came down from Blackpool to stay at Bedford Close, Chenies to clear up everything. Their mother was to spend the rest of her life down under so, as a result, there was a lot of phoning to be done across all those thousands of miles. I travelled to Bedford Close every day that week, coming back with a trailer load each time. It's surprising what you collect when you are interested in making model steam engines so, when the time comes to clear my lot up, there will be several lorry loads, mainly model making materials and machinery, but also a lot of old British motorbikes and parts.

The little Fowler tractor, along with Jim's Myford 'Super Seven' lathe, were crated up with a lot of things from the house and sent to Australia. I was to have the partly built Fowler showman's engine, a beam engine and a Stuart Turner vertical engine plus a set of drawings and castings for a Dore-Westbury milling machine, whilst Frank would be going back to Blackpool with the Fowler plougher. I was a bit disappointed with this, but that was their mother's orders and, although I had done a lot of the work to build it, Bert and Jim had done all the paying, so who was I to argue about it. After all, I had brought a lot of money's worth of bits home, of which I have since made good use. Frank gave us a ring quite often for a chat to see how things were going. One Sunday he phoned, giving me a big surprise by saying "Do you think you can come and pick up this ploughing engine as I haven't got the time to look after it properly and it's starting to go rusty. After all it's a Challis product and should be with you so I will write to Australia to tell them what I have done". He didn't have to tell me twice to come and pick it up, so the following weekend I would be up the M6 to Blackpool to spend the weekend with them and bring little *Princess Mary* back with me. My son had just bought a new Hyundai pick-up, so this would be my transport for this trip.

We loaded the engine up, fixing it down to a piece of board, so that it would not roll about while travelling and then made our way back towards home on the Monday. This was the middle of winter and, as we had left it a bit late starting back, we would get back onto the M6 and press on to get as far as possible in daylight. We had got back to the Birmingham area when, in the mirror, I could see lights flashing and gaining on us fast, it was a police Range Rover. I glanced at the speedo which was on 85 mph and I thought that this was it. They rocketed past us, meanwhile I was already braking, expecting them to pull up in front of us, but it must have been our lucky day, they just went on into the distance, then, a few miles on, we joined the queue of traffic, so the cops must have been on their way to sort things out.

Many hours were spent making new parts for the little BB1 as I was not happy with lots of things. The drawings were wrong in lots of places and many of the parts didn't even look right to me. Although it performed quite well, I intended to have things looking about right before it went to any rally. I worked hard on it until mid-summer and, as by then it was looking good and performing well, I entered it for the Woodcote rally. Here many questions were asked and hundreds of photos were taken, so I packed up that evening really happy. There was no security at the model tent, so I took *Princess Mary* back to the top of the field where my caravan was standing. The ground was quite steep and very rough from where cattle had walked about while the ground was wet, but it had now dried out rock hard. I had fixed a piece of nylon rope to the perch bracket and was struggling up the hill with it when a young chap, who I would think was in his mid-twenties, came up to me and said "Is that a BB1?", to which the answer was "Yes" and a long conversation started. I soon learned that he had got a pair of the real things at his father's farm in the Peak district of Derbyshire. To my surprise, he was living in the next village to us, about two miles away, so, when I told him that I had grown up on ploughing engines and had worked them for a living when they were in their hey day, he was over the moon. He said "You must come to Buxworth to meet my parents and talk steam ploughing, then you can have a look round our tackle. You should join the Steam Plough Club as you are the sort of person we are looking for. Genuine steam plough men are few and far between". He was Dr. Tony Marchington, now the proud owner of that famous Fowler showman's engine *The Iron Maiden*.

At the end of the summer, I made my way to Derbyshire with the little BB1, as the Buxworth steam group had decided to run a small rally for a few local people who owned steam engines. This was run in the big car park at the village pub, the 'Navigation Inn' and I had been invited, rather a long way to go, but well worth it. Tony Marchington had his pair of BB1s, *Fame* and *Fortune*, side by side on the canal bank and I was perched at the side of them. All three of them were ticking over all the weekend, a very impressive site and admired by many steam followers, meanwhile Tony was telling them that I was the cat's whiskers with ploughing engines.

On the Monday morning, I hooked up my caravan and made my way up to the other end of the village, to Barren Clough Farm, the home of the Marchington collection. Here we spent most of the week, which was a very enjoyable one, as I was helping to get the ploughers back home and pack them away for the winter. This brought back many wonderful memories, as this was the first time that I had juggled with the levers of a ploughing engine since I left Wards of Egham many years ago. They say that if you learn something properly as a youngster, you never forget it and, believe me, this was once in my lifetime where this showed up. Everything came back to me as if I had only left them the day before.

That week I met all the Marchington family, Frank, Milly and their three sons. They all made us feel very welcome and, between them, they soon started me back in the steam scene, so I feel that I owe them a lot, as I am sure that had it not been for them, I would not have joined the Steam Plough Club or met the many steam enthusiasts that I know today. We have since travelled to Derbyshire several times each year, a distance of over 160 miles each way and we now know almost every inch of the road from Mortimer to Buxworth. We like the country up there very much and the people there even more. We are always made so welcome and could not be treated any better if we were part of the family. I have passed on lots of tips and told them many things about ploughing tackle that they knew very little about and I am sure this has been very much appreciated.

I went back to Derbyshire the next summer to help take the ploughers to their first big rally which was at Lyme Park in Cheshire, close to Stockport and what a time I had there (the BBC film 'A Gamble on Steam' was made here and it has since been shown several times in our area). I got well and truly roped into this event, all unexpectedly, but it was all worthwhile. I had my 2in. model and the two big ones to look after all the weekend, then help get them back home again. While trundling along the A6, with sometimes about half a mile of traffic behind us, it brought back a lot of memories of the times that I had with Wards, working around the London area. The tram lines had been our biggest problem as the trams could not overtake us, so we kept pressing on until there was a break in the oncoming traffic, when we could dive across to the wrong side of the road, to stop and let them go by, perhaps three or four at a time. They used to run about every ten minutes, so it didn't take long to get a few behind us, all clanging away at their bells, which were foot operated, followed by a mouthfull of slang from some of them as they came by.

I have taken the little BB1 to many rallies all over the South, having some wonderful times with thousands of admirers and if I had as many pounds as there have been photos taken of both it and the six furrow anti-balance plough, I would now be pretty rich. It's hard to believe, but I get asked many more questions about the plough than I do of the engine. I think this is because most people know what a steam engine looks like, but a six furrow Fowler anti-balance plough is a different story and it's amazing how few of today's generation have ever seen one. They are big clumsy things, made in several different designs, but all did the same job and in the right hands were capable of doing some real good work. My 2in. model plough was made in ten months without drawings or castings. I made up my mind to make it through being asked so many times "Where is the plough and the other engine?".

I was up in the Peak District spending some time with the Marchingtons at Barren Clough Farm, where Tony has a very old anti-balance plough, a very rare one with rack and pinion travelling axle, so I spent a couple of days taking close up photos and some of the main measurements. This gave me something to go by, but I would have to go quite a bit bigger and heavier, as this one is very spidery compared to the later versions and, of course, was five furrows whereas I wanted six to go with the BB1 engines. I sized it all up very carefully and when you have spent thousands of hours working one of these monsters you know just about what everything looks like. My main problem was getting the right size channel-steel for the frame, the real thing is made mostly from 6in.x3in. channel-steel, so I needed 1in.x$^{1}/_{2}$in. and this was just about unobtainable. I used two pieces of $^{1}/_{2}$in.x$^{1}/_{2}$in.x$^{1}/_{8}$in. angle-steel welded together, which works wonderfully well and looks just right. I fabricated the wheels by turning the rims from big chunks of steel plate, which were over 1in. thick, but this didn't take long on my big lathe. The spokes were cut from steel discs, two for the furrow wheel and two for the land wheel, the furrow wheel, of course, being higher and narrower than the other one. The small wheels at the ends are known as 'skid wheels' or 'depth wheels', these I turned from lumps of aluminium as I did the steering wheels.

I now had the biggest job on my hands, this was the skifes (the main body of each plough) six rights and six lefts. On the real thing these are steel castings and weigh about 2cwt each. They are a very awkward shape to make and, on working out the size of each one, to cut them from solid steel I needed nearly 4 feet of 4$^{1}/_{2}$in.x$^{3}/_{4}$in. steel bar. I managed to get this from our local blacksmith, but I was then in for some hard slogging as a lot of it had to be sawn by hand. I marked out the twelve of them, then set about them with a 1$^{1}/_{4}$in. drill, then a hacksaw and finally the milling machine. In a couple of weeks, I had twelve skifes, which looked just about perfect and the weight of the set was less than a quarter of the weight of the piece of steel that I had started with. The rest of it was in a wheelbarrow full of swarf from the milling and drilling machines. With everything put together, then painted the usual Fowler blue and red, it looked very impressive and worked as good as it looked. I was more than pleased with it, but how far was I from the correct size for everything, one day I might find out.

My second visit to the Lyme Park rally came up and again I was left in charge of the two big ones along with my little engine and plough. Tony had by then purchased a six furrow anti-balance plough which we had with us at the rally, so here was my chance to check on how far I was out with my model. After spending most of the day with my 'stick of inches', paper and pencil, I found that I was within a cat's whisker with just about everything and believe me this really made my day.

I was getting pretty well known by several steam clubs and model societies, so I was being asked by several of them to go to their meetings and give talks on steam ploughing, one of these clubs being the Reading Society of Model Engineers. I made my way to Prospect Park in Reading, which is where they have their railway track and headquarters, taking my little BB1 with me and then had it in steam with the plough alongside. This was admired by many of the members and many questions were asked while we were having our cups of tea at the end of the meeting. While we were chattering, one of the members came over to me and said "Would you be interested in making another one of these to make up the pair?". My answer was, "I have been thinking of this for along time but so far I have not been able to get my hands on a set of castings, they seem to have all dried up". He had a little grin to himself and said "I know where there is a full set going begging" and told me the whole story.

His home, before he came to Reading, was at Ashford in Kent and he had been apprenticed at the railway works there. As part of their training, they had been going to build a pair of 2in.-scale Fowler BB1 ploughers (the same as my own), but as far as I could gather, they did not even finish the first one of them. When the guy that was in charge of the apprentices retired, he took the castings home with him intending to build it himself in his retirement, but had never got down to it. He was now getting rid of it all to make room in his workshop for a railway loco he was in the middle of building. I asked how much it would be going for and he said "Offer him £50. I was down there with him last weekend and he wants to get it out of the way so I am sure that if you go down to Ashford with £50 in notes, he will be quite happy". This was the Thursday evening, so I phoned him at the weekend to make arrangements to go and have a look at what was going.

We made arrangements to meet at his house around mid-day on the Monday, so I set off from home in good time to make sure that I would find his house by mid-day. I got a bit lost in the town which was quite busy, but once on the right road, I soon found his home and arrived there spot on 12 o'clock. He took me into a spare room where he had laid everything out on the floor and believe me, when we had got it all into my Audi estate car, it was a full load. There was a full set of jigs, in all shapes and sizes made from heavy pieces of steel plate, a set of front and rear wheels, formers for the boiler plates plus many more. (The racket it made on the way home was unbelievable, so I was glad when we reached home.)

With everything loaded up, we went back in for a cup of tea and to get settled up for the load of bits that I was very pleased with. I said "How much do I owe you?", expecting to pay a fair sum for all the jigs alone, plus at least £50 for the castings. He cast his eyes around the heap of ironmongery and said "Will you give me £40 for it?". I promptly said "No. I will give you £50 and I will be more than happy, if you will". I paid him, shook hands and I was soon on my way home with almost as much noise behind me as there is from an engineering works, but it was all worthwhile and the No.2 engine is now well on the way.

I was at the Woodcote Rally for the third time and as usual was having a browse round the stalls when I noticed that the NTET had for sale a new edition of the 'Traction Engine Register'. I already had one of the early ones and thought that, by then, there must be a few more engines come to light, so I purchased one of them. That same evening, I was sat in my caravan having a scan through it to see what was new and to my surprise amongst the Marshall rollers was No.83412, the one I had carefully looked after for 12 years, I could hardly believe what I was seeing. Just after the war, we had been told that all the other engines that had gone to India had come back to be sold off at Bordon, but my pride and joy was not amongst them, so we thought that she was still back in Calcutta or somewhere in India. The burning question was, how had it come back and been sold off unnoticed?

On the Monday evening, I found the phone number of the guy at Oxford who had compiled the new register and gave him a call. It's hard to believe, but he told me exactly where she was in less than one minute, so I said to him "Are you sure that this is the right one as the work's number is correct but the registration number is wrong". He promptly said "It was re-registered when it came back from India. Is the one that you are looking for the one that was registered in Reading in 1927 as RX 2099? If so, this is the one". I could hardly believe what he was telling me after all those years. With pen and paper at the ready, I soon had the address of where she was standing, although I already had some idea that this was a long way from my home, as the location in the register was Flint, which, of course, is in North Wales. She was owned by Tunnel Cement and was at Seffn Mawr Quarry, Mold. I did a bit of research myself and found the phone number of the quarry manager, so I gave him a ring to tell him what I knew about his engine. He said "You have already told me more than we ever knew about it, you must come and have a look at it then we can have a chat about it".

Within a week, I had hooked up my caravan and was making the long trip to Mold. I soon found the quarry, which is up a narrow road up into the hills and made my way into the manager's office. We had a long chat about the roller, then he said "You had better come and have a look at it before you make your way back home." I expected to find it all spick and span but, as we made our way down to the building where the old girl was standing, he said "It is in a bit of a state at the moment", this I soon saw. When we reached the open fronted shed I saw that she was almost buried with parts of earth moving machinery and the like, but worst of all, she was covered in about an inch-thick layer of limestone dust. My wife was with me and she has said several times since, that there were tears in my eyes as we came back up the yard to the office. Before we left, I said to him "You should be locked up for letting a wonderful tool like this get in such a state", to which his answer was "We have had to cut our labour force quite a bit and our fitters can hardly manage to keep the stone working machinery going so I can't see much being done to it for a long time". I said to him "Do you think the firm would consider selling it?". He told me that "Tunnel Cement is a big concern so this would have to go through a lot of departments before anyone could say yes but, if you write me a letter explaining what you know about No.83412 and that you would like to buy it, I will see what I can do". That afternoon we left Seffn Mawr Quarry a bit disgusted at the state she was in, but, perhaps I would be able to purchase her before long.

We made our way back towards Chester, a city that we had never had a look around and found a very nice caravan site on the outskirts of the city. We spent best part of a week here and, on exploring Chester, found it to be a beautiful place. On our way through, from Mold to Chester, we passed through a small town called Padeswood and here is the cement factory where all the stone from Seffn Mawr Quarry is used. What a place this is, it is a town on its own and a place where a stranger could soon get lost.

The weeks and months went by with not a word from the cement people. I was thinking that they didn't want to play, otherwise I would have heard something before now, or had my letter not been passed on to the people concerned, so should I chase them up again. We had spent a weekend at a rally in Derbyshire and was spending a week at Buxworth with the Marchingtons, when I realised that, from here to Mold is a much shorter trip than from my home at Mortimer. Out came the maps and the route was soon sorted out, this would be Macclesfield, Holmes Chapel, Middlewich and Chester. The next morning, we were away in good time and so were in Mold, having a meal before mid-day, then on to the quarry, where the manager was more than surprised that I had heard nothing, so he gave me the London address of the firm so that I could write to them directly myself. This I did, but still I heard nothing for weeks, by when I had more or less decided to forget about it. Then a letter arrived from the Padeswood cement works, saying that they had decided to let their own workers restore it at the Padeswood works. There would be a steam club formed and they would like me to join this club and become a committee member, going to the works whenever I wished to help in the restoration of the old girl.

From then on, I made many trips to Padeswood to see the old Marshall being stripped out and got ready for restoring. There was very little to be done in the way of repairs, as she was in quite good shape apart from the boiler lagging, which had rusted through in places and a little bit of welding needed on the coal bunker, so she was soon ready for painting. The fusible plug had not been out for many years, but this had to be removed for the boiler inspection and this was where the first bit of trouble started. When it was eventually shifted, it pulled out part of the thread in the top of the firebox. In most makes of engines, the plugs are $3/4$in. BSP, so the firebox would now have to be built up and rethreaded. This should be no problem, as there were some good welders at the works. They had a wonderful workshop and stores, which was stocked with just about everything that was needed to run a place like the Padeswood Cement works and in that stores was something very unusual, a set of $^7/_8$in. BSP taps, so the damaged thread was cleaned out, then tapped out to $^7/_8$in. and a new plug made in the workshop to suit, so the problem was over.

New lagging panels were made and fitted then she was ready for painting, but this, as far as I could see, was the first thing to be wrong. The guy in charge of the job was Mervyn Foulkes, he had written to Marshalls for information about the colour and the lining, but they had told him that the colour was Mid-Brunswick green, so this was what was ordered. I was not too happy about this, but they did not seem to be too fussy on the colour, so Mid-Brunswick green it would be. I had seen this engine delivered new to Newbury District Council and, after a few years, had myself carefully looked after it for another 12 years. The colour was rather unusual. It was not maroon, but more a purple brown or plum colour so, with its extra wide stainless steel boiler bands, she looked very nice and when she was taken from me, most of the paintwork was still in very nice condition. With the painting and lining finished, the old girl looked really smart once again, but this was ruined by the short metal cab that had been fitted. The brass 'Britannia' which was fitted on the front of the saddle on all Marshall rollers, had long been missing, so I said to Mervyn "If you make a new full length wooden cab, as she was fitted with when new, I will make you a new brass 'Britannia' for the front," so this was decided on. The carpenters at the works set about this job and when finished it looked very nice. While this was going on, I had made arrangements with a Marshall owning friend in Sussex that, when the rally season was over, he would lend me his 'Britannia' for a pattern to cast the replacement.

At the end of the summer, I went off to the Amberley Chalk Pits Museum where his engine would be stored for the winter and returned home with this valuable piece of brass work. I still had some moulding boxes and sand that I had managed to get hold of from Wilders of Wallingford, many years ago, so some scrap brass was rounded up and my portable furnace dug out from the back of the workshop. I soon had a very nice casting of the Marshall trade mark ready to be buffed up and taken to Padeswood, where it was soon fitted and so finished No.83412 ready for any rally. If ever anyone gets the chance to purchase this wonderful old engine at some future date, if you remove the 'Britannia' you will find my name and the date stamped into the back of it. I haven't been in touch with the Padeswood people for a couple of years now and, as I have neither yet seen the old Marshall at a rally, nor have I seen any thing about her in 'World's Fair', I can only assume that she must be just laying idle in the shed where no one can see her. What a great shame this is, but I expect the problem is that no one will spend a weekend to drive the low-loader as it all has to be voluntary work.

Through each summer, I still go to the different rallies with my little BB1 and plough, often getting the chance to get up on the footplate of someone's ploughing engine and have a few pulls or, perhaps, even spend a whole day doing just that. It's a bit of an effort to climb up into one of these monsters at almost 85 years young, but once up there, I can still hold time with the next best one that comes along. I still have the gentle touch of the regulator and can manage all the other levers as well as I did over 70 years ago. Almost two years ago, I spent almost a day at Hadlow in Kent helping to make a film 'Farming with Steam'. Here, I had a few hours on a Fowler AA6 with a 5-furrow anti-balance plough, plus spending a lot of time talking about how it was done, how we lived and survived the long scorching summer days, which I can assure you was no picnic. As I have said many times over the years, none of today's generation would stand for what we did, we were a breed apart from the others.

Photograph: Buxworth Steam Group.

'This illustration gives the driver's eye view while stood on the footplate of a Fowler BB1 Plougher. There was no shelter of any description for the driver and after a hard day's ploughing during wet or wintry weather, it was a relief to relax in the warm living van ...!' **JOE CHALLIS**

Chapter 11

'Reminiscences'

O ver the last few years, I have been to many different clubs to give talks on steam ploughing and have passed on many useful tips to steam plough engine owners. I will finish off this book with some more useful tips for the would be steam ploughman, as there are many things to know about this job that are not in books. The people that worked ploughing engines when they were in their heyday, are now a bit thin on the ground.

As I have said many times, the most important part of a ploughing engine is that lump of ironmongery that hangs under the boiler, ie the rope drum, its rope and the coiling gear. If these are not working properly you will get nowhere fast. The oiling of these parts is quite easy as, on most of the Fowler engines, there is an oil box on the back end of the left-hand hornplate, which is close at hand to the footplate and this box has three pipes leading down to the main parts. The drain pipe from the tray under the link motion takes care of the coiling gear, so the only two parts that you must make sure of with the oil feeder are the pulleys on the 'monkey head' and the jaws of the clutch. If these jaws get dry, your clutch will fly out and there is no way that you will hold it in but, if oiled properly, there is no way that you will get it out whilst under load.

The coiling of your rope will depend a lot on the way your engine is standing, the ideal position for your engine is to lean slightly away from the work. If the headland is sloping the wrong way, you can nearly always overcome this with a few shovels full of earth under the low rear wheel. It is surprising how little earth it takes and this can always be found within a few yards from the point where the cultivator has turned or the plough has pitched in. If you try to work with your engine leaning into the work, the rope will not turn properly at the top, often putting two or even three coils on top of each other, these then go down with a bang, often crossing over one another, thereby sometimes tying a knot which can be very harmful to the rope.

The drum brake must also be taken care of and kept oiled, for if it runs dry it will judder, making a grunting noise and taking a lot of power from the other engine. This also wears the brake blocks out quicker than normal. If you have had a heavy storm or wet night or weekend, on no account should you start working until the water has been mopped out of the cavity between the gear ring and the brake. The oil and water mixture is as slippery as ice, causing your brake to be useless, so the rope soon goes all over the place (I have known it to come outside the guards and get into the teeth of the pinion). If you have a look at the top of the drum, where the brake band rests, there are a series of slots for draining the water out, but these often get blocked and, even when clear, they do not take all the water out, so a piece of rag used as a mop is always the drill before starting after a rain.

If you are using the old singles with tank-steerage and are setting out to start a field where the ground is uneven, always hook the rope from the other engine onto the front of yours and then make your way backwards across the field. Most of these engines have a brake on the steering shaft, just below the steering wheel, screw this on so that you can just turn the wheel, put the toes of your boots into the hole where you shovel the coal from and make your way across the field. This way, with your knees against the coal bunker, you have much more power than when just stood on the steering step. Your toes will stop you from being lifted off the engine if you decide to hang on when there is a hump or hole on one side. Also, this way, your rear wheels will often iron out the lumps and will give you the message when to hang on, but never go backwards with someone stood on the step steering for you, I have always found it is far better to do it yourself.

One of our biggest problems was getting the engines from a narrow country lane into the field, often through a ten foot gateway, but this could nearly always be overcome with a few shunts and a bit of careful regulator control. With your implement behind you, stop just before you get to the gateway and uncouple it, then take your engine past the gateway until the rear end is level with the entrance. If the field is on your right, put one of your wheel spuds in front of the left-hand front wheel and go forward another foot or two so that you are now on full left lock. Now place another of your spuds with the flat side up behind the left rear wheel, then reverse back steadily. That wheel will not go over the spud, so instead it will slip, taking the stress from the axle and allowing the other wheel to do the work. Your front wheel spud should now be put slanting behind the wheel and this will slide the front of your engine over about a foot each time, so with a few shunts you are soon crossways on the road and ready to go straight into the gateway. Once inside, pull out a few yards of rope to deal with the implements. If the field is on your left you simply reverse the procedure.

Some of the gateways were just about impossible to get through, so one gatepost had to come out and this could be done with very little damage to it. You get your front wheels through the gateway, then put the rear wheel against the post, pushing it slightly to loosen it, then put a sack round the post, get the sling chain and thread it through the ring on its end, so forming a slip knot which can be dropped over the post (making sure that the sack

260

is under it). The hook end of the chain is then put over the top of the wheel and down onto one of the spokes, then gently go backwards and the post is lifted out with very little damage, ready to be put back into place when you are out of the field.

There was nearly always some good coal to be used, so keeping steam up was no problem, if you fired them the right way. This was always a thin fire, keep the clinkers out of the firebox and just enough fire to cover the bars. With a BB1 or K7, you could pull in a full length of rope with the regulator wide open and the steam gauge would stay on the red mark all the time but, as you shut down a bit, when the cultivator got near to you, they would start to blow off, so on would go the injector.

A BB was just a bit slower making steam, so that is why the firebox was lengthened by 3in. on the BB1 and this made all the difference. One more thing that we always made sure of, was to keep the ashpan cleaned out, as a fire on both sides of the firebars soon burns them out.

If everything is kept well oiled, there is very little that needs to be done to a ploughing engine. I have thrashed them, day in and day out, with seldom a spanner or hammer needed, but it is always best to have your tools, so that you know where to find what you want quickly. Don't have your toolbox like a marine store, a place for everything and everything in its place. I always found that, if ever a tool was needed in a hurry, it was whilst travelling on long journeys from job to job and the crankshaft was spinning at high speed for hours at a time. This is when it is not easy to see a bearing that is running a bit warm.

There was always one thing in our toolboxes that was not used on the engines, but was always kept in a small sack in one corner of the front box. This was a few rabbit snares which we were experts at setting, living chiefly from the farms either by fair means or foul.

If you have a long journey in front of you, always get going early in the morning. It is an old saying that "Every hour in the morning is worth every two in the afternoon" and I have proved how true that is many times during my lifetime. A BB1 is a wonderful engine for long journeys, as they are geared low in low gear and the reverse in top gear. I am sure that, in the right hands, it could hold time with a three-speed road engine. They are light on coal and water, as there is so much power on tap all the time and you never change gear for hills, their normal load is peanuts to them.

Another task that needs doing correctly is the fitting of a new rope. First of all, you must find a field long enough to take almost all of your length of rope. You must then get your engine stood nice and level, or better still leaning slightly away from its work. With your rope pulled out almost to its full length, the next job is to bend the end of the new rope at right angles, at a point about 2 feet from its end. This is best done using a piece of 1in. water pipe about a foot long, place this over the end of the rope, then put this in the coupling on the back of the engine and bend the rope to a sharp right-angle.

Drive a bar into the ground in front of the coiling lever, this will stop the lever from following the drum round (which it tends to do with no rope on it). One of the gang now stands by the 'monkey head' while the driver engages the clutch and starts the drum turning (the clutch lever will have to be held up while you are doing this as, with no load on it, it will not stay up). The coiling lever must now be watched carefully to see when it reaches it lowest point, then put a chalk mark on the bar in line with the top or bottom of the coiling lever. Run the engine while the coiling lever does its full travel, up and down, to make sure that you are right with your mark (it is time well spent), then stop the engine as soon as it reaches its lowest point again. Push the drum round backwards so that the slot, for the rope to pass through, is at the front in line with the centre of the front axle.

Now get a small bar or piece of pipe about the same diameter as the rope and push it through the wheels on the 'monkey head', this must now be adjusted so that the bar is resting on the bottom wheel and laying flat on the bottom of the drum. The rope must now be passed through the wheels of the 'monkey head', then through the slot at the bottom of the drum and clamped up good and tight with the clamp bolt. If you have made a good right-angle bend in the rope and pushed it back tight to the drum before clamping up, your first coil will start properly.

The rest of the gang now hang onto the rope and keep it tight, while the first four or five coils are wound on. You must now put a good load onto the rope for the rest of its length, the ideal load is the sister engine in top gear with the drain taps open. Make sure that first bed goes on properly as, if this one is not right, none of the rest will be.

I have found in the past that all ropes are not the same, you get one that goes on perfectly, then another one will need to be wound on two or three times (with a good load on it), before it runs properly. It seems that some are not twisted as tight as others, so they are, therefore, slightly bigger in diameter and must be loaded heavier to pull it into shape. One thing to remember is to always use a swivel shackle to couple your rope to the load, then stop pulling about every 200 yards so that the swivel shackle can spin back and allow the rope to unwind any twisting.

Boiler care was very important, as we were nearly always under pressure with a long list of farmers waiting for us especially during and just after harvest time. However, we always found time to wash out the boilers every fortnight. Most Fowler engines have a brass plate, that can be seen from the footplate, which says "Wash out the boiler after every hundred hours working" and this worked out to be about a fortnight for most traction engines. On the ploughers, we always clocked up about 200 hours in a fortnight and, depending upon where our water had come from (which in those days was nearly always from ponds or streams), the mud would be up over the first row of stays. A ploughing engine that is on full song from daylight until dark in the long days, consumes a lot of water.

A dirty boiler is the cause of priming, also, when an engine is running on half steam and half water, it does a lot of harm as it washes the oil off the pistons and valve faces, thereby ruining the gland packing. The regulator becomes much harder to move, as it is sliding on mud instead of a nice smooth face, thereby making hard work for the driver. Unlike the market gardens around London and the big flat fields on the east side of the country, the fields in my part of the globe are all very hilly, some of them quite steep and working a ploughing engine on steep hills is a far different kettle of fish to working on the flat. Many times, I have started working in the morning with the engine head down on the hill but, by mid-day, the other half of the field would be steep uphill or vice versa and on this type of going the driver has a lot more to think about than when on level ground.

The length of the boiler on a plougher makes it far different to a normal traction engine. I have worked ploughing engines good and hard for hours at a time, with the water just showing in the bottom gland nut of the gauge glass. At times there would be water coming from the piston rod glands, as the water at the front of the boiler was close to the cylinder block and if your boiler is dirty, you are then soon in trouble.

Many drivers think that working head uphill allows you to press on regardless, but this is not so, as, with a ploughing engine, you must make sure that you keep your boiler well filled or you can do a lot of damage to the front end of your tubes and the tubeplate. A ploughing engine on full song for hours at a time, with no water at the front end, will soon have red hot tubes and they will soon be burnt out.

All these things were drummed into me by my father on the Basildon Estate with the K7s when I was only knee high to a grasshopper. With well over five and half thousand acres on that estate, I don't think that there was one really flat field and some of the hills were really steep, so I had a good training on this type of going. Keeping your boiler well filled whilst working up a steep hill is no problem, although your glass is full all the time, there is no way that you can see where the water level is. However, there is a way that allows you to tell if you are on the right line.

On top of the boiler, on most Fowler ploughers, there is a master valve for the injector and water lifter steam pipes. Underneath this, inside the boiler, there is a pipe which feeds this valve and it draws its supply from a hole at the cylinder base. This means that you can fill your boiler right up when stood head uphill, as the injector will not work once you start feeding it with water instead of steam.

Another tip (once again from my father) for keeping the water level right in this position, is to slacken off the gland nut at the master valve and leave it like this while working on the hill. As a result, whenever you move forward, when the water is high enough, instead of a wisp of steam coming from the master valve gland, it will be water.

A further tip while working uphill is to keep your engine well scotched up. A small wedge shaped block is useless for this as, if the field is sloping out and the rope is tending to pull you back, you only have to have the cultivator hook into a big flint or something and you are back over the block, away down the hill a bit quicker than you came up, with nothing that you can do to stop it. The scotch block that you need for this is a piece of a tree trunk about 12in. or 14in. diameter, by about 2 feet long, with a piece of light chain stapled to the centre of one end and a hook on the other end of the chain. This is then hooked onto the side of the tender, so that, as you move forward, it is pulled along with you and then, when you have moved far enough, you can stay put on the footplate using the chain to pull the block up behind the wheel. The block needs to be pulled up so that it stands on end behind the wheel, then reversing back onto it pushing the end of the block into the ground. This way you have a block about 18in. high to get over. This is all very fine, but on really steep slopes you can't just rely on this block, you must put the big sling chain (which is always pinned to the coupling on the back of the tender) through the wheel and back to the coupling, this way you are doubly safe.

All through the Thames Valley, from Maidenhead northwards to Oxford and beyond, on both sides of the river, the fields are all hills or valleys. The Chilterns on the Oxfordshire side and the Berkshire Downs on the other. Going west through the Kennet Valley is about the same, right through to Marlborough and the Wiltshire Downs. These are some of the areas where I grew up and worked ploughing engines for a good few years, nine of them at Basildon, two in the Chilterns with Wilders of Wallingford and several years through the Kennet Valley and into Wiltshire with Wards of Egham.

Whilst on the subject of burnt out tubes, something else has crossed my mind. I once had the pleasure of coaxing home, from wildest Hampshire to Egham in Surrey, a 10-ton Aveling & Porter roller that had received some of this treatment. At Hurstbourne Tarrant, on the A343 Andover to Newbury road, there is a long steep hill which, like much of Hampshire, is all chalk. On this sort of going, unless there is a thick coat of stone or tarmac, enough to keep out the frost in hard weather, you get trouble. Chalk, when frozen, blows up just like the carbide in our gas lamps, when water had been added. Well, this is what had happened here. The bright spark that was driving her had spent over three months on this hill scarifying then punching up and down over 6in. coats of 3in. limestone, all the time with about half a glass of water, resulting in doing a lot of damage to the front of the boiler. He had finished the job and was to move onto Picket Piece, near Andover, but had phoned Egham saying that he could not go until something had been done to his tubes, as they were all leaking at the front end.

When Sid Ward arrived with the boilersmith and found what had been going on, he sacked the driver on the spot, as there was nothing to be done apart from fitting a new set of tubes, the existing ones being burnt so thin that there was almost nothing left. Yours truly clicked for the job of getting her home. I always made it a rule, when travelling on strange roads with the ploughers, to keep the glass filled to the top as, if you find yourself at the top of a steep hill with half a glass of water, a lot of valuable time is wasted whilst filling the boiler to make her safe to start down. It is also nice to know that you are all right for a couple of miles, if you find yourself running low in the tank.

Apart from the cylinders, which is fed by a force pump, all the other moving parts are fed by oil cups with syphons. These, if looked after properly, give very little trouble, but it is best to renew the syphons occasionally, as they sometimes clog up or stop working for some unknown reason. I always kept a few ready made ones in a small tin in the toolbox. These syphons are easy to make using pieces of about 20G copper wire and a few strands of knitting wool, but they must be the correct length (all the Fowler oil cups are a standard size). You must make sure your syphons are long enough to almost reach the shaft that they are feeding, but with enough wire to bend over at the top of the feed pipe to stop them from dropping any further. This is most important as, if the wire gets into the bearing, it makes a right mess of it. However, it must be close enough to the bearing to make sure that the feed end of it is below the bottom of the oil cup as no syphon will work if the outlet end is higher than the feed end.

One thing to remember, is to make sure that the wool at the feed end goes right to the end of the wire, as it's the wool that syphons the oil not the wire. There is very little else that needs to be oiled apart from the pulleys on the 'monkey head' and most of all, the jaws of the rope clutch. If these get dry, your clutch will work its way out and you will wonder what has happened. The three syphons, in the little cast iron box, that feed the upright shaft and drum stud, etc are all the same as the ones in the other oil cups.

It is not much use having two good engines, if your implements are not up to scratch. We used to reckon that they were our bread and butter, so every spare half hour was spent on them, so keeping them in good condition. The cultivator was the one that was used most and, no doubt, took more pastings than the rest of the implements put together. It seemed to stand up to its work remarkably well, being built very robustly and about the only thing that gave us trouble were bent tines, but this was to be expected as they were not made for removing tree roots. While we were clearing orchards around the London market gardens, our cultivator really took some stick as there were many large roots still left in the ground that had been broken off when the trees came out. Some of these were about 4in. in diameter and did our tines no good at all.

On normal going a cultivator gave very little trouble if kept oiled properly. The wheels, etc had a very hard life, as the dust and grit worked their way into the bearings, then mixed with the oil to form a grinding paste. As a result, the drill for oiling was little but often. This is especially true for the front wheel turntable, I have seen this taken apart several times and every one of them had square ball bearings instead of the original round ones. They had been ground away by the mixture of sand and oil, but they still seemed to work quite well.

One thing to remember, if you are working very hard ground, is never pull the lever to drop the cultivator tines in after it has turned unless it is on the move, this will smash the tine points as fast as you can put them on. Good drivers and cultivator men are always on the look out for tines that have lost their point as, if left for only a couple of pulls, a dull point on our ground in the Thames Valley will be finished, as the point will then fit like a square peg in a round hole. Some of the later cultivators were fitted with an hydraulic cylinder to lower it steadily into the ground, but these never seemed to last very long. As with the wheels, the oil and dust on the cylinder's piston rod soon ruined the seal, letting the oil pour out as fast as you could fill it up, making it a useless piece of ironmongery.

The harrows, or drags as they were sometimes called, gave very little trouble. The main thing being the tines which, on our soil, would wear out fairly quickly, meaning that they would have to be taken to the nearest blacksmith to be sharpened or, as we would say, drawn out to a chisel point and hardened. For travelling on the road, the tines of the fold up wings would have to be taken out each time and then replaced when you reached the next field. This sounds a bit of a bind but, if you go the right way about it, is no problem and can be done by a good team in a very short time. These tines have several holes drilled in them, at about 1in. intervals, starting from the top to about halfway down the part that fits in the socket. With something in these holes (we used a piece of thick wire made up like a giant key-ring), the tines could not fall out if the wedges holding them worked loose and came out. The rings were easy to take out and replace, but when removed, we marked the hole with a chisel to enable us to replace it at the correct depth quickly, thereby saving us a lot of time.

The fold up wings are pretty heavy and are just about as much as two can lift. This was always done by numbers (1, 2 and up), always standing with your feet close together, as if you do heavy lifting with your feet apart, you are asking for trouble. We often had fields with sides curved inwards like a rainbow, so with both engines right into their corners, the harrows had to go another 50 yards further out in the middle of the pull. As a cookboy on those Oxfordshire hills around Goring and Crowmarsh, I have spent many hours travelling on the wing, hanging onto the rope guard over the skid wheel. This way, the side that you are on goes into the ground deeper, so pulling the harrows that way and it's surprising how far out of straight you can get by doing this.

The plough is the most important implement of the lot and, if you are hoping to do a good job, time must be spent keeping it up to scratch. Today, with the big tractor ploughs, they don't seem to take much pride in their work and, as long as it is turned over, that is all that matters. How things on the farms have changed over the years. Anything seems to do these days and I am sure that if we had turned out work like some that I see being done today, we would have had our marching orders a bit quick. Each plough skife, mould board and coulter is fully adjustable on the Fowler ploughs, as are the travelling axle and skid wheels for depth so, if you know your job, some good work can be done with these monsters. Using chains and weights, it is surprising how much trash you can bury. I have ploughed fields of mustard that was almost knee high and made a perfect job of it.

The best way to set your plough up properly is to put on a new set of plough shares at both ends, then stretch a line from the tip of the front one to the tip of the rear one, then any error on the ones in between can be set by the stepped washers or set screws (whichever you have). Using their fixing bolts, the skifes can be moved sideways and up or down, this way all the points of the shares can be brought into a straight line. You must now set the coulters to suit each plough. With the blade type, the front edge needs to be just a little behind the tip of the share and with room for two fingers between the end of the blade and the share. I am not going into using disc coulters as we never used them. They were not much use on our stony ground, but I would think that the setting would be about the same as for blades.

The next job is the mould boards, which are best set with a line, first along their bottom, then along their outer edges and they can be adjusted by the stay bars. With the earlier ploughs this was not so easy, as the stays, instead of being straight, were cranked at right angles and slid in a bracket with a nut and washer at both top and bottom. The drill with these was to just slacken the nut and do the rest with a heavy hammer, then tighten up again, hoping that it didn't move while you were using the big spanner.

When steering the plough, you don't sit straight behind the wheel, but sit slightly sideways and lean out towards the work you have done, looking along the furrow making it easier to keep the furrows straight. The best reason of all for this position, is so that if the rope on the engine is not coiling properly and you are directly behind the steering wheel, it is quite easy to get a smack in the face with the wheel as, when the rope jumps, you are inclined to pitch forward whilst the wheel is coming back towards you.

As your plough shares wear, you will see that the point begins to turn up and so tends to lift the plough out of the ground a bit. However, the shares are reversible, so when they are placed on the opposite end they tend to dig in and you will straight away notice the difference. You are then ready for a few more acres before scrapping the shares. While looking at some of the ploughs that turn up for a demonstration on ploughing, I see that some of the shares are held in place by nuts and bolts or by nails. This is entirely unnecessary, as a small wooden peg does the job just the same and is so much quicker and easier when the time comes to renew them.

While around the farms, we always had our eyes open for used rick pegs, which had held the thatch down on the corn or hay ricks. They were nearly always made from seasoned hazel and were very tough and ideal for our requirements. With a good sharp pocket knife, they could be put into shape with no problem, so this was a job for the guy that was sitting on the back of the plough as he made his way across the field.

If your shares are a bit slack on the spigot of the skife, a piece of leather will put this right. We always used the tops of worn out boots for this job and believe me, we went through boots at a fair rate. This was especially true for the drivers, as we always shut the firehole door with our foot. This must have been done many times in a day and of course the door was almost red hot all the time and so, did the soles of our boots no good at all.

Some of these tips may be useful to some of the present day owners of ploughing tackle who were not as fortunate as I was in getting such a wonderful training as I had from my father and those Basildon Estate Fowler K7s. During my nine years at school, I must have spent as much time on the ploughers as I did at school. Almost every day, all through the spring, summer and autumn, I would go straight from school to the ploughers and be there until almost dark. I am sure that this paid off, as by the time that I left school, at fourteen years young, there was very little that I didn't know about running a set of ploughing tackle. When I started earning my living with ploughing engines everything to me was just a playgame and I never looked back

I was a full blown driver for Wards of Egham at sixteen and a half, and in charge of their best set three months before my nineteenth birthday (but Sid Ward thought that I was about three years older) and I think that this must be a record. Judging by some of the things that have been spoken about me in the past, I think I must have been a bit of an ace with steam engines.

While working for Fords of Wokingham, I had the job of bringing home, from way down in Hampshire, a 14-ton Marshall 'S'-type single cylinder roller which had been badly neglected and was just about a total wreck. The big end was hammering like a blacksmith and what appeared to be water was running from the front end of the tubes, although, this turned out to be from the wash out plug ring at the bottom of the tubeplate. The plug had been cooked up through working on hills with not enough water to cover the front end but, luckily for us, the tubes were still dry. With these Marshalls, below the bottom of the smokebox door is a small lid for cleaning out the ashes, so I opened this and chiselled out the rubbish, leaving the little cover open, so that the water could run out instead of coming back through the tubes as a constant trickle. Unfortunately, if it got worse, we were in trouble, as the bridge of the plug and the nut that held it were one big cake of rust, obviously having never been shifted for years. Mr. Ford had taken our works' foreman and myself out to this roller and was to pick us up later in the day after we had struggled along for a few miles. We started off, but before we had covered the first mile, the rear axle bearing on the right-hand side started to grind and made expensive noises, so we had another problem on our hands.

On these Marshalls, there is an oil cup on the side of the hornplates with a copper pipe down to the axle bearing and this, by the look of things, had been blocked for months. I unbolted the steel plate that is bolted to the front of the footplate to cover the axle and removed the pipe. Sure enough the hole into the bearing was blocked solid and was almost as hard as rock. With this cleared, I thought that we would be back in business again, but this was not to be as the oilways in the bearing were worn away, so no oil could get through. George, our work's foreman said that there would be no axle left by the time we had got back to Wokingham. I had a little grin at him and said "We are not sunk yet" and got busy with the scarifier hand wheel. By screwing the scarifier down, I lifted the engine and sure enough the oil started to run, so I said to George "If we do this every few miles with cylinder oil we will make it" and it worked.

269

We had not gone far that day, when Mr. Ford came to pick us up and he followed us along for quite a way before we found somewhere to pull off the road for the night. This was a wide place on the side of the road, but before we reached this, we had a steep hill to go down, but the daylight was fading fast, so to save time I left her in top gear, whereas I should have changed down. We got about halfway down with the reverse lever well back, but we were still hammering along at a fair bat when disaster struck. The front cylinder cover gasket blew out and we were away. We reached the bottom of the hill safely, but George started to panic and he said "What are we going to do now?" and Mr. Ford said "We are surely in trouble now?". I said to them "Don't panic. I expect there is some asbestos string in the toolbox or living van", however they both seemed to think that this would be of no use.

While I was taking the cover off, George found a roll of asbestos string, so I cleaned off the old bits of gasket with my pocket knife and put one turn of the string around each stud until I had a complete circle round the cylinder. The cover was put back on and not a wisp of steam came from it, leaving them both flabbergasted. We parked her away for the night and made our way home. I was dropped off at Mortimer, whilst George and our boss went on to Wokingham only to come back the next morning for another session with the wreck.

While she was steaming up, George told me what Mr. Ford had said on their way home, his words were "I just can't make young Challis out, he is a proper genius. Whatever the situation he is always so calm and collected". They were both a bit concerned about our journey, as we still had a long way to go, but I was really enjoying it as I always liked a challenge and this was certainly one of them. Our journey took us almost three days, whereas with a good engine it would have taken me only one day.

Only a few years ago, something was said in front of me and I don't think I have ever been so embarrassed in my whole life as I was that day. It was during my first visit to the Egham Royal Show with my little Fowler BB1 and plough. The now late Jack Ward was then a big name at Egham as well as at the show, being the son of Sid Ward who had been my boss for a good few years and someone had told him that I was there. He came to the model tent, where I was just inside the door with my engine in steam. We had a long chat about the times when I was with Wards, then off he went, saying that he would be back shortly. The day went on then, about mid-afternoon, Jack came back with a few more of the big wigs, including the Mayor.

The model tent was just about solid with people, so there was no way that they could get through the crowds, so they came in behind the stand that I always take to display my engine and plough. They were packed in like sardines and Jack, who like his father had a pretty powerful voice, put his hand on my shoulder and said "Meet Joe Challis, an ex-employee of ours and one of the best steam ploughmen this country has ever known". I could have dropped through the floor. I never ever thought that I was any better than anyone else at this game, but I always enjoyed my work, hard as it was. Steam engines have always been part of my life, especially the ploughers, I grew up on them and would like to go out on them. I would just love to do it all again with nothing changed.

Apart from both villages being very much larger, Basildon has changed but very little over the last eighty years. The Park, with its miles of brick and flint walls and the exterior of the mansion are just about the same as they were when I was a schoolboy. But sadly, most of that beautiful interior had been taken out before it was handed over to the National Trust. I still often take a trip back to Basildon, calling in at 'The Crown Inn' at Lower Basildon, where they do a very nice cooked meal (with a cheap rate for pensioners), then drive away into the hills, stopping to browse across the fields bringing those golden memories flowing back. Those wonderful times I spent there as a schoolboy with those Fowler K7 ploughers. It is still beautiful country and must be some of the prettiest in Berkshire with those narrow winding lanes, hills and valleys, just about the same as they were eighty years ago.

My favourite spot was always Radington Hill. This is about half a mile past Primrose Cottage (my birthplace) and was where I used to collect many different kinds of wild flowers, some of them very rare such as Monkey and Bee Orchids. Each year, I always topped the list for the school's wild flower display and, years later, we used to take our two sons there to do the same and they too always came out top. Years later, we did the same with our twin daughters and their teachers, once again they were always first with their wild flower displays. In my will, I have asked for my ashes to be scattered here when the time comes.

Across the top of this hill runs that ancient earth works, the 'Grim's Ditch' and about a mile further on in the next valley is the start of the oldest road in Europe, 'The Great Ridgeway', which stretches right across Berkshire and away through Wiltshire, a wonderful trip on a motorbike. Only a few weeks ago, I went back to Primrose Cottage and was shown over it for the first time since we left it in 1923. The exterior of it still looks very much the same, but inside it is now very different, as both cottages have been made into one big one and very nice it is too. I have also recently been back to Upper Basildon and spent an evening with Clive Williams who has written a very interesting book on the history of Basildon. I was able to help him out with a few things that he knew nothing about, as there are only a handful of us left that were there when I was a boy.

My number two 2in. scale Fowler BB1 is well on the way and with luck could be on show soon. But sadly the little 1in. scale replica of the Basildon Estate 8 hp Fowler is still here unfinished. Perhaps, one day my sons, grandsons and great-grandsons will get down to finishing it off.

Photograph Buxworth Steam Group.

'Visitors to steam rallies that are held in different parts of the country most weekends during the Summer, will see many smokebox doors, most bearing the maker's name and the town where built. There will be many of each make that will be the same as each other, but you will only find one like this as it was the one and only to be completed ...!' **JOE CHALLIS**

Appendix I

WILDER Ploughing Engine No 1, BL 4150

This engine can claim to be both the oldest and one of the youngest ploughing engines in existence. Its history provides an interesting insight into a small country based agricultural contracting and engineering firm 70 years ago.

R. J. & H. Wilder of Wallingford were long established agricultural contractors with both thrashing and ploughing sets operating in the Oxfordshire and Berkshire area. In 1926 they decided to build a pair of ploughing engines of their own. It is thought that the reason was that the Oxford Steam Plough Co., later known as Allens of Oxford, had been building their own engines based on Fowler designs for some time. There was obviously rivalry between the two companies - of which more later.

Wilders already had a number of old Fowler ploughing engines in their yard including 1054 and 1109 of 1868 and 1281 of 1869. On 24th June 1890, when owned by Noah Paxman of Clifton Hampden, one of the engines subsequently owned by Wilders blew up on Wargrave Hill. The riveted seam between the firebox backhead and the outer wrapper failed killing the driver Walter Henry Woodward. His grave in Chalgrove churchyard is marked by a simple cross carrying his initials and by a memorial stone which records his name and the date and the following " ...who was killed by the explosion of an engine". The memorial was "erected as a mark of respect and sympathy by his fellow workmen and other friends". Wilders bought both the sets that Paxman owned.

Wilders therefore had the basis for building an engine of their own. When the author spoke to their chief designer in 1980, he said that when he was an apprentice in the 1920s, the only engineering drawings that he had seen at Wilders were rough chalk sketches on sheets of steel. This is probably not the case when you consider the items of the new engine that they both designed and manufactured as listed below:

The principal sources of components for the engine are as follows:

R. J. & H. Wilder   Boiler, smokebox and chimney
Cylinder Block - including piston and valve
Crankshaft
Trunk Guide, Crosshead and Connecting rod
Road Gearing - except for final drive gearwheel
Tender
Back Axle

John Fowler & Co.   All other components (some off engines being broken up, others bought new from Fowlers). Wilders restraked the back wheels one of which appears to have been made up from two originals.

New castings were made by Walter Wilder of Crowmarsh, just over the river Thames from Wallingford. R. J. & H. Wilder then machined them. Walter Wilder also used to do Allen's castings - they do not appear to have let family ties interfere with business!

Wilder's design used a 200 psi boiler (tested to 400 psi) and an inside admission piston valve cylinder block of 12 in. bore and stroke. Whilst externally looking like an Allen boiler, the Wilder in fact has more tubes and is one column of stays shorter in the firebox than the surviving Allen boilers. The crankshaft has three bearings and the big end is counter-balanced, however, as an original Fowler flywheel with a balance weight cast into the rim was re-used, whether true balance was achieved is questionable. The Stephenson link motion is arranged such that the links are up when the reversing lever is forward - this means that the rods are open as opposed to crossed and also thoroughly confuses casual observers who think that the engine is moving the wrong way!

Despite obviously being able to achieve high standards of workmanship some parts of the design are far from perfect. For instance, the gear change mechanism is a collection of flat bar with the wooden running board as an important support member. Wilders retained the original Fowler tank steering. This has two hazardous features, to turn left you steer to the right and, as it drives through straight spur gears, it can throw you off the engine with great ease. The engine also retains the original Fowler friction band drive system. Rather than using drive pins, the rear wheels are locked to driving drums by bands which must be tightened to achieve a positive drive. Whilst you do not have the game of lining up pin holes, the bands do have a habit of loosing grip at embarrassing moments.

The engine came out in March 1927 and was paired with one of Wilder's 12 hp Fowler singles. They carried out three jobs with a five furrow plough. The first was on part of the former Basildon estate at Lower Basildon on the A329, the second was for a Mr Pullen at Church Farm, Appleford (a village name all steam enthusiasts will remember) and the third at Steventon, thought to have been for a Mr Cauldwell. For these jobs the driver was Wally Ilesdon and the cook-boy was Joe Challis. Joe plays a part in the engine's story 69 years later.

After this the engine went back to Wilders for adjustment - apparently if it stopped on a dead centre it took two men to pull it over. At about this time representatives of the Oxford Steam Plough Co. actually stopped the engine on the road as they thought that Wilders had copied their design of piston valve single. In fact, the designs were different but the incident shows the rivalry between the two.

Wilders did build a second engine but it was never completed. It was included in their auction when they gave up steam cultivation contracting. One account says that it was being towed down the road one day when the flywheel fell off. The boiler may have gone to Jersey for steam sterilising market gardens nurseries.

The engine was used for a few years paired with a 10 hp horizontal shaft engine, Charlie Smith drove the Wilder and Joe Challis' mother's cousin, Tommy Street, drove the 10 hp The engine was finally sold when Wilders gave up steam ploughing in 1936. The sale was held on 16th September and included five sets of ploughing tackle. Catalogued as Wilder's number 6 set the engine was lot 32. It was bought by Joseph Griffin of Bruern Grange, Shipton-under-Wychwood, Oxon for £70 subject to Wilders carrying out some mechanical work. His reason for buying the single ploughing engine is interesting. He could see that a war with Germany was coming and was concerned about the possibility of loosing one of his pair of K7 (15270/1) engines to enemy action. The Wilder engine was his insurance policy. The second engine was lot 33, catalogued as unfinished but with the boiler as having been tested to 320 psi

Joseph Griffin appears not to have been in a hurry to take delivery of the engine because Wilders eventually sent a bill for storage at their canal wharf site for £14. This he agreed to pay subject to Wilders delivering the engine to Bruern Grange. Two of Wilder's men drove the engine over, however when they were near the end of the journey the nuts holding the piston rod packer in place came off. The packer came back with the piston rod, turned slightly and was then pushed back by the crosshead. This bent both the studs which should have been holding it in place. Joseph Griffin's son Bob had to go out and replace both the studs before the journey could be completed.

The engine was not required during the war. In 1948 Bob Griffin retubed it and spent 6 weeks pulling out trees around his house. This was to be its last work in steam for 48 years. In the early 1960s it had several changes of ownership, eventually being preserved by a consortium of Jack Wharton, Arthur Napper, Bill Tame, Eric Fillmore, John Hirons and Tony Stockwell. It was moved to Arthur Napper's yard at East Hagbourne where it stood between the old Fowler singles 1368 and 2013. The present owner first saw it in steam in October 1975 when he assisted Bill Tame in using it to wash out the boilers of the other singles. At this time the lagging had all been removed and it was clear that major boiler work was required to make good the external corrosion that had almost completely removed numerous rivet heads and pitted the plate to a depth of $5/32$ or more.

In late 1979, it became known that the consortium of owners were prepared to sell. The author of this appendix was the successful buyer. The engine's new home was to be near Wantage to go under cover with Fowler BB1 15206 and Marshall portable 53360. The engine was loaded at Jack Whartons using his recovery vehicle to winch it on but this was not available to unload. Once at its new home, therefore, ramps were put in place, the engine was put in gear and a long(ish) chain attached to a farm tractor which then pulled. The compression in the cylinder was sufficient to stop the engine overtaking the tractor, the author remembered to steer back to front and solid ground was reached. Restoration then proceeded in bursts and pauses with the pauses being somewhat longer than the bursts.

As purchased the engine was complete apart from the top of the whistle, the 450 yard cable, three lagging bands and the lagging sheets - it still had even the spuds and the chimney damper. In view of the boiler work needed a complete strip down and rebuild was decided upon.

The first job was to dismantle the engine. This went reasonably smoothly apart from both rear wheels being seized solid on the axle. Eventually one was freed, the other remains locked solid to this day. The reason for the seizure became clear when the free wheel was examined. Wilders had bored and bushed the back wheels to fit the new axle, but had failed to drill the oil holes through the new bushes. With only water finding its way along the axle, the two had simply rusted together.

The inside of the boiler barrel was in almost perfect condition, but the wastage on the outside meant it had to be replaced. The barrel is in two sections each with a lap seam. The tubes put in in 1948 were carefully drifted out and the complete boiler went to Colin Wait near Bristol. Colin and his team of helpers made a superb job of manufacturing a new barrel which faithfully following the original design. When the time came to re-assemble the various castings and brackets onto the boiler, everything lined up perfectly even down to the original packing under the trunk guide support still being the required thickness. The original smokebox tubeplate was re-used and the 1948 vintage tubes were put back in - how many engines can say that they have a 50 year old set of tubes that are good for seasons to come? To complete the boiler work, Colin also made a new smokebox and ashpan and replaced some broken stays. Whilst only having one injector and no pump when originally built, the opportunity was taken to mount a second clack on the new barrel, this will be coupled to a new injector in due course. Two Fowler pattern blowdown cocks have also been fitted.

Following the return of the boiler unit in 1987, work came to a halt as employment changes and other interests took over the available time. The engine was also 60 miles away from home. In 1995 the author of this appendix and his partner Neil went to the Great Dorset rally as spectators. There we learnt that 1996 was to be a Fowler special year. We decided to aim to get the engine to the event in the best state we could. At this stage the engine was a boiler on wheels with the crankshaft castings and the cylinder block loosely bolted in place. The remaining thousand and one items were scattered around numerous outbuildings, attics and store cupboards. Whilst a lot had been cleaned and painted before being put away, they all needed to be attended to before being refitted. There then followed many hours of driving on the A34 and getting home at midnight as weekends were spent working on the large items and re-assembling the small ones.

The decision was made to follow Wilder's paint scheme of green with red wheels, but to use a dark green rather than the original acidic mid green. Some items such as the gear guards still had traces of the original Fowler painting and lining hiding under the later Wilder paintwork. Photographs were taken to provide a permanent record of 1860s Fowler paint schemes.

By 13th May 1996 the boiler was thought watertight. A gentle fire was lit using scrap timber and the water raised to lukewarm. The boiler was pumped up to 160 psi at which point the joint between the cylinder block and the boiler barrel started leaking badly. We had suspected that this might give trouble as Wilders had machined the block to a larger diameter than the barrel. To achieve the original joint they had used many loops of copper wire and much red lead and putty. This was the way we initially tried. After this failure we had to remove all the fixing bolts and lift the block off again. This we did whilst the boiler was still hot. A new seal was constructed using a fibrous compound called 'Fibrine' which was held in place with expanded aluminium mesh normally used to repair car body panels. In order to put the block fixing bolts in place, the author had to lower himself through the manhole and slide along the top of the tubes - not to be undertaken if you suffer from claustrophobia.

After a couple of trial runs the boiler was ready for the official pressure test to 300 psi on 21st June. This was passed with flying colours. To celebrate, the water was partially drained out, the cylinder top blank removed, the safety valves fitted and steam raised to 70 psi to try out the new whistle. At this time the piston and motion were still awaiting refitting.

By mid July we were ready to fit the crankshaft, flywheel and motion shafts. This was done by towing the engine under a suitable lifting beam using the Fowler BB1 and then winching back using the BB1's cable. All went together well once we put back the ³/₈ in. packer under the nearside crankshaft bearing. By this time, the valve gear radius link had been built up using 'molecular metal'. The original components date from 1868 and were very worn. To date the building up has worked well with no signs of wear or pieces breaking out - it is very much simpler and cheaper than remaking or building up with weld.

Finally on Sunday 4th August all the motion was in place. Once again steam was raised and with 50 psi on the gauge the regulator gently opened - the crankshaft rocked backwards and forwards as though driving a set of steam yachts. The piston valve, despite having taken accurate measurements, was obviously not set right. We resorted to setting in steam with the engine ticking over. The valve was found to be extremely sensitive with a quarter of a turn on the spindle making the difference between an even exhaust beat and the engine trying to run both ways at once. With less than four weeks to go until the Great Dorset the weekend finished with the writing of a very long list of 'essential things still to do'.

The following weekend the cable drum was winched under the engine and jacked up into place. Then it was time to raise steam again to drive to within range of the 3-phase welder to finish the tender repairs.

Monday 19th August was the day of the boiler inspector's steam test. Steam was raised on both the Wilder and the Fowler. Everything went satisfactorily apart from one of the safety valves not reseating cleanly. This problem was later cured by filling some casting flaws with silver solder and refacing the valve in the lathe. The valves are the same diameter, but have different seat designs, one is conventional but the other works like a poppet valve. You get no notice that it is about to lift - just a nasty shock! The valve springs were replaced during the rebuild as the bottom ends of the originals had corroded very badly and might have broken off.

That afternoon Joe Challis, the cookboy from 1927, came over to see the engine in steam and to supervise our cable splicing. A number of lengths of ³/₄ in. cable from Fawley power station had been acquired and the intention was to make up the 450 yards needed to fill the drum from four of these. Unfortunately, the cable was made up with more strands and finer wires than a conventional steam plough cable. Joe told us that the foreman in the working days would have expected a splice to take about half an hour - it took us five, so no acreage bonus that day. Without Joe's help we would still have been there the next day.

The following Monday a third length of cable was spliced on in the hope that it would reach the length of the Dorset field. A final job was to bolt the engine's nameplate, *William*, into place. The name was chosen in memory of Bill Tame, a former Wilder employee, former part owner of the engine and friend who had provided help and guidance to the author of this appendix since the BB1 was acquired in 1968.

The next day it was time to board the lowloader and travel off to Dorset

- engine plus Fowler living van, light traction wagon and water cart. The wagon was loaded with bits still waiting to be refitted. On arriving we thought we had time to catch our breath but no, please could we shunt around to provide a backdrop for the BBC Holiday programme who were recording that week's edition on the field. Having duly moved about and drowned out the presenter with the whistle - the sound engineer didn't realise that a ploughing whistle is meant to carry to the other side of the field - it was time to wrap up for the night.

Next morning, the first job was to fit the steering linkage casting to the front axle following repair by Colin Wait. Then on went the toolbox, spud racks and the spuds. Colin caulked up a few minor weeps on the boiler barrel and then the engine was steam tight.

The next five days were spent alternating between working the engine and carrying out running adjustments including dismantling the big and little ends and the crosshead twice! The idea was to do some hard pulls to shake everything into place. This was successful, but by the end of the week whenever somebody picked something off the ground and asked 'is this yours', we always answered yes! The cable splices held when pulling both the plough and the cultivator, unfortunately we were 50 yards short for the longest pulls - apologies to the Daniels and their McLaren who had to shunt around the ploughed field to get coupled up. The week was spent in the living van. We had brought a tin bath with us - after a long dirty day you can't beat lying back in a bathfull of water hot out of the engine injector in front of a blazing fire in the cast iron range and with a pint of gin and tonic.

Joe Challis came down for one day and drove the engine around the field pulling the Fowler wagon. He thoroughly enjoyed himself, but got a ticking off when he got home for getting oil on his anorak!

Following the Great Dorset, the engine went back to Brian Snelgar's yard near Salisbury. Winter work included fitting two blowdown cocks, timber lagging and sheets, plus tracking down and rectifying a mysterious knock. This was found to be due to the flywheel key being loose resulting in the flywheel overtaking the crank at certain positions. The cure was some welding followed by much filing and rounded off by more molecular metal. A further length of cable was also spliced on giving almost a full drum of 450 yards.

In 1997 the engine went to two working rallies, the Stanton Drew Steam Up near Bristol and the Great Dorset once again. This time we were able to work every day rather than having to take time out to bolt bits back on! One of the highlights was when Joe Challis came down and drove a session whilst we were cultivating - we were more than happy to stand back and leave Joe in charge of the engine as he had been more than seventy years before.

There are still things to be done to complete the restoration of the engine - fitting a second injector and putting planks back in the gearing to cut down the gear noise being just two - but she is now able to give real pleasure as she does the job of work she was designed to do all those years ago.

Acknowledgements:

William (Bill), Harold and Marge Tame

Bob Griffin

Joe Challis

Bill Smith

Colin Wait and his team

Robert Hodgson

and all the others who have offered advice, help and encouragement over the years.

© James Hodgson, 1998.

The Steam Plough Club

Full details of membership and the aims of the Steam Plough Club are available from:

Mr. Simon Fisher (Membership Secretary)
THE STEAM PLOUGH CLUB
Warren Farm
Ightham
Kent
TN15 9AP

The
National Traction Engine Trust

Membership of the National Traction Engine Trust is open to those who, whether engine owners or not, have a genuine interest in the preservation of self propelled steam road vehicles, portable engines etc.

Full details of membership are available from:

J. R. Cook (Membership Secretary)
THE NATIONAL TRACTION ENGINE TRUST
'Dolfarni'
Church Lane
Kirkby la Thorpe
Lincolnshire
NG34 9NU

An oblique view of the west front of the house at Basildon Park. Designed with a restrained use of ornament, but an unerring sense of balance, and built in a particularly beautiful Bath stone, the Palladian villa-style house was built between 1776-1783 to the design of architect John Carr of York.

Appendix II

A Short History of Basildon Park

Basildon was built between 1776 and 1783 by Sir Francis Sykes, a close friend and ally of Warren Hastings, who had made a large fortune in the service of the East India Company and who was created a baronet in 1781. Sykes - who came of a Yorkshire family - had previously lived at Ackworth Park near Doncaster and this may explain why he employed the architect John Carr of York, most of whose other work is to be found in the north of England.

The plan Carr adopted was that of a Palladian villa, with a main block joined by one-storey links to separate pavilions containing the domestic offices. Designed with a restrained use of ornament, but with an unerring sense of balance, and built in a particularly beautiful Bath stone, the house is undoubtedly one of Carr's masterpieces. The Sykes family fortunes began to decline after the death of the first baronet in 1804 and in 1838 his grandson was forced to sell the house and estate - which at that time consisted of about 2,500 acres - for the comparatively large sum of £97,000.

The new owner of Basildon - the Liberal M.P. James Morrison - had been a pioneer of many new business tactics, his most famous dictum being the idea of 'small profits and quick returns'. Morrison had by this time built up a modest haberdashery business in the City into a vast enterprise with international interests. His close friend, the architect J. B. Papworth, was commissioned to complete some of the interiors which Sir Francis Sykes had left unfinished - notably the Octagon Room - to heighten and embellish Carr's lodges on the Oxford road and to design other buildings on the estate, while some smaller alterations were also made after 1844 by David Brandon. James Morrison died at Basildon in 1857, but his widow continued to live there fore another 30 years, after which it passed to their son Charles. The last of the Morrison family to live in the house was his sister, Ellen, who died in 1910.

Basildon might well have been one of the lost country houses of the 1920s, 30s, 40s or 50s, because the threats to it were as numerous as they were various. Unlived in by the Morrisons after 1910, it was put up for sale in 1928 and bought by the 1st Lord Iliffe, the publisher and newspaper proprietor, who wanted some of the land to add to Yattendon, where he had already built a new house. The house and park at Basildon were then sold to Mr. George Ferdinando and he had a scheme to sell the house re-erected in America for a million dollars. Fortunately, he could not find a purchaser and he only sold some of the decorative detail, which mostly ended up in a specially created Basildon Room in the Waldorf Astoria Hotel.

The house had already been unoccupied for nearly 30 years when World War II broke out and it was requisitioned. During the next 12 years, it served a variety of purposes: the English used the park for practising tank warfare and two units of the 101st Airborne Division of the American Army completed their training there before 'D' Day in June 1944, and after the invasion of France, returned to prepare for the invasion of Holland, in September 1944. After the War, the Ministry of Works used it as a billet for prisoners of war. By the early 1950s, despite some basic repairs carried out before derequisitioning and its return to Mr. Ferdinando, Basildon was in a very poor state and appeared to have no future. As well as the need for extensive repairs at a time of strict controls, the losses of detail and the effect of 12 years' hard use had to be made good: the combination was a particularly daunting one. It would not have disappeared immediately, but it was not difficult to imagine the growing hold of rot and the increasing temptation to rob the structure of lead and fittings, and within a few years Basildon would have become a shell that no one thought worth stabilising, and the site would have been cleared.

Meanwhile, Lord Iliffe's elder son, the Hon. Langton Iliffe, had in 1938 married Renee Merandon du Plessis, born and brought up in an old British colonial house on a sugar estate in Mauritius. The young couple lived first at Carlton House Terrace, but, after the war, began to search for a house in the country, near the Yattendon estate - and preferably Georgian, since they both shared a love of eighteenth century art and architecture. Basildon, though much larger than the sort of house they had first envisaged, seemed to fit the bill in every other respect, and in 1952 they courageously decided to buy and restore it.

Lady Iliffe later described the impact the house made on her and her husband, and how its saving became a cause for them. It was a formidable challenge for not only had they to carry out the repairs - all but one window had to be replaced - but they had to work out a plan for living in the house. An early idea was to start with a splendid apartment on the principal floor and seal off the rest of the house, but in the end they decided to tackle not only the main block but the flanking wings. With the aid of the architect Mr. Winton Aldridge, a lifelong friend, they made their plans for repairs and adaptation, and in September 1954, two years after they began work, they moved in.

Twenty-five years later, Basildon Park was handed over to the National Trust with the hope that Trust would protect the property for future generations to enjoy. Founded in 1895, the National Trust - the greatest conservation society in Britain and the country's largest private landowner - readily took up the challenge and Basildon Park, which lies eight miles north-west of Reading on the Reading-Oxford road (A329) between Pangbourne and Wallingford, during 1998 is open to the public as follows: HOUSE: 1st April-1st November: daily except Monday & Tuesday (but open Bank Holiday Monday) 1 p.m.-5.30 p.m. (closed Good Friday). PARK: Garden & Woodland Walks: 1st March-27th March: Saturday & Sunday 12 p.m.-5 p.m.; 1st April-1st November: same days as House 11.30 a.m.-5.30 p.m.

Photograph: Buxworth Steam Group.

'Pictured here is a typical steam plough living van that was home for a gang of five men for a week and some weekends during busy periods. The gang was comprised of a foreman, two drivers, cultivator man and cookboy. The beds were not too special, but we could always sleep fairly well, as after about 16 hours hard slogging each day, we rolled into them dog tired. ...!' **JOE CHALLIS**

Index

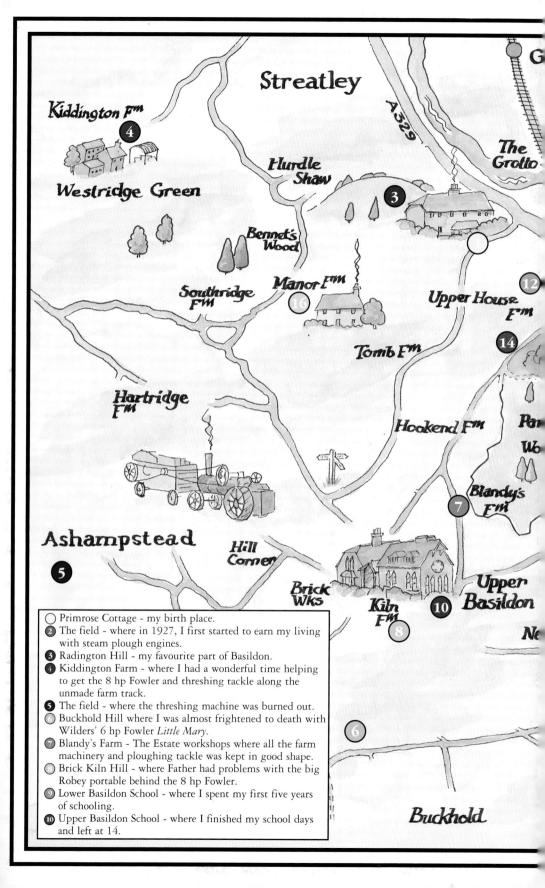

Streatley

A329

The Grotto

Kiddington F^m

④

Westridge Green

Hurdle Shaw

③

①

⑫

Bennet's Wood

Southridge F^m

Manor F^m

⑯

Upper House F^m

⑭

Tomb F^m

Hartridge F^m

Hookend F^m

Par Wo

Blandy's F^m

⑦

Ashampstead

⑤

Hill Corner

Brick Wks

Kiln F^m

⑧

⑩

Upper Basildon

Ne

⑥

Buckhold

○ Primrose Cottage - my birth place.
② The field - where in 1927, I first started to earn my living with steam plough engines.
③ Radington Hill - my favourite part of Basildon.
④ Kiddington Farm - where I had a wonderful time helping to get the 8 hp Fowler and threshing tackle along the unmade farm track.
⑤ The field - where the threshing machine was burned out.
⑥ Buckhold Hill where I was almost frightened to death with Wilders' 6 hp Fowler *Little Mary*.
⑦ Blandy's Farm - The Estate workshops where all the farm machinery and ploughing tackle was kept in good shape.
⑧ Brick Kiln Hill - where Father had problems with the big Robey portable behind the 8 hp Fowler.
⑨ Lower Basildon School - where I spent my first five years of schooling.
⑩ Upper Basildon School - where I finished my school days and left at 14.